LIFE AMONG THE DOCTORS

Books by Paul De Kruif

OUR MEDICINE MEN

MICROBE HUNTERS

HUNGER FIGHTERS

SEVEN IRON MEN

MEN AGAINST DEATH

WHY KEEP THEM ALIVE?

THE FIGHT FOR LIFE

HEALTH IS WEALTH

KAISER WAKES THE DOCTORS

THE MALE HORMONE

LIFE AMONG THE DOCTORS

PAUL DE KRUIF

Life Among the Doctors

⫸ ⫸ ⫷ ⫷

IN COLLABORATION WITH
RHEA DE KRUIF

To paint nature here, as everywhere,
you must have lived in it a long time.

VINCENT VAN GOGH

HARCOURT, BRACE AND COMPANY

NEW YORK

COPYRIGHT, 1949, BY

PAUL DE KRUIF

first edition

꧁ ꧂

THIS BOOK IS FOR

DONALD C. BRACE

꧁ ꧂

⇶ ⇷

It will be observed that the first person singular and the first person plural are both used in the narration. This has come about because the chronicle has grown out of many years of intimate collaboration. Its views in respect of the art, philosophy and religion of medicine and its overall plan and continuity have been hammered out in thousands of hours of discussion of the strange events in our life among the doctors and to all of this Rhea de Kruif has contributed as much as the undersigned. Rhea has participated in gathering most of the material; she has taken part in countless conferences in which we have been public health consultants or reporters. In the narration of these phases of the story, it is *we* who are doing the telling. When the undersigned has had to go it alone—never so happy—this is told in the first person singular.

PAUL DE KRUIF

※ ※

THIS BOOK is the story of the fight by responsible men of medicine against human disease. These pioneers have also had to fight against a few human beings—powerful but irresponsible—who have handicapped them in their struggles.

As this book goes to press comes news that these medical pioneers are now to be freed from a great deal of their frustration by self-constituted "authority."

The daily press reports that the responsible leaders of the American Medical Association at their annual session have acted so that one or more self-appointed "spokesmen" can no longer act or speak in an irresponsible manner.

The American Medical Association has taken an historic step ahead for the health of the American people.

※ ※

Acknowledgments

»> «<

For every facility for the study of life among the doctors, thanks to DeWitt Wallace and Lila Acheson Wallace. For guidance into subjects of interest to large numbers of readers, thanks to DeWitt Wallace, Kenneth W. Payne and William Hard, Jr. With the exception of the opening chapter, events in this chronicle were linked closely with our medical reporting for *The Reader's Digest* during the past nine years.

For her expert and devoted attention to the preparation of the typescript, thanks to Eleanor Nevenzel, our faithful assistant.

»> «<

Contents

➤➤➤ ⋘⋘

PART ONE

TWO MEN IN CONTRAST

꘍꘍ ꘍꘍ ꘍꘍ ꘍꘍

THE WHITE HOUSE   DECEMBER, 1939

Alone with the President: His close-set, dark-circled eyes were intense. His face was stern after a short smile. He had changed since I had seen him three years before.

"This plan for preventive medicine," I said, "at the start wouldn't require more than a hundred million dollars a year."

The President's eyes, saying "impossible," wilted me. His face became grave. "That's out of the question, now," he said. His face clouded with what seemed clairvoyance of some vast coming ordeal, some looming sorrow.

"We won't have a hundred million for that," he explained. "We're going to need all the money Congress will appropriate—for ships . . . tanks . . . guns . . . bombers."

꘍꘍ ꘍꘍ ꘍꘍ ꘍꘍

CHAPTER I

Death Has Priority

⇛ ⇚

TO tell about life among the doctors you have to have lived among them for a long time; with me this experience began thirty-six years ago. To tell about them truly as the more or less earnest and struggling servants of mankind that most of them are, you had better not be a doctor—that is to say, an M.D.—yourself; and that I am not. Yet, first as a microbe hunter and then as a writer, I've worked intimately with many men of medical science and practice, sharing their joy at saving the lives of people who—perhaps the year before—would have died because science couldn't have saved them. I've lived, too, through their desperation as they stood helpless, watching human beings die despite all available devotion and knowledge.

At their best, medical men are the highest type yet reached by mankind. They are the first to show how we may fuse the power of science with the faith of religion to build a new humanity. At their worst (and this is fortunately true of a small minority of them), they are little better than legalized murderers. Taken all in all, doctors—so great has become their power over life and death—can be described as the strangest body of human beings inhabiting the earth today, a sort of new species mutating from *Genus homo.* To tell how they surpass all miracles in human history, or neglect miracles available, or sometimes make commerce out of human flesh and blood—it's as if you were trying to tell of life among Eskimos or aborigines to people who did not know that they existed.

3

Why, to tell about life among doctors, is it better not to be an M.D. yourself? The answer demands plain speaking: unless a physician was ready to give up his profession, it would be next to impossible for him to describe life among doctors—because the free swing of truth in his story would be hindered by what is known as medical ethics.

These rules or principles governing the conduct of medical practitioners are a system working for good and evil. It's good that medical ethics keeps most doctors from being abortionists and restrains the majority of them from the fee-splitting that encourages needless and sometimes dangerous and even deadly operations. On the other hand, a doctor who knows that certain of his colleagues have killed patients through ignorance or negligence does not tell the public, naming names. That would be "unethical." Again, a doctor who would openly tell the world that the use of some new preventive or cure is being hindered by medical super-conservatism or by physicians whose commercial toes would be stepped on—such a crusading doctor would be in danger of being fired from his medical society, especially if he named names.

As a result physicians are frustrated in cleaning their house of its abuses. They are held back from taking a bold lead in putting to rapid use all the healing and the medical mercy that their wonderful new science now makes possible. That is why the life-saving progress of medicine is slow, despite today's blooming power of a science that can now ease so much pain, that bids fair to lift the ancient three-score-and-ten ceiling over human life, and right now could keep millions of people from dying.

I have admitted that this conspiracy of silence, keeping doctors from tattling upon each other, has its good points as well as its bad. Without it, physicians whose patients die through no fault of the doctor would be the prey of malicious medical competitors. Here is another element of justice: it is often difficult to prove that the death of this or that patient was actually due to ignorance or neglect on the part of the physician; maybe the patient would have perished despite the combined efforts of the greatest medical team in the world.

Yet for many years, and more and more, it has irked me that so many people go on needlessly suffering and dying. If the self-improvement of doctors is inevitably slow for the above reasons, where does that leave us—the hundreds of millions of us who are fed up with being sick when we no longer should be, who are appalled at continued needless dying? The answer is simple. The doctors will be as competent as we, the non-doctors, demand.

At the end of the 1930's this became clear to me. At this time I had no great hope that any writing I could do would accelerate public demand for good medicine. My plans were far more ambitious. It seemed to me that, to enforce their yearning for life, the people must have a leader, a champion. In that year, 1939, I believed we had found the man who might lead us out of our medical valley of shadows. Wasn't Franklin D. Roosevelt the man who could rally all of us to demand that the doctors mobilize for a nationwide fight for life? Alas, Mr. Roosevelt showed me that not life but death had priority. He put me kindly and firmly in my place, showing me the fatuity of my aspiration to be a behind-the-scenes public health politician. It was Mr. Roosevelt who inspired this present effort to write about life among the doctors.

II

On a gray day in December, 1939, face-to-face and alone with this remarkable man, it became clear to me that the idea of his becoming history's first political public health champion was less than bright. It was a day of major disillusion. I had no religion in the orthodox sense, having had it beaten out of me at an early age by the obvious hypocrisies of my Calvinistic Dutch upbringing. The mercy of science to strengthen and lengthen human life and to conquer human pain—that was my faith, that was what held my life together. I went to the White House, confident that an all-out war against needless dying could be started. At last such a campaign was becoming good politics; there was an upsurging mass interest in good medicine; the President was the world's master politician. Why shouldn't he take the lead in this now possible fight for life?

I came away from the White House knowing that in the immediate years ahead the power of science was not going to be used primarily for life. Timing is everything, they say, and that day the President showed me my timing was not good.

When you lack inside political information, it's remarkable how your logic can fool you. I went to him, hot with the irresistible reasonableness of launching a nationwide preventive death fight right now. What was there to stop such a campaign in our country? What if across both oceans super-gangsters were perverting science for mass murder justified by ideologies both right and left? All the foreign ideologies, from Nazism to Communism, promised pie for everybody—not now, but in the far future. But here in America we weren't misled by such nonsense. Here we were for the greatest possible good for everybody, *right now.* Our peculiarly American philosophy made most of us unwilling to die for any political theory before we really had to.

The country would be as good as unanimous for Mr. Roosevelt if he'd stage an all-out fight for life. Wasn't the President a man who hated war?

It was clear that now was the time to put this good fight into action. I was bemused by the elegance of my own logic; for me the issue went deep below the opportunism of politics. Now was the moment to make this new death fight the spearhead of social progress. Towards what? Towards a human brotherhood where there would be a stronger, longer, more decent, more contented and loving life for everybody, at the end of which we wouldn't much mind dying, the way we don't mind going to sleep at the end of a good hard day.

That's what drove me towards the White House. For me it was the day of days.

III

This December noon I was to have lunch with Mr. Roosevelt, alone, with plenty of time. From the woods and dunes of Lake

Michigan's eastern shore I had come as a sort of courier, sponsored by Surgeon General Thomas Parran of the United States Public Health Service. Tom Parran believed too much in me. This gentle, gray-haired, ruddy-faced man—the first in our history to try to make the question of life-or-death a national issue—had the notion that the Dutch in me would click with the Dutch in the President. Tom Parran had chosen me to put a plan for a formidable expansion of preventive medicine before the President. We had planned an attack against every preventable disease and death. In my inside pocket, this campaign was boiled down to a little memo, two type-written pages, just the length (so insiders told us) that the President would be likely to read through to the end.

The plan was practical, economic, not crackpot. The need for an immense expansion of public health laboratories was pointed out by C. C. Young who in Michigan had built the finest public health laboratory in the world on a shoestring. He had demonstrated to Michigan's politicians that they were swindling Michigan's taxpayers so long as there were not the laboratories to keep Michigan's people from unnecessary dying. The economic desirability of wiping out tuberculosis had been injected into the plan by Detroit's Dr. E. J. O'Brien. He had taunted the city fathers into understanding that they were the opposite of budget-balancers so long as they let Detroit's people rot to death from preventable TB, and so on—for every death, from pneumonia to preventable cancer.

Might the President doubt the practicability of our plan because of a possible disinterest on the part of the American Medical Association? A group of politically powerful physicians, led by Dr. L. G. Christian, of Lansing, Michigan, felt that co-operation of the medical organization in such a public health campaign could be assured.

The economics of the health plan had been approved by Mr. Marriner Eccles of the Federal Reserve Board; the politics of the memo had been discussed and given the blessing of Mr. Harry Hopkins. We all hoped there was history in the making on those two pages in my pocket.

Since the memo proved that it was immensely more costly to

maintain needless sickness and death than it would be to wipe them out, Congress would hardly dare to stop this plan if the President sponsored it for 1940 legislation. It would mean votes for the President if he was going to try for a third term or, if not, for anybody he would choose as heir-apparent. Just the same, as Pa Watson led me in, my mouth was a bit dry, legs a bit rubbery, and forehead dampish. There sat the man who could make our dream or break it.

"Good to see you again, Paul." His head was thrown back in greeting. His close-set eyes were intense, dark-circled. His face became curiously stern after a very short smile. He had changed, fantastically, since I had last seen him three years before. After the briefest greeting chit-chat, I sensed that now you didn't tell him, he told you. He had mutated (as the biologists say) from the man I'd known.

IV

Three years before, when he had given lunch to the President's Birthday Ball Commission for Infantile Paralysis Research, he had shown such vivid interest in the fight for life that he had planted the seed for the confidence with which I had now come to the White House. That day in 1936 the President had been a blend of the charming, brave, and pitiable. I remember him walking into the Red Room with such effort that it hurt you to watch him. Then he was one of us, or so it seemed. Circling round to be introduced to him by his great friend and supporter, Keith Morgan, whose arm he held, I was the last. To all the members of the Commission before me, the President had said informal words, flashing his smile. To me, before Keith could get out my name, Mr. Roosevelt simply stuck out his hand and winked, as if to say, "You and I know what the score is, don't we, son?"

The Very Important Persons of the Birthday Ball Commission were overwhelmingly Republican, and it was marvelous how he disarmed them at the big oval luncheon table, giving them his first-name treatment right down on their level. His attention to the report on our progress (or lack of it) against polio was close. His questions were shrewd and convinced me that here, at last, was a president who could easily be persuaded to make the overall death-fight a major issue.

This 1936 day will always be memorable because that same evening, along with two other men, I dined with the President in his study. Before the dinner was wheeled in, he shook us his own special cocktail, teaching us its chemistry with a winking gusto that reminded me of Henry L. Mencken. Here was not only a president but a fellow-drinker, and not only that but a barkeep. He was every inch of him not a president. When one of our little company, eagle-eyed old Otto Carmichael, the Hoosier Rabelais, told him he was going to have to pack the Supreme Court to keep the New Deal going, the President answered, never, it wouldn't be cricket, it wouldn't be democratic. To Arthur Carpenter, the able manager of the Georgia Warm Springs Foundation, the President painted with an almost religious emotion a picture of the coming care for the crippled.

That night he showed himself a fighter for the lowly and forlorn, but for just a moment the patrician, the master, flashed out in him. Every American who wanted to work should have the right to a job. "But," said the President, "if they won't work, we'll have to give those fellows the soup-kitchen." I shot back at him that Americans really not wanting to work were in the enormous minority and even these were probably most of them malnourished, not loafers. He nodded. He wrinkled his brow, looked at me, pondering, waiting for a suggestion for mass medical attack (which I then certainly didn't have). He was an open-minded groper, in 1936.

I can see him now as he sat, strong, tired, and pitiful, waiting to be lifted onto his little wheel chair by his factotum, Gus Gennerich. The President looked up at me. "Come and see me often, Paul," he said for a good-bye.

V

From that day of lunch and dinner at the White House to this day in December, I hadn't seen the President again. Now he had called for me. His handclasp hadn't lost its trick of making you think you were one of his special friends. He was still genial, but with grim overtones. In a few minutes I felt that the human first citizen of 1936 had metamorphosed into an unmitigated top man, 1939. During the almost two-and-a-half hours he talked to me he exaggerated his old mannerism of tossing his head, especially as he announced plans or decisions. It was soon clear that his old preoccupation of jobs and welfare for all Americans had been replaced by preoccupation with a surely coming battle for the survival of a world in danger. He seemed to me to be in training to become President of the World. It was tough for me to get a word in; it was a fascinating and alarming soliloquy that I listened to. His dark-circled eyes hinted tragedy and flashed power, personified.

As I listened, waiting for an opening to present our plan, the situation seemed to me a bit comical. Thrown into the ring with such an overwhelming character, what could a sand dunes boy from Michigan do? Through his hard hitting talk, telling me, telling me, telling me, I looked sharp for an interlude that had to come sooner or later. For a moment he was silent, eating, and I presented the possibility—in highly general terms—of increasing our prosperity by beginning to build America over. Harry Hopkins had told me that the President still had faith in our American system of more or less free, competitive enterprise. I hazarded that, under this competitive system, much of the public money that would be needed to rebuild America—making our country stronger, more productive, healthier, more beautiful—could pay itself off like any toll-bridge or power dam. Amortization!

For a moment I thought I had him, telling him that in my pocket there was a specific, concrete example of such a self-amortizing project. By spending a moderate sum of money for personnel and facilities for a nationwide attack upon preventable TB, venereal disease, pneumonia, mental disease, cancer accessible to early treatment, and so on—the savings from no longer having to *maintain* all this needless sickness and death would build up into a sinking fund. This might pay off the initial public health expenditures in a generation. Amortization. I hit hard with that word. The savings could retire the initial health bond issue.

What's more, more healthy people would release new human energy. This, flowing into production, would add billions to the nation's wealth.

He looked at me, woolgathering only slightly. "We're not talking of pain, misery, death," I said. "It's economy. It's costing us billions to be sick and to die." So I gave him our slogan.

He looked interested, for an instant. "You see, Mr. President," I urged, "it's no different from Boulder Dam paying off its cost of construction."

I had said one sentence too much. "Have you see Coulée Dam?" he countered. "Yes, this past summer," I answered.

"Well, we expect Coulée to start pumping water for irrigation late in 1941," he said. "Of course you know for what?"

"To irrigate the Quincy Plateau, to reclaim millions of acres of land that's failed in dry-farming," I answered, proud like a bright boy who knew his lessons.

"Correct," said the President. "Coulée will start pumping late in '41," he repeated. Then he looked at me earnestly. "Do you know what I want to do with Coulée in 1941, if Congress will let me?"

—Just a moment. *Here he was telling me he expected to be President again, in 1941.* He was going to run for a third term. He was giving me news no reporter then knew, something so secret that his intimates didn't know it. Something—maybe—lurking in the sub-cellar of his ambitions and dreams . . .

I steadied myself. Deadpan, I asked him, "What is it you intend to do with Coulée?"

Now he became animated. "I'm going to take John Steinbeck's Okies, hundreds of thousands of them now in California, and move them up there, and make a green country for them."

Though this had nothing to do with our health plan, yet I was happy. Now our health plan could hardly fail. Hurrah for Roosevelt, 1940. If we could only sell him public health, too, the fight for life would have a matchless leader. His unguarded confession that he wasn't going to let go of his power, at first shocking me, now began to delight me. I must sell him the vision of physically underpar millions who, just as much as those Okies, needed a public

health Coulée. Now I gained courage. I caught and expanded the
President's limited vision of rehabilitation. I became metaphoric.
Along with the green land for Okies there could be a promised land
of longer life, greater vigor, and freedom from pain for many
millions.

I was ready to pop our memo at him, ask him to read it, and
bid him good afternoon. "The point about this health plan," I
said, "is that, at the start, it wouldn't require more than a hundred
million dollars a year."

The President cut me short.

"That's out of the question, right now," he said. He broke it to
me, but kindly. His face became grave. "We won't have a hundred
million for that," he explained. "We're going to need all the money
Congress will appropriate—for ships, tanks, guns, bombers." He
accented each killer word.

In America, too, it was going to be a choice, if not between guns
and butter, then between guns and health. There went our hoped-
for fight for life. So that was that. What a man, just the same. What
a politician—first things first. He knew his Congress. To be sure
of the coming needed money, the billions for death, it would be
best not to confuse the good solons with requests for a mere hundred million for life. The President was keeping things simple.
Who could argue? Billions for death, or civilization itself might die.

So I didn't take our health plan memo out of my pocket.

VI

His sureness, his energy licked me. I had let Tom Parran and
the rest of them down. I should have stood up to him. I had caught
the President in a contradiction, in mental confusion, and knew it.
He had revealed his determination to be President for a third term.
In that third term he was planning the peaceful project of green
land for the Okies. Yet too, in that term, he was going to be Commander-in-Chief in the coming Armageddon. The two projects
couldn't go on together. Why didn't I put it to him? If there was
going to be war, the Okie project would have to go out the window.

On the other hand, if the Okies were going to get their green land, then there wouldn't be war.

If I had been tough enough right then, I'd have asked him: "Mr. President, are you using those two contradictory prospects simply to give our health plan the brushoff? If you're meaning to start the Coulée project for the Okies in 1941, you must mean that war can be avoided. Then why can't there be money to begin building stronger and longer-lived Americans as well as happier Okies?" This is no *esprit d'escalier* on my part. I thought of asking that, right then.

Instead I made a last feeble argument, asking him, since we were to have all that armament, wouldn't it be wise to build the maximum number of healthy men to man it? He didn't even answer that one. He was right. It wasn't man-power, it was horse-power, it was kilowatts that would win the war. Machines first, men second, and a second-rate man could kill men with enough first-rate machines.

When the President saw that he had me licked, some of his old geniality returned. He began talking gaily about doctors in general; it was a profession he did not hold in too high esteem. He switched from our public health plan—which did not involve any radical change in medical care since the practicing physician is not a major factor in the control of preventable disease—to medical care in general. He was definitely on the side of the bold handful of Washington, D. C., doctors, who were trying to establish a local, prepaid group health plan and were being kicked around by the American Medical Association. It was easy to see that he was back of the Government's prosecution (really shadow-boxing) of the American Medical Association in that minor fracas. At the same time, master politician and feeler of the public pulse that he was, he knew that the almost unanimous opposition of the doctors' organization—the most solid of all our country's unions—made plans for Government medicine hopeless.

On this issue I had no argument with him. Our medical men— somewhat less than perfect—are still the best in the world. They don't want to be run—and inevitably bureaucratized—by the Government. Present distribution of medical care is far from perfect, granted. So is distribution of houses, clothing, meat and groceries. There was no evidence that socializing any of these necessities (including medical care) would bring plenty within the reach of everybody. On the contrary.

Toward the end of our talk, though he had shown himself completely cool to expanding preventive medicine as proposed in our health plan, he said there was something he wanted to do, not too expensive, for the care of our neglected sick. The President wanted to build hospitals in blighted areas, especially southern. But the American Medical Association would surely fight him in Congress on that one.

Then he asked me his first and only question of the day: "How can I get organized medicine's support in the project of building these hospitals?"

I answered, and not at all jokingly, that he'd have no trouble on that one if he could only secure the support of the Editor of the *Journal of the American Medical Association*, in short, of the then leadership of American medicine.

VII

It had taken more than two-and-a-half hours of the time of the busiest man in the world to teach me that our health plan was licked, cold. What the President had taught me was more than I'd learned in any equal time in my life. I had seen what power does to a genial and friendly man. What good would it do us, even if Surgeon General Thomas Parran did have the solid backing that was unquestionably his in the Congress? It was clear that Congress wasn't running the country. The strong man in the White House was running it and he didn't mean maybe. This day I had seen the degree to which Mr. Roosevelt knew he was a man for history, of destiny. He was the coming Commander-in-Chief and when he spoke of ships, guns, tanks, and bombers it was with enthusiasm that was curiously reminiscent of boys who love to play with tin soldiers and cannon on the floor. Only this game was getting ready to turn deadly. Remembering his face, stern, willful, sure of power,

I could see him as if up on Olympus, getting ready to chuck thunderbolts at his rivals and down onto mankind's helpless myriads. Our plan for a fight for life, indeed. Now death had priority.

That day Mr. Roosevelt showed me clearly the kind of man you have to be to run a big country in time of danger; you've got to be tough about the suffering of millions today to make possible the happiness of millions tomorrow. You have to be a man of your time, not ahead of it, a realist, which Mr. Roosevelt exquisitely was, as against prophets like Tolstoy and Gandhi.

This day the President had given me a terrifying peep into the responsibilities of those who press the buttons controlling global strategy. Europe afire today; tomorrow the world flaming. How do you fight such a conflagration but with fire still hotter? He made me smile, bitterly, at our idealism. Would we still recommend that he spend his time putting over a health plan that might mean a mere saving of American lives as against saving—civilization? Of course not; to any realist, ridiculous. The President knew which side of science to use to save civilization. He was anything but blind to science as some have claimed he was, not to one side of it. Our men of science and industry would produce limitless metal, TNT, new deaths. Our science would rub out the gangsters; if necessary, whole peoples. No leader had ever shown greater faith in, or more lavish generosity in support of, that kind of science.

It was awesome to listen to him; it was shivery to watch his clamp-jawed sureness. . . . *Thou shalt not kill.* The President was a Christian, at least an Episcopalian, and certainly realistic and practical. From the Old Testament he could choose another command . . . *Eye for eye, tooth for tooth, hand for hand, foot for foot.* That answered better today's awful exigencies. If you had to kill, you should kill the right people, justly, eye for eye, et cetera, but from thirty thousand feet up in the sky could the boys on our side be sure they were blasting the right ones or the right number?

This day, best of all, the President had taught me to distinguish clearly, at last, two sides of science which till now as a whole I had tended to worship indiscriminately as the hope of mankind. Dutifully scientists—truth-hunters—would multiply old and concoct new

and horrid deaths. Dutifully other scientists—truth-hunters too—
would find ways for our doctors to palliate the new super-slaughter,
staunching blood, mending smashed bones, anointing seared skin,
soothing crazed brains in a fantastic race of miracles for death
against miracles for life. It was creepy. Unless you had the vision
to get far above it and take a long and truly global view, it was
all of it more than a little wacky, and I didn't have the requisite
vision or brains. (It was plain to me that day in Washington that
proximity to power which plans and executes global strategy is not
for the likes of me.)

What was there left then? Tolstoy, Gandhi? Tolstoy had wonderful words; Gandhi had remarkable personal courage; but could
words or personal courage stop the leaders who push the buttons
for more and more scientific and interesting global wars? What was
left but the doctors?

I kept being haunted, after that Washington day, by the story
told by the man of Galilee, the one about that man who, after the
priest and the Levite had both passed by the poor fellow who had
fallen among thieves, stopped and bound up the wounds of the
victim and poured in oil and wine. That man was the good Samaritan. You remember the man of Galilee, after telling it, asking:

"Which now of these three, thinkest thou, was neighbor unto
him that fell among thieves?"

Religion had failed to make men neighbors. Beautiful words had
failed. It was the *act* of the Samaritan that made him a neighbor.

With their new and fantastically growing power over pain, over
death, and over misery, our modern doctors could now multiply
acts of mercy *ad infinitum*. I do not say that this will ever make the
cruelty and murder of science ridiculous and finally intolerable. Yet
it is this possibility that makes me want to write as truly as possible about the bright and the dark side of life among the doctors.
Cy Young, the man who urged me on to it and about whom presently I'm going to tell, was, in his single-mindedness for life, the
strangest possible contrast to the first global ruler, the President.

※ ※ ※ ※

The director was living on borrowed time, between two deaths. In 1933 he had been next to miraculously cured of what should have been fatal cancer. Over a period of twenty years he had saved more lives than all Michigan's doctors put together. He looked like a British colonel, only brighter than most of them. Now he sat chain-smoking cigarettes, coughing terribly, drinking whisky-soda, coughing. He was not kidding himself that he had much longer to live.

"Forget the President's brushoff," he growled. "Hell, Paul, as a politician you're a good writer. Get back to your workbench. This science is turning the docs into a new breed of cats. Find 'em and tell the world about 'em."

Then he couldn't go on, for coughing, and his face was gray. We were low because he wouldn't be with us long. He encouraged us very much and we were sad he wouldn't be here to read about himself in the book for which we then had no title.

※ ※ ※ ※

CHAPTER II

Doctor to Five Million

》》 《《

THE power in the hands of the plainest physician is the best gift of God, so far, to mankind. From having been hardly more than a bedside consoler fifty years ago, every doctor now more and more has the actual decision as to whether a patient shall live or die. This power is not human. It is chemical. It is not magical, but it is immensely greater than any doctor who uses it.

Take simple examples. Sulfonamide crystals—God's powder, they've been nicknamed justly—have brought small-town surgeons a life-saving mastery as great as that of the most expensive city specialist, when faced with the emergency of the attempted rescue of a victim of perforating appendicitis. In such a fight the humblest surgeon now has far more chance for victory than the most celebrated knife-man had ten years ago. Similarly, sulfadiazine and penicillin, in the hands of a country doctor, can cut down the lobar pneumonia death rate far more drastically than the most potent serums could do it in the hands of the savants of the Rockefeller Institute Hospital in the 1920's, and this is equally true with the often fatal cerebrospinal meningitis.

This chemical revolution was exploding on a dozen other fronts of the fight for life. From somewhat bumbling though admirable bed-side comforters, rank-and-file doctors were being transfigured into life-savers.

When I began working among doctors as a microbe hunter years ago, many physicians were pretending to save lives but mighty few were doing much more than stand by while nature did the trick for them. It was the microbe hunters, sanitarians, and public health men who were doing the life-saving. Mister Leeuwenhoek, a Dutch janitor, gave his discovery of microbes to Mister Pasteur, a mere chemist. Leaders of the medical faculty fought Pasteur viciously when he tried to put his first life-saving weapons into their unwilling hands.

In my early days among doctors, knowing that public health's live-saving was not primarily done by M.D.'s, I asked myself—just what *is* a doctor? In human history that learned degree has been conferred upon a grotesque variety of people—saints profound in Church doctrines, dignified doctors of divinity, cooks on old sailing vessels and in northern logging camps, capitalists who endow universities, generals who direct mass slaughter, chiropractors, osteopaths and horse doctors.

The real doctor—or what's called in the loftiest medical circles "the physician"—is the man at the bedside, the man with the knife, and the man legally entitled to write a prescription. Though I am a Ph.D. in bacteriology, most M.D.'s (except in academic circles) address me as mister; this used to irk me, but it does so no longer. I am happy to go by the title mister, and to call all who are not M.D.'s—mister. The M.D.'s—from the time they receive their diplomas—are intensely proud of being "doctor"; and at last they are gaining the right to this pride. They are becoming the front-line soldiers in the fight for life.

Now that this fight has spread far out beyond the microbe hunters and healthmen of yesteryear, the physicians are on the verge of adventures even more astounding than the conquest of microbes. Proteins, liver extracts and yeasts, anti-biotics, synthetic vitamins and hormones—as the doctors learn how to use them—give promise not only of lengthening human life but hint a transfiguration of humanity.

If the rank and file doctor still doesn't believe this, who can blame him? I used to, but don't any more. While I still remained a bit ironical about physicians who sneered at this new science without so much as trying it, a man not himself an M.D., though a doctor of public health, began setting me straight.

II

It was very fine to be alive in the same world with this curious man, Clifford Caudy Young. Though we had lived only ninety miles apart in Michigan for many years, though he had every right to be called the state's first citizen, my self-complacency (thinking I knew too many remarkable men already) had kept me away from him till 1938, just the year before the President blasted our health plan hopes. C. C. Young was the builder and master mind of the Public Health Laboratory where a death-fighting army spots microbes and makes serums and plasma—all free—for all Michigan's five million people. From the world over healthmen and microbe hunters had been making pilgrimages to this modern shrine from which life is dispensed for nothing. Maybe it was because he was such a determined enemy of his own notoriety that I had passed him by so long.

He was hardly ever mentioned by any title but plain "Cy" Young. If by doctor you mean a man who carries a black bag about, who is licensed to write prescriptions, who obscures diseases and their symptoms by Greek and Latin names, who has the legal right (with or without adequate training) to cut into people's bellies, chests or brains without being held responsible for consequences, then Cy Young could not be called a doctor. On the other hand if by doctor you mean a man who dedicated his life to giving death-fighting tools to all physicians, who fought savagely to save all human life regardless of its moral merit or its bank account, who battled commercial traffic in life-saving blood with such bitterness that he made it an infamy for any human being to die because of a lack of dollars to buy blood—then Cy Young *was* a doctor and one of the greatest of our time.

"Cy Young will be remembered as saving more lives in the past twenty-five years than all us Michigan doctors put together," said L. G. Christian, a distinguished physician, the day Cy died.

Cy Young became unforgettable the moment I met him. His gray eyes were eager and sad. His eyes blazed intensely from a pain-lined face that had a sad, haunting compassion. His eyes seemed to be boring right through me wanting to get some incredibly mysterious news across to me. He was tall and burly, looking like a prematurely old English colonel who had seen too many wars, yet he moved with springy vigor and always eagerly, as if an unseen hand beckoned him.

The first day I met him he made no bones about it: he was not quite a five-year "cure" after a desperate operation for an almost 100 per cent incurable cancer of the kidney. That, he said, explained the furious urgency I noted in him. He said he was moving so fast to meet a deadline, to make his state health department laboratory a center sending out every weapon of medical science to wipe out microbic maladies, to combat virus deaths, and then (what no public health laboratory had ever presumed to do) to shove back old age.

"You may think I'm nuts," he growled, "but I'm working to get all that power into a network within thirty minutes of every doctor in Michigan." He was a tremendous fan for doctors good and bad because he said this science would end up by making the bad ones pretty good. It wasn't Cy himself who was responsible, mind you; about himself he was detached and impersonal; it was this wonderful science!

As I sat in his beautiful tile-walled administrative office with its fireplace and paintings of his champion dogs and its big light windows, and looked at him, dressed with an offhand English elegance, a man of the world, immensely cultured—it was impossible to associate this man and his surroundings with my notion of what a public healthman should be. His fierce eyes took in my puzzlement and he laughed and began telling me how he had got to be the breed of cats (his favorite expression) that he was. (This narrative beginning that October 1938 day took Cy and many others six years to tell—up to and beyond that day he died in the exceptionally poignant spring of 1944.)

III

He had legitimately inherited his own pioneering. His mother was the first white child born in Kansas Territory and Cy himself had left home for good at the age of thirteen, going along with men down the Chisholm trail to stake land claims in Oklahoma. From his mother's story he was a strange independent youngster. He fell into a deep hole and when a neighbor offered to help him out he snarled, "Let me alone, this is God's business." Then he scrambled out himself. A neighbor woman asked him to take her sick cat away and get rid of it, and he killed the cat instantly before her eyes, telling her (without words) that she'd have to take the consequences of her cruelty.

In high school at Rochester, New York, he blended sophistication with scholastic brilliance. A heart-breaker and gambler, he hung round the corner drugstore in the widest peg-top pants of the early 1900's and finished the four-year high school course in two. By mysterious financial operations at the Saratoga race track in the summer he supported his chemical engineering education at Lehigh and then went back to Kansas University to graduate, take his Ph.D. in chemistry, and become Director of the Kansas water survey.

In those days around 1910, keeping folks from swallowing each other's microbe-laden discharges was about all there was to public health. Doctors had little or nothing to do with it, and Cy had little or nothing to do with doctors. Swat the fly, no roller towels, individual drinking cups in trains—these were his public health slogans in Kansas. In the cultural desert that Kansas then was, Cy made his own oasis and sent off to Wales for a first edition of Fox's *Book of Martyrs*. As a camp sanitarian in the army in World War I he began to be thrown with doctors and his gray eyes began to note the first gleam of a hint of a change in their then benighted bedside art. They were beginning to be exposed to bacteriology, to chemistry, to all the new science now lavishly applied to make our boys more efficient killers.

This gave Cy his own private dream of a new kind of doctor, so in 1919 he came to Michigan as state bacteriologist when to Michigan's doctors microbe hunting was not much more than a name. Those days Michigan's diphtheria death rate was the highest in the U. S. A., as many as 1,200 children dying in one year. He might well have asked what the state's good doctors were doing about it. Hadn't diphtheria antitoxin been discovered way back in 1896? Wasn't it already known that large doses of anti-diphtheria serum, given early—one or two days after the onset of the sickness—were almost surely life-saving? It was Cy Young's shrewdness to ask these questions of himself, and not publicly of physicians.

Altogether the state's condition in regard to preventable death left a good deal to be desired. Typhoid epidemics exploded, even at Ann Arbor, under the noses of the professors of the University of Michigan Medical School. Also smallpox persisted in Michigan —a pestilence that should have been obliterated long ago by vaccination. Cy's new quarters as state bacteriologist testified to the community's low esteem of public health work.

The laboratory consisted of three dingy rooms and an alcove. Its most impressive apparatus was an array of meteorological gadgets acquired in days when disease was thought to be due to noxious air. Cy called his little staff of five young men and women together.

He climbed up on a chair before the dusty shelves and one after another he smashed the ridiculous barometers and thermometers to bits on the laboratory floor. "Now—we'll start from scratch," he growled amiably. His technicians could only look glum at what remained—a leaky sterilizer, an old microscope, a few hundred test-tubes and a dozen Petri dishes that had bottoms but no tops.

Cy got wind of an auction of surplus World War I equipment at a nearby Base Hospital and bought $50,000 worth of gleaming microbe-hunting tools for $4,000. Then, though his experience was principally that of a water-supply sanitarian, he began reaching down into the throats of Michigan's children to track down the why of the infamy of the state's ten to twelve thousand annual cases of diphtheria.

He was a martinet. Night after night with his technicians he rolled thousands of swabs. He seemed not to have to sleep and stayed later than the rest to finish sterilizing gallons of culture medium. Mornings (Cy the only one not sleepy) they hurried out to schools—Cy taking care earnestly to ask not only the permission but co-operation of the local saw-bones—and here they made children stand in line saying "ah-h-h" and gagging at throat cultures. Then Cy gave Michigan's citizens (and the doctors) the news that hundreds of seeming healthy kids were spreaders of the choking death.

Though this survey was exactly as far as Cy's duties extended, his hatred of this needless death had no bounds. The new toxin-anti-toxin preventive had just been perfected; the Michigan Health Department hadn't a sou to buy any of it; hardly a practicing physician in the state had so much as heard of it and even if they had, wouldn't this preventive take away their business of *treating* diphtheria—and sometimes curing it? Cy was a great beggar, for others. He wrote to a drug house pleading for enough of the new preventive to stage a demonstration to show that diphtheria could be wiped out of an institution where yearly it took its toll of many poor little idiot children. From the drug house he received a cool reply that he could purchase the preventive at any corner drugstore.

"Damn them," growled Cy, "that'll be the most expensive two-cent stamp they've ever mailed out."

Covering his fury, Young sought an audience with Michigan's Governor Alexander J. Groesbeck, already famed as the most economical administrator in Michigan's history, a stern man whose veins were reputed to contain ice water. Cy hid his own unorthodox belief that the greatest sin is to put a cash value on any human life. He set out to prove to the Governor, in very quiet words and respectfully, that preventable death when allowed to persist wastes money.

"We're hospitalizing around 10,000 cases of diphtheria a year," Cy argued. "And that's costing the taxpayers over $500,000." Groesbeck looked at him, dead-pan.

Then Cy took a gamble, looked into the Governor's cool eyes

and right through him: "I'll cut your diphtheria death rate in half in ten years' time if you'll get me $75,000 a year to immunize the state's children," he promised.

It was the rankest kind of shot in the dark. It had never been demonstrated on a large scale anywhere. Would the doctors sanction such a cut in their business? How the devil would you get the children together for mass immunization—it had to be done before school age to be effective. Would parents permit wholesale shots into the arms of their children? Hadn't there been disasters where the preventive went bad, killing kids instead of protecting them?

Groesbeck looked at this strange apostle. The Governor's coldness hid a warm heart that beat with Cy's against suffering. His cold brain that knew a man when he saw one made rapid calculations—but not in terms of money. He did not permit himself a smile. He said: "I'll try to get you the money. I'll sponsor a bill for free diphtheria preventive and antitoxin."

Then Cy had to turn himself into a politician—even worse, into a lobbyist which was dangerous for any state civil servant. Drughouse lobbyists (with the aid of a Christian Science legislator) stalled the diphtheria bill so that it was as good as dead the last day of the 1921 legislative session. Cy sniffed around the state capitol and discovered a merry group of state representatives who called themselves "the assassins." They had appointed themselves killers of all legislation that was contrary to Governor Groesbeck's wishes. The head killer was a humorous cove, George Welsh.

"What a salesman Cy was," said Welsh, remembering. "He wanted every kid to live, yet he was practical, and he never wanted a damn thing for himself!" Yes, said Welsh, the assassins would turn themselves into life-savers—for Cy. At 4 A.M. that last all-night legislative session, George Welsh (what a humanitarian, said Cy) marched down the aisle with a big bunch of newspapers under his arm, placed them under the seat of the Chairman of the Ways and Means Committee, lit them under the solon's behind, and amid the flames George shouted that he was smoking out the antitoxin bill.

George and Cy were like kids raising hell. They button-holed a venerable legislator just returning from one of his necessarily frequent prostatic trips to the washroom. Didn't he remember, hadn't he told them of an awful diphtheria epidemic in Sanilac? They all but propped the old gentleman up while he told the legislature how the black diphtheria back in the 'eighties had killed 75 children in his home town and what were we but murderers to allow this to go on? When tears were dried (the old man was really good in there) the antitoxin law was passed unanimously in the dawn of that winter morning. Cy and George Welsh and the assassins hurried to the hotel singing that they were a little prairie flower growing drier by the hour—which they remedied all the rest of the day. Cy was an epic drinker in dark hours and sunny.

The new law gave Cy not only the money to buy diphtheria preventive but much more than that. Writing up the law with George Welsh, Cy said he knew he could manufacture these life-saving materials far more cheaply than he could buy them from drug houses. So they framed the law—it was really a historic frame-up— so that Cy's state laboratory would be credited with every dollar he'd save by setting up his own diphtheria-fighting factory. The $75,000 profit piled up in two years was enough, plus a small state grant, to build the first unit of the present 22-building laboratory northwest of Lansing, Michigan.

The consequences of the antitoxin law were almost historic; Michigan's death toll from diphtheria faded far more swiftly than Young had promised, so that now hardly more than forty children die yearly instead of twelve hundred; and the former $500,000 hospital bill for diphtheria has all but vanished; and on diphtheria alone Cy saved Michigan more than all the money expended for its modern laboratory that fights every kind of death. Deep in him Cy knew he might really have made history. Though the doctors hadn't raised a finger to help him originally, yet they didn't seem to mind the loss of their diphtheria business and many of them did become anti-diphtheria inoculators. Cy knew that if all of them, or even most of them, had pitched in, then the choking death would have been stamped out of Michigan utterly so that not one baby would die. If this made Cy sad, he never showed it.

Though some kids still needlessly died, *more would die if the doctors got their backs up and began to buck him.*

I V

Young had a trick of getting along with and using the strangest variety of citizens. In the early 1920's, with the help of salt makers, he started gunning for a disease that was none of his official business whatever. In those days goiter was so prevalent in the state that it was called "the Michigan disease." There were goiter wards in many city hospitals; the cutting out of enlarged thyroid glands was a splendid business for surgeons, and Michigan goiters contributed more than their share to the hecatombs of sliced-out thyroid glands that were a good part of the foundation of the early prosperity of the Mayo Clinic at Rochester, Minnesota, and the Crile Clinic in Cleveland, Ohio, where the goiter business became the greatest example of surgical mass production.

Young (because it was hard for him to sleep any length of time) was a restless continuous nighthawk reader, and at the beginning of the nineteen-twenties he learned that simple goiter seemed due to a lack of iodine in the human body, and that the disease had actually been prevented by feeding iodine pills to a few hundred Akron, Ohio, school children. How to get that preventive to everybody in Michigan? Cy mulled over it. You certainly wouldn't start off by selling the idea to surgeons who were sending their children to college—partly—by highly profitable cutting out of goiters!

Young started his new battle by a curious flanking attack, getting chummy with Michigan salt manufacturers. He got the State Health Commissioner to call in a group of these salt men. They heard the amazing news—that goiter nowhere in the world was considered a public health problem, but that a state survey (instigated by Young) proved that, where iodine was lacking in drinking water, there goiter deformed and partly disabled as high as 90 per cent of children. And vice versa: where iodine was abundant, there goiter was not.

Interesting and so what, said the salt men. Just this—if the salt men would fortify all table salt with just a trace of sodium iodide—it wouldn't cost them more than $25,000 a year, and they could charge that off to promotion—they would share the glory of wiping this disease out of Michigan. Cy prodded their consciences. He talked to them quietly, not evangelistically, and it was hard for them not to keep looking into his gray eyes, so intent, so earnest. If science can guard a few hundred children in Akron, isn't it a shame to withhold it from the millions of Michigan children threatened? He melted the salt men.

Today the disease that used to kill many new-born babies of goiterous mothers, that prepared the ground for fatal thyroid cancers, that sapped the strength of scores of thousands, is vanishing from Michigan.

V

Young was able to pull off the astounding variety of his raids on disease and death because he was a wizard at keeping in the background. His name appeared on no scientific publications celebrating the goiter victory. He was one of that unhappily rare breed of men who instinctively know that you can get anything done if you don't care who gets the credit for it. Hating personal notoriety, Young never set himself up for a mark by denouncing the doctors for their lamentable backwardness in preventive medicine. On the contrary he shrewdly bribed them into public health interest by giving them new tools for their trade of fighting sickness. "Preventive medicine—what's that?" he would say, looking at a doctor innocently.

In the early 1920's he had to step carefully to avoid hurting the medical profession's toes, commercially—because, after all, wasn't treating sick people a business like another? Who could deny that Young's new-fangled science was a threat to the doctors' pocketbooks? "Don't think of it," said one distinguished old Michigan physician to his son who wanted to enter medicine. "You'll not make a living, my boy. Diphtheria's on the way out. So's TB. Why, son, *my* father put me through medical school on typhoid fever—and where is it now?"

Up north among the Norway and white pines he planted around his summer house on the shore of yellow-emerald-blue Torch Lake, Cy pondered how to fetch the doctors. He was a simple thinker. His horse sense told him that his job was simply individual health multiplied by 5,000,000. It was the family doctor who had personal contact with individuals. Young had a lucky day when Dr. L. G. Christian came to his laboratory asking help, help. Christian remembers that day as marking his start in scientific medicine.

"In the middle 1920's, in Lansing, Michigan," said Greg Christian, "we docs were totally incompetent to practice scientific medicine. About all we could do was to tell the difference between an acute appendix and lobar pneumonia," said Greg. "We didn't even have labs where we could do a simple blood count."

Greg remembers his first contact with Young as a bit terrifying. "I've read in a medical journal of a guy drawing blood from a patient with bad St. Vitus's dance," said Greg to Cy. "Then you took the blood serum, and shot it into the patient's spinal column, and it was supposed to help."

"Where did you get that wild idea," growled Cy, glaring. "For God's sake, don't try it. No, I won't help you! Do you want me to be an accomplice to murder?"

Greg, who has a fast-burning temper, looked at Cy, thinking, what a bull-thrower. Then Cy softened. "If you need any kind of scientific lab work, Dr. Christian," he said, "come and see us, we'll always be glad to help you."

Greg remembers this as the beginning of modern medicine in Lansing and then Ingham County and then spreading statewide into Michigan's burned-over sticks. Greg became Cy's medical missionary and undercover medical press agent for the state laboratory. He was, though quick to "burn," very genial with his round face and merry brown eyes glittering behind his spectacles. Greg began teaching more and more Michigan doctors how, for every preventable death Cy was knocking out, they would find another disease (not yet preventable) to fight more effectively (and profitably) if they would just get a little scientific information into their heads and use Cy's laboratory.

That was Greg's salty way of putting it. So now Cy's laboratorians began giving Michigan's doctors blood tests to dominate diabetes by the scientific control of their new insulin treatment; to trace chemically the devastation of kidney disease; to diagnose pernicious anemia. All these tests were free to the doctor, mind you. They took nothing away from the doctor's fee and the doctor felt good because his conscience told him he was doing more for his sick people than just comforting them and giving them a pain-killer and something to keep their bowels open.

"My God, did I use that laboratory!" said Greg, reminiscing. "Every patient with a fever and a heart murmur had blood drawn and Cy's folks would look for the green streptococcus. Every patient with suspected pneumonia had his sputum typed for pneumococcus."

Greg beamed. "Nothing was too much for Cy and his gang to do. I got the notion people were infected with the intestinal parasite, giardia," said Greg. "I sent bushels and bushels of you know what to Cy's lab and they never protested," he said, chuckling.

Within ten years of the time of his coming to Michigan, the number of physicians using Cy's laboratory service free, starting from a handful, had passed 5,000 and included nearly all of the state's doctors outside Detroit where hospital and commercial laboratories were already available. Cy opened branch laboratories to bring this new science quick to backwoods doctors in life-or-death emergencies. Laboratories independent of the state health department broke out like a beneficent rash in Michigan's hospitals. Young himself became a legend among Michigan physicians. By serving them, not by talking. By the devotion of men like Greg Christian. That was lucky because Greg—deadly honest—was on the way up to anonymous power in the mysterious medical-political world of the hospital coat-rooms. Greg was a fighter you didn't monkey with, and you'd better have him for a friend.

VI

By now Cy's Lansing laboratory had become world-famous. Far ahead of the current hullabaloo about venereal disease, Cy had sensed the need of a simple syphilis test to replace the expensive and ponderous Wassermann reaction. Out of his budget Cy finagled a substantial sum of research money. Keeping his own name out of it, he helped plan, encouraged, and in fact fathered the inexpensive and accurate Kahn test that has made possible today's uncovering of millions of cases of the pale horror, and Cy saw to it that all credit went to Reuben Kahn.

It was a shrewd business stroke as well as life-saving science. All states outside Michigan and 12 foreign countries bought Kahn syphilis test materials from Cy's laboratory, in a few years netting more than $150,000 which Cy proceeded to tuck away for a rainy day in his death fight. Young now began to see a vision of the laboratory's self-supporting future. Public health too expensive? He'd show 'em how to make public health pay its own way; he'd teach the world how to get public health for nothing. Then, one night, driving back from Detroit alone, he was doubled up by devastating pain and when he got home, here was hemorrhage. From a kidney? In the next few days he help diagnose his own kidney cancer and hopped the train for Baltimore to take the months of agony of deep-X-ray bombardment to shrink the tumor, ending up with a terrific operation to remove it by famous Dr. Hugh Hampton Young.

VII

From the edge of death Cy dragged himself back to Michigan, gray-faced and poisoned by X-rays. Would he live two years more? Possibly. This was 1933, and he came back to trouble. The state's new serum law (how enthusiastically he'd finagled it!) empowered him to make and to give Michigan's people, free, not only diphtheria preventive but smallpox, typhoid and rabies vaccines and serums for lockjaw, pneumonia, and scarlet fever—for any infection for which a proved specific preventive or cure existed. It seemed socialistic. Greg Christian had had to fight hard at a State Medical Society meeting to keep the physicians from issuing a pontifical resolution against it. But that wasn't now the danger.

The trouble was that Cy hadn't the laboratory space to make these life-saving biologicals. More and more progressive doctors were clamoring for them; the doctors were almost unanimous for Cy; it was only a minority of old fogey medical politicians who opposed this free life for the people. How to get the serum-factory? It was the deep depression, and the state's financial cupboard was bare. Cy called in two men from his outlandish assortment of cronies, and they were the farthest possible remove from doctors. Representative Joe Green was a small, gray-haired worldly-wise solon who knew where the political bodies were buried. Representative Tracy Southworth was open-custard-pie-faced, genial and who could help liking him? These two took Cy to see Relief Administrator Louis Nims.

Cy worked his mesmerism upon this dark-haired, handsome and able man. Did the federal government want to do something besides leaf-raking and boondoggling? He showed Nims plans for a new laboratory building, cost—only $500,000.

But where was the necessary local sponsor's contribution? Without it you simply couldn't get federal money and the state hadn't a sou. Then Young produced the $150,000 his laboratory had netted from the sale of those Kahn syphilis test materials. It was perfect timing. "The time to shoot bear is when bear are around," growled Cy, chuckling to his young laboratory key men when they all were celebrating.

It was victory as Cy designed his functionally beautiful new laboratory building and even then he sensed that his time was not too long and that buildings are really nothing. Bricks, tile, and steel don't save human life and who were going to be the brains for the hundreds of searching hands now working in his modern citadel against death? "It's Michigan's five million people you're working for," Cy was always haranguing them, getting that excitement into the lowest-paid clerk and lab-swipe. The danger to his pet, his baby, his life, this laboratory, was that the best he could pay his best men was a pittance. One morning Dr. J. T. Tripp, his key man, indispensable to all serum production, laid a telegram on Cy's desk.

Tripp was a slender, drawling, dreamy-eyed chemist. Lanky, Yankee, and dependable was Ted Tripp and imaginative in new tricks to save money in serum production and to make serum more life-saving—and Tripp was poor as a church mouse. The telegram Cy now read offered Tripp three times his present pay and the chance, maybe, ultimately to become a drug house magnate. Cy brooded. He dragged at his perpetual cigarette. He jumped up and in his always hurried manner walked Ted to a big window. Then Cy swept his hand with drama towards the site of still another pro- jected production building. *"Somebody's* going to have the fun of building it and running it," Cy said. Then he turned and jabbed Tripp hard on the chest and looked him hard in the eye.

"Do you want money or do you want fun?" Cy asked him.

Then he chuckled. "You didn't know, Tripp, that I was a mil- lionaire one time? Another guy and I discovered an alum lake in Colorado. Got out a big pile of the expensive stuff. Deal closed to sell out with my share a million bucks and there weren't any taxes those days," Cy laughed, bronchitically.

"It hadn't rained in that month in the country for years. That very night—cloudburst. Washed the whole pile of alum back into the lake. Deal canceled."

Cy looked at Tripp. "I've never worried about money again. My money problem was solved for life by that rainstorm," said Cy. Tripp stayed around to have fun.

In twenty-five years only one of his key men left Cy for the higher pay that drug and biological manufacturers were constantly offering them because of the superb lab training Cy gave them. Young brought all of them up from nothing, worked them like dogs, trained them like dogs—it was a good way to handle people because aren't we more firm as well as kindly with dogs than we are with human beings? Yet again he flattered them, making them share his vision. He was incessantly calling huddles of his laboratorians from low to high around enormous charts dramatizing their death fight's progress. He'd drag at his cigarette; he'd sweep his long powerful fingers down lines indicating waning whooping cough or pneumonia—

"Lowering Michigan's death rate is *our* life work," he'd growl and then cough terribly as if he himself were not for life much longer. He'd drag at his cigarette and point to zero death rates at the chart's baseline. "That's what it's fun to gun for," he'd say.

VIII

Towards the end of the 1930's Cy had stretched his miraculous survival from that incurable cancer to five years. He slept less and less. Against all advice he chain-smoked right through fits of asthmatic coughing. By this time I had come to know him closely, and there was a swift recklessness (seemingly) in the moves he made to build his baby, that laboratory, into the most powerful death-fighting instrument ever known, anywhere. He was a scientist, administrator, political finagler, businessman and more than a bit of a brigand. His methods were impolite, indecorous, sometimes not quite legal and in the strictest sense, occasionally, hardly ethical.

For a long time he'd dreamed of a division to fight virus deaths now that visible microbes were on the way to be conquered, and no state health department in the country had a virus laboratory. It was 1938, and the National Foundation for Infantile Paralysis was getting set to disburse its huge March of Dimes money for the fight against polio. A grant had just been authorized for a long-term search to find a sulfa or some such magic bullet to cure polio and it would be like looking for a needle in a haystack with almost sure defeat at the end of it. Here was the money, a polio virologist had consented to try it—but he had no laboratory. Alas, he was *persona non grata* mainly for racial reasons; you know what I mean. High up in the penthouse of the Hotel St. Moritz, in New York City, Cy and I talked it over.

He jumped up suddenly. "Let me have that feller," Cy said.

"It'll be an almost sure wash-out," I said. "It's more than likely they'll never find an anti-polio chemical—"

"How can I get that grant?" roared Cy.

I told him the awesome name of the scientist whose word was law in the Foundation. He was the big man not only in the Foundation but in the hospital of the world's then greatest research laboratory. He was in New York City right now. "Let me go and proposition him," Cy roared again.

I remonstrated. Cy, coughing and lighting another cigarette, pulled on his coat and put his elegantly sloppy hat down over his eyes and hurried out the door. The days that followed were unforgettable. Triumphantly in a couple of hours he hurried back with the okay of the tsar of polio science for a polio grant as good as in the bag. The homeless virologist would be happy to migrate to the sticks of Michigan. But to house him Cy had no laboratory space at all.

Cy grabbed the telephone, long distance, "Yes, that you, Cummings?" This was Dr. Don Cummings, the 34-year-old engineer-microbe-hunter-doctor that Cy had already picked out to become the laboratory's heart and directing brain. "Buy all necessary materials at once to build a virus lab on top the east animal house," Cy commanded.

"You say we haven't got the money?" Cy said. "Fine! But buy all necessary materials today. There's a polio outbreak in Detroit. Emergency. You know. Time to shoot bear's when bear's around!"

Cy dropped the telephone back into its cradle and laughed and laughed and took a gulp of whisky and a deep drag on his cigarette. He alarmed me. Quietly now he told me that building, without the state money to back it, might mean his own and Don Cummings' hides as public healthmen. The state's red tape required three bids on every building project. "Don will do it, don't worry," said Cy.

That very afternoon Don closed all necessary contracts. All items had to be approved by the state purchasing agent. That day Don wangled blanket approvals without a cent to back him. When Cy got off the plane and hurried to the laboratory two days later, trucks were rolling into the grounds and bricklayers were already busy.

Cy hurried over to the office of the State Administrative Board. Yes, what he'd done was irregular, if not criminal. For Michigan's threatened children! Three weeks after the board members had signed the virus laboratory appropriation, the virologist was in the new laboratory shooting paralytic death from Detroit's children into monkeys. So began a search that might mean a step towards a coming preventive for polio. And here was Cy's modern virus laboratory, the first in any state health department in America, that would begin to search out means to spot and fight all kinds of virus infections for Michigan's doctors.

As he felt his own time running out, Cy's training of his key youngsters to their coming responsibility for life or death became more laconic, abrupt, savage. Ted Tripp called Young by phone, confessing they were caught short on serum against a scarlet fever outbreak. "We do have one batch that meets Scarlet Fever Committee standards," said Tripp.

"Does it meet our own?" asked Cy. "No, not quite," Ted admitted.

"Would you shoot that stuff into your own kids?" Cy asked.

"Well—no," Ted answered.

"Then what the hell are you bothering *me* for," Cy rasped and banged up the phone.

His laboratorians were doglike to Cy if for no other reason than because he wanted nothing at all for himself. They knew he himself was getting a pittance for running a multi-million-dollar business and at the same time they knew he'd fight for their last miserable dollar. One autumn all the workers—Cy himself excepted—got the word by letter that a ten per cent contribution to the party in political power would be expected from their next paychecks.

Cy hurried out to see the party big shots. "Stop monkeying with my kids," he said. "They're too poor now. They won't pay a penny. If you've gotta have that kind of graft, just come and see me personally."

For his now more than 250 workers Cy turned his laboratory

into a death-fighting university. He made them all feel as if a discovery as famous as the Kahn test might lurk in any humdrum microbe-hunting routine.

"Go ahead and try it—if it amuses you," said Cy to Dr. Pearl Kendrick, who believed she could turn a dubious vaccine into a real whooping cough preventive. For ten years Cy guided her work and got financial support for Kendrick. Working overtime, nights, in addition to her duties as Director of the Grand Rapids branch laboratory, she developed the now world-famous vaccine that has helped cut deaths of children from 529 in 1920 down to only 36 in 1945 in Michigan.

IX

Cy's prestige among public healthmen and philanthropic foundations was now immense, and his laboratory was recognized not only as a developer but a mass-testing instrument for new death-fighting weapons. The remote and austere Commonwealth Fund in New York City advanced him $100,000 to fight Michigan's pneumonia. Michigan's doctors were beginning to change from kindly bedside bumblers into crack diagnosticians and public healthmen, thinking not only of individual patients but, as Cy did, in the terms of the lives of Michigan's five million. Greg Christian prodded Cy onward. "You're giving us the chance to type pneumonia, you're giving us free serum, with that and these new sulfas," said Greg; "if we could spot pneumonia the first day—we'd knock the hell out of your pneumonia death rate, just as we did diphtheria."

Cy arranged that doctors could send qualified office girls to the state laboratory for microbe-hunting training to type and spot pneumonia microbes. His serum against the most common types of pneumococci—free and instantly available—cut Michigan's pneumonia death rate in half even before the coming of sulfas.

Amid his life-saving triumphs he was curiously versatile experimenting in fields completely removed from chemistry and microbe hunting. He bred champion spaniels and French poodles. He built beautiful furniture and household utensils out of rare woods that he collected from Africa and Australia. He became a skilled worker in silver, and he was a collector of everything under the sun except such obvious items as stamps or coins. He accumulated buttons that became a museum of the history of buttons from all parts of the world. He owned what was probably the world's outstanding collection of pipes from those smoked by Chinese opium addicts and prehistoric Indians to those given him personally, by Harry Lauder. Yet he was no hoarder, and he lavished the objects of his collections and the results of his craftsmanship on anybody interested but particularly upon people who might befriend the laboratory. He collected modern first editions whose coming value he predicted with uncanny literary insight, but most of all he collected people.

He lived outside himself completely.

He stopped a forlorn woman walking a very sick spaniel in Washington Square in New York City, glared at her kindly, told her: "Madam, your dog is dying. Let me take care of it and I'll get you as fine a red spaniel as you've ever seen, in place of it."

This woman turned out to be a great artist in ceramics and this friendship was the beginning of Cy's own ceramics collection.

In a dingy down-at-the-heel little tavern, where he stopped to drink on his way up to Northern Michigan, he saw that the child of the proprietors was severely cross-eyed and immediately by long-distance phone arranged for a curative operation with the ophthalmologists at the University Hospital. Mind you, he'd never seen these saloonkeepers before and very likely would not see them again.

He loved life and was a stoic at his own life's ebbing, and more and more savagely he hated the death of any human being who did not have to die. He lived the life of two active men because he slept so little, and he knew sleeping more wouldn't stave off his own particular inevitable.

In his last years every tragedy became his own and was the signal for his staging a fight to avoid its repetition if that were practicable. In 1943 in a Michigan hospital a workman, smashed up in an automobile accident, died of shock because he couldn't immediately contact friends who'd guarantee that hospital that he could pay for live-saving plasma. Cy saw red. Plasma must be free. For everybody. His young executives in the laboratory, his doctor friends, all told him that was ridiculous. At $30 per pint, the price of commercial plasma, it might cost $600 to save one life! It'd bankrupt the laboratory.

That year Cy was feeling a misery worse than that of his old bronchitis in his chest. Recurrence of his cancer? Hardly—it was ten years since that miraculous operation. But he was white-faced now, instead of gray, and we all were worried. He pulled himself together. Those so-and-so's—letting that guy die because he couldn't reach into his pocket to pay for the blood! He went to Governor Harry Kelly. Coughing continually, he recited his death-fighting swan-song.

"You can *bury* a baby for $125," Cy told the Governor. "It might cost all of $500 to save that same kid with plasma you'd have to buy at the drugstore. If you want to bring *money* into this argument, it'd be a damn sight cheaper to let the babies die!"

That speech started Michigan's historic state-wide free plasma program, in 1943. From the time Michigan's people began giving their blood, free, for Cy's lab to process into plasma, the use of this wonderful life-saving fluid by Michigan's doctors has increased eightfold. Already they've saved the lives of thousands of premature babies, mothers in childbirth, smashed-up motorists and injured workmen and patients who, without plasma, could not have been built up to stand desperate, life-saving operations.

As I sat by Cy's bedside in the spring of 1944—he was off his feet for good now—he told me how he had pulled off the last of his great raids against needless death.

"I just made Harry Kelly see that it isn't cricket to make human blood an article of commerce any time that blood might save a human life," he said.

"That gag is something for the big book, Cy," I said.

"You'd better jot it down then, son," he said with just the faintest sadness in his smile. "You won't hear it again."

Though he was the opposite of religious in any orthodox sense, there was little doubt that Cy would be ready to face St. Peter that spring of 1944. From his laboratory more than 2,000,000 doses of life-saving serums and preventives were going out free to Michigan's doctors, who, in the same time, were sending in more than a million specimens for free diagnosis. If it had not been for Cy's lab, Michigan's people would have had to pay millions of dollars for these products and for their examinations—and the majority would not have got them because they were too expensive.

There never had been a year when the wholesale commercial value of the laboratory's production hadn't far exceeded the state's total budget for running it. Yet Cy's state laboratory—call it socialism if you want to—had generated plenty of death-fighting free enterprise in the best sense, according to our American profit system. Spotted all over Michigan there are now 156 local hospital laboratories bringing science to local doctors—for people who can pay for it.

As he lay dying—it was a second cancer, this time of the lungs, that was killing him—Cy planned new fights for the lives of Michigan's five million. He mapped out a plan for free penicillin for all who might not have the wherewithal for this new yellow magic. If he had lived, this actually might have come true.

In the spring of 1944, Rhea and I brought him wake robins from our Wake Robin valley, and we will not forget the way he touched those flowers that are the symbols of life's re-awakening. He lay there, a shadow of the old Cy, in St. Laurence Hospital in Lansing. He lay there in a curious contentment, because—in contrast to the overwhelming majority of pioneers—he had trained his successor. This was the lean-faced clean-lined Donald Cummings. Don was an engineer, then a Ph.D. in bacteriology and, yes, an M.D. which Cy never was. Cy had worked the miracle of Don's getting his medical education and degree during the years Cy was training him as a public health laboratorian.

"Don will be able to meet the docs on their own ground," said Cy, laughing, but not boisterously as he laughed in the old days.

In the same St. Laurence Hospital at that moment Don Cummings was putting one of Cy's earliest death-fighting dreams into successful action. He was demonstrating that rigid outside microbe-fighting controls bid fair to wipe out the deadliest enemy of America's newborn babies—epidemic diarrhea of the newborn—the curse of our nation's hospitals that brings the worst sadness to thousands of mothers every year. What a discovery for Don to make his bow with, as the new director!

Cy was outwardly a violently anti-sentimental man but you couldn't blame him when, just before he died, he permitted himself an expression of the fierce love that smoldered in him. Just before he died Greg Christian and Don Cummings were alone with him.

"I've never had a brother," he muttered to Greg Christian who had so valiantly sold Cy's laboratory to Michigan's doctors. "Greg, you've been my brother," he said. Then he turned weakly towards Don Cummings. "I've never had a son," Cy said so low you could just hear him.

"Now, Don, you're my son."

All those twenty-five years Cy had remained the almost completely anonymous doctor to Michigan's five million, and if he could come back to his beautiful laboratory grounds on DeWitt Road in Lansing today, I'm sure he would protest with his old-time gruff goddamn. Over the entrance of the 22-building institution that he built from nothing the state has put up a plaque carved in stone. It has no words of eulogy. It says simply—C. C. YOUNG PUBLIC HEALTH LABORATORY.

PART TWO

THE TOUGH MAN FROM TEXAS IS GENTLE

The Nazis were at the English Channel; even Churchill thought they might soon be across it. Many of us were spooked about their hopping the ocean and infiltrating this country. At a medical jamboree in California, we listened to certain doctors calling the President that S.O.B. in the White House; then we felt better at what followed.

This black summer it seemed as if all able-bodied doctors would have to stop working for stronger life for everybody and start patching the smashed-up and dying. It was just then that we heard of sick people brought into an Alabama hospital, stuporous, demented, sometimes moribund. A few cents' worth of a pure chemical sent these doomed folks walking home the day after they'd been carried in, dying.

In cold scientific print the doctor who saved them dared to call it a miracle. To us it seemed next door to resurrection.

CHAPTER III

Famine-Fighter's Miracle

⇛ ⇚

THIS 1940 summer, while the old civilization seemed to be cracking up and while some people were getting ready to hop a ride on the wave of the future, it was impossible to get going on my book about the doctors, "the real guys," as Cy Young called them. We were haunted by the seeming correctness of the fearful predictions the President had made, that gray day in Washington the December before.

Then on a pleasant early summer day I sat alone with Henry Wallace in his big office in the Department of Agriculture. I looked up to this plain-faced man with somnambulist's eyes because his hybrid corn was a promise of an upsurge in the world's food production. This morning Henry had just returned from a portentous cabinet meeting. Over the teletype we stood reading the sinister progress of the Nazi Panzers. Off the record he confided the defense budget of astronomical billions that would be needed. I remember well kidding him—he was a radical economist—about this being a wonderful chance to scrap our monetary system, because you never did have to think of paying for any war till after it was over, and this coming Armageddon we'd absolutely never be able to pay for at all.

Our common interest had been a possible fusion of religion with science to build a new humanity. New humanity? Science would do damn well to keep us alive at all. This morning I saw Henry Wallace, the politician. He was F.D.R.'s henchman. He was committed to fighting death with death still more deadly—how deadly he did not tell me. I left Henry and felt scared and lonely.

Then Rhea and I came down through an exceptionally thick high fog, landing under a low ceiling at Mills Field, San Francisco, and the terror seemed much farther away. The danger seemed negligible when Dr. Karl F. Meyer—a big, tough yet sentimental man who can laugh no matter what—was there to meet us giving us the hello in his Swiss accent. Karl immediately injected us with his serum of optimism.

Karl Meyer had brewed his cheerful medicine from the cool common sense of his Swiss forebears who had maintained their democratic oasis through centuries of the rest of Europe's suicidal insanity. He had blended this with his acquired California breeziness. Karl was in his middle fifties, walked with a mountain-climber's stride, and with his close-cropped mustache and clear-cut, lean face he reminded you of a German Feldmarschal. Rhea and I demoted him to Feldwebel (top sergeant) because he incessantly ordered and pushed us around showing us the marvels of California —from the dry wine at Geary Street Solari's grill to the model Okie camps in the Central Valley.

He was one of the world's very top microbe hunters, versatile, as good in the midnight quiet, alone, in the ivory tower of his Hooper Foundation laboratory as he was teaching olive cannerymen and tuna-fishermen how to keep microbic death out of the food they supply to the world. Many years before Karl had cleaned the murderous botulinus toxin out of California's canning industry. He'd made it the safest in the world by a remarkably foolproof system of sanitation and inspection. Farmers, fishermen, canners, California's biggest businessmen looked up to Karl as their scientific tsar.

Yet in his work there was nothing of the tyrant. Karl got all his effects by letting guilty parties decide—*voluntarily*—what to do after looking long and hard at devastating and always simple facts. "Den dey become Christians," Karl would say.

He was scientifically world-famed for a gory epic of killing and cutting the inflamed brains out of sick horses to discover the virus of equine encephalitis, also fatal to humans; he laid the foundation of a vaccine to guard against it and for the sanitation that will one day wipe it out.

He was nobody's yes-man. He had fought a knock-down battle with authorities of the U. S. Public Health Service. They'd maintained the bubonic plague principally endangered us by sneaking into sea-ports on rats from ships from foreign lands. Karl and his crew of outdoor searchers spotted the black death lurking in the wild rodents all over our American West.

He was an institution in California. His general medical learning was as immense as his fiercely kind appearance was impressive. Yet to California's doctors, big businessmen, fishermen, university presidents, and labor organizers, Karl kept himself way down low, calling himself the "janitor." He might have become a high-paid tycoon of West Coast industry. For no money—aside from his pittance as Director of the Hooper Foundation—he was on call day and night. For anything. For guiding high echelon strategy in how to cut down California's death rates. For the scut-work of personally spotting possible typhoid bugs in a few pounds of California cheese.

In any walk of life Karl Meyer would pass for a big shot; in everything he did he acted like a servant, but of everybody.

II

This June I watched Karl go to work on the doctors of one of California's most prosperous county medical societies. He took me along to the annual stag dinner (dining being a secondary consideration) to which he had been invited as the speaker of the evening. Since Karl held somewhat advanced social views on medical care, the gleaming streamlined fleet of Cadillacs, Buicks and Chryslers parked around the roadhouse where the learned meeting was held, made me wonder. Here was not so much prosperity as affluence and in our country in any profession prosperity and acceptance of democratic ideas (even sensible Swiss ones) are not bedfellows.

Karl saw my worry and smiled. "Never mind, Paul," he said, smiling cheerfully. "Vat ve must do is to be able to dr-r-rink dis evening." Then, around midnight, when most of us should have been beyond concentration upon scientific or social questions, came the speeches.

Karl Meyer got up, calm, steady, not having to hold on to the table, and quickly the room was quiet. To the majority of his hosts, any liberalization in the practice of medicine was rank communism. Karl talked straight out to them, loud and clear. He told of kids dying in the Okie camps for want of decent medical care; he told of white-collar-class mothers without means for the medical care of their children. Gently he suggested that most of his listeners were too far along in their prosperous grooves to be able to change. Then he outlined necessary changes in medical education that would turn out a new generation of community and scientific-minded doctors . . .

"Or, gentlemen, you vill have nothing but government medicine."

I watched them all around the big U-shaped table, curiously sober now, antagonism in the faces of mighty few of them, groping puzzlement on the serious faces of almost every one of them. They were strangely like obstreperous kids being talked to as if by a wise uncle and wanting to understand. Then hard applause. Then silence.

In between the evening's Rabelaisian jollity I'd been listening to the hide being taken off Mr. Roosevelt—obviously for my benefit. He was a menace. He was going to make all of them serfs of a socialistic government. He was a sonofabitch, net and period. It was lucky that ethyl alcohol is soothing to my emotions. Mildly I kept protesting that the President knew medicine would only be socialized over the dead bodies of practically all of America's doctors, that he hadn't the faintest intention of making them government serfs and that—master politician that he was—he knew he couldn't even if he wanted to.

Yes, but what about the Murray-Wagner bill, that would mean Government medicine? I told them it was only a trial balloon, that the President hadn't an intention of pushing it. They all looked as if they didn't believe me.

And now, to my dismay, following Karl's speech the President of
the medical society asked me to make a few remarks. Karl winked
at me through the vinous, smoky murk and made signals for me
to give them the works. It was a short speech, very slow, not in
these exact words but to this exact effect:

All this evening I've heard a certain man being taken apart.
Wasn't this man, after all, Commander-in-Chief of the armed forces
of the United States . . . (impressive pause) . . . at a moment
when we all knew we were as good as alone against the most powerful and barbarous bastards in history?

Up jumped the President of the medical society. He raised his
glass. "Gentlemen," he said, "to the President of the United States!"
To a man the doctors jumped up, drank the toast and then cheered.

It was Karl Meyer's common sense and courage that had softened them up for it. This was a high point, a highlight in the
last nine years of observing the doctors. It flashed over me then
that, though their new science had put it within their power to
become a new kind of man, this evening they had shown themselves as human beings no different from any other guild of any
other prosperous Americans—automobile dealers, undertakers or
any American small businessmen. They were, at bottom, loyal
Americans and their griping about the President was, figuratively,
skin-deep; it was no deep conditioning. And how could it have
been? They were a highly prosperous group of Americans, not
fenced in. What they knew (or better, thought they knew) about
medicine's threatened serfdom had come to them in the form of
dire threats of it, published in their medical journals, and in the
form of certain rumors circulated down to them through the mysterious political channels of the national and state medical associations.

Watching them jump up to toast their president it came to me
that, just as these good physicians were fundamentally loyal to
their country, they were loyal to their calling, according to their
conditioning—which after all had been engineered by the politicians who rule the doctors just as politicians rule other unions.
Faced with the threatened death of any man or woman or child,

every one of these physicians would have worked to the limit of strength and knowledge to save life, regardless of whether or not the patient could pay. All of these doctors did some "charity" work, some of them a great deal of it. Probably most of them more or less soaked their well-off patients in order to be able to treat poor people for nothing. It was a loose and really unfair system, and many of them would have admitted it, but it was the only system they knew.

That night I had seen Karl setting strange thoughts buzzing in their heads. It was too bad Karl Meyer had so many irons in the fire. It was too bad that the unorganized but numerous top level doctors of the country (top level in their sense of community responsibility as well as technical skill) couldn't arrange for Karl to talk his economic good sense to medical societies, nationwide.

Yet deep down I believed it wasn't economics so much as organic chemistry that was going to change the doctors. A shift of one double-bond in a single chemical molecule might add more to their strength against death than all the communistic, socialistic or new-dealistic planning in the world.

III

Back home at Wake Robin all that summer I swam in Lake Michigan and worked in the sun house, digging into the scientific reports of a strange new science done by a doctor whose work hinted the promise of carrying organic chemistry's magic into every level of medical and surgical practice. His name was Dr. Tom Douglas Spies [rhymes with ease].

In order not to be too ignorant when meeting this character, all summer I dug through scores of his scientific publications containing hundreds of astounding case histories and full of the names of organic chemical compounds of which I'd barely heard. It was a new world. Tom Spies was surely an adventurer in a new epic against human misery apparently worldwide and involving countless millions. The cause was apparently a lack of certain exactly known chemicals (vitamins) essential to life. This seemed a discovery even more hopeful for humanity than that of the microbes which cause disease and death.

This chemical starvation was not confined to the have-nots or to Mr. Roosevelt's ill-fed one-third of a nation. It seemed able to strike anywhere, and even though more prevalent among Southern poor peoples, it could be found among mink-coated ladies on New York's Park Avenue.

Tom Spies, mark this well, hadn't isolated or synthesized any of these key life chemicals himself. What he was doing was to experiment with them in a novel manner on sick human beings. He was using these new synthetic vitamins in a disease detective hunt. He was uncovering a vast hidden hunger. Having spotted a given chemical deficiency, Tom Spies then cured these sick people. His saving of some of the very sick ones was even more spectacular than Roux and Behring's first antitoxin rescue of children doomed with diphtheria in the late 1890's.

As I studied the scientific protocols, the speed of these chemical cures awed me. Into Hillman Hospital in Birmingham, Alabama, certain sick people were brought on stretchers. They were stuporous, demented, sometimes dying. Ten years before they wouldn't have had a fifty-fifty chance of coming out of the hospital alive. Now Tom Spies worked what he dared to call, in cold scientific print, a miracle. A few cents' worth of a given pure chemical often sent such doomed folks walking home the day after they'd been carried into the hospital, dying.

It was next door to resurrection.

This was one highlight of the beginning of a revolution in medical science. Instead of people dying from the presence of microbes infinitely small, here were people endangered by the mere absence from their bodies of tiny amounts of specific chemicals that ought to have been there. Here was yesterday's vague science of A-B-C-D-E vitamins, transformed by organic chemists into life-saving power that was as magical as it was unexpected.

Out of cheap coal, petroleum, lime, water and air, these supercooks, the chemists, had refined to crystal purity the vitamins hidden in the bones gnawed by cave-men, the soups and stews of slaves and peasants, the salads and roasts of kings. These were chemicals that God—by whim or oversight—had put into foods in amounts that were marginal, yes, stingy. Now it was clear that Tom Spies was getting ready to teach rank-and-file doctors to use them abundantly. Maybe to change humanity, to raise mankind to a new level of life.

I V

Mid-August of 1940, Tom Spies met me one hot Alabama afternoon at the Birmingham airport. You would not have taken him for a physician; he didn't carry his bedside manner about with him publicly. He was tall and heavy-set; he seemed strong but not burly, and there was a hint of the artist about him. He was bare-headed with a shock of unruly dark hair, and his eyes (their color I can't name to this day) were brooding yet looked into mine directly and right through me. He was from Texas. His voice was low-keyed and he talked in a verbal shorthand in sentences where a few words summed up chapters of what I felt was an immense medical experience.

Before we'd gotten into his car from the plane (no preliminary amenities) it was clear that for Tom Spies the one fact in the world was the existence of a chronic chemical famine that his human experimentation was revealing. Human beings were chemically imperfect or broken down and he was out to fix them. His science was very expensive and what it needed was money, money, more money. Incandescent ambition flashed through his low-voiced talk. He wanted no money for himself; he worked for a pittance; he had never received a penny in fees from a patient in his life; the money was needed only to uncover and then cure this newly revealed chemical starvation for vitamins and proteins that he believed was nationwide, no, worldwide.

Next morning at Hillman Hospital I found myself in an atmosphere electric with the hope that is peculiar to medical discovery. It was a poor people's clinic. That was a requirement of entrance for all patients: inability to pay. Here I saw such a co-working of patients and searchers that it was hard to sort the sick people from their doctors, dietitians, and nurses. Through this hurly-burly of destitute, sick, convalescent, and newly healthy humanity Tom Spies moved calmly, not in a professional white coat but with no coat at all, no tie and with his collar open. For days I listened to him talking to hundreds of these people. Excepting for those there on their first visits, he seemed to know all of them by their first names.

Though this clinic was in the deep South there was no professional condescension in the treatment of the Negroes. The clinics were separate, but the same doctors and nurses, dietitians and social workers took care of the patients whether they were black or white. Unless you listened sharply to his diagnostic questions and to his orders routing some to chemists for blood tests, some to the ophthalmologist for eye examinations, some to the nutritionists for dietary prescriptions, you would not have taken Tom for a practicing physician. There was the devotion of dogs in the eyes of the sick people as they answered his questions. He was one with these hundreds of people, many of them almost too sick to walk, others sitting with their heads bowed in their hands as if they were feeling, for the first time in years, what strength meant, and vigor.

There was chiaroscuro in this clinic. Here sat a mother with inflamed eyes, breaking into a sudden storm of weeping, paying no heed to her brood of children climbing around her. Close by stood a millhand, strong at last after years of having been too weak to work, now giving Tom Spies a slap on the back that, if he hadn't been a solid man, would have sent him reeling. There was a mixed democracy of suffering and new hope that was new and strange to me.

Those hot days I kept at Tom's heels and kindly he demonstrated my ignorance of vitamin deficiency diseases. I had thought you could divide them into pellagra, beriberi, scurvy, rickets, and a few other rather easily detectable conditions. Now among these hundreds of people Tom showed me the subtlety and complexity of what he called "chemical starvation." Some of the patients were merely weak, or weak and stupid. There were those who said they couldn't work, and hardly walk—no other signs or symptoms. Close by sat some with an exaggerated nervous drive, but down-hearted—next to others with burning eyes and inflamed cracks at the corners of their mouths. Some seemed outwardly healthy but Tom's examination revealed their inflamed mouths and tongues. A few were short of breath from damaged hearts. Again there were those whose only sign of sickness was chronic, years-long diarrhea. Though undernourished, malnourished, it was a complaint common to all these people that they were not hungry.

In this confusion, Tom Spies—not seeming to be trying to teach me—began to show how he and his doctors, nurses and nutritionists discovered what was chemically lacking in these people and how these deficiencies could then be chemically corrected. It was outlandish how the new synthetic vitamins were tools for diagnosis and at the same time, cures. *It was by curing these people with a given chemical that Tom found they'd been lacking it when they were sick.* The crowded rooms of the clinic were merely the concentration point of his vast laboratory of hundreds of square miles, including the slums of Birmingham and huts of the farmers of the surrounding country.

Into these so-called homes went Tom, the other physicians, nurses and dietitians, and social workers, to learn the most minute details of the lives and especially the diets of fathers, mothers, children and even the dogs of the family. Every year thousands of people poured into the Nutrition Clinic at Hillman Hospital. Here Tom and his staff looked for signs of their hidden chemical hunger—in their eyes, their mouths, on the skin all over their bodies, in their stomachs and intestines, in their blood and by delicate neurological tests, and in many with all such signs lacking they found symptoms of this chemical hunger revealed only by their heavy hearts or their nervous despair.

It was a stern science. Rigidly these sick people would then be held to the diets that had brought them their chemical starvation. Then, one at a time, Tom would add huge doses of the new synthetic vitamins to their inadequate food. One pure B vitamin at a time—thiamin, riboflavin, nicotinic acid, pyridoxin. Under this dosing, if a disease sign or symptom would vanish, that was the diagnosis of a given chemical starvation, and at the same time its relief. Tom explained that these chemical starvations were almost never single. If one vitamin proved lacking, chemical hunger for others was almost always there.

What baffled me about Tom's new science was its surface simplicity; what excited me was a hint that here might be a chemical hope for miseries that were not only physical but mental, moral and even in the broadest sense, social.

"Is this chronic chemical famine confined to the deep South, or even to your Birmingham region? I've heard that hinted," I asked Tom Spies.

"Nobody knows. It hasn't been tried sufficiently anywhere else, the way we're trying it," he said. "And we've only begun to scratch the surface."

v

These exciting days the testimony of my own eyes watching events at the Hillman clinic made me wonder about the unsolved illnesses, stupidities, economic dislocations and hatreds of millions of underpar people in Michigan, New York, and California.

I saw women brought into the Hillman, crying uncontrollably, forgetful, weak, unable to care for their families. They were no different from many northern, eastern, or western women coming into old-fashioned doctors' offices. Those doctors would have wagged their heads, muttering "neurasthenia," or "psychoneurosis" and they would have treated these women by telling them they should have a good rest and to try to take a brighter view of life. But here at Hillman, following huge doses of one or another of these new pure synthetic vitamins, I saw such women changed from sad to gay, cheerful human beings within a few hours.

Their nervous breakdowns were chemical.

At Hillman Hospital I saw children who might best be described as little sad old men and women, from photographs taken of them when they were first brought to Tom's clinic. They were always tired, listless, often dunces at school. See, here were their former deplorable records. Now here at Hillman, back for their check-ups,

I saw many of these youngsters, chemically transfigured, mischievous, energetic, some average students, others now A students heading their classes.

"Can it be that the so-called I.Q. isn't always hereditary—is it often chemical?" I asked Tom Spies.

He was conservative. "There's been no real survey, anywhere," he said, smiling.

Big, blond, kindly Dr. J. W. MacQueen, the director of Hillman Hospital, was listening. "You don't find these chemical problem children only among Alabama poor kids," he interrupted us. "My own boy was supposed to have been brought up on a good diet. He was restless, fidgety, unable to concentrate at school," said MacQueen. "You remember, Tom, how you spotted the trouble. Thiamin, nicotinic acid, and riboflavin. Now he's a different youngster!"

At Hillman clinic I saw records of men who hadn't worked for years. They'd been despaired of by social workers as no-gooders. They were like millions who, country-wide, were laughed at as shovel-leaners on W.P.A. Here were the records of how synthetic vitamins had brought them back to work, liking it.

"Just ask this man," said Tom, introducing us. This wiry citizen chuckled, explaining it. He hadn't been able to hold a job—till just lately—since he could remember. Then shots of these vitamins in the arm and then big doses of vitamin pills and he'd begun to get hungry and started to get stronger and now he was a ship-builder.

"For Uncle Sam," he said proudly. "Doing heavy weight-lifting, not minding how much overtime. Now we've got money enough for plenty of good food for the family," he said.

When the man had gone, Dr. MacQueen took me aside. "That's the kind of man who'd have been called no-good southern white trash—when he was sick," he said.

"But surely, Bill," I answered, "there are millions of real southern white trash." I was certain he'd agree, because MacQueen came from a high southern family, the kind that are at the top of one of the most exquisite caste systems in the world, the kind that ask,

"What's his family background?" and then, when it's no great family name, look faintly down the nose and lose interest. Now Bill MacQueen interrupted me and, mild man though he was, said fiercely:

"Watching Tom change thousands of these people has convinced me there's no class of people deserving to be called white trash."

MacQueen's eyes had the look of a man who'd been wrong all his life and had at last seen a light. "Tom's proving that their so-called no-goodness is chemical," he said.

In the evenings of these astounding days, Tom Spies tempered my enthusiasm. "These new vitamins aren't cure-alls," he said.

There were many human deteriorations, breakdowns of morale, mental diseases for which nobody's yet found the chemical answer. "Not *yet*," he underlined it, smiling and with a faraway look. "The physicians have only just begun," he said, "the investigators have only scratched the surface."

I mustn't think these chemicals were permanent cures, any more than they were cure-alls. He showed me records of how his group brought malnourished people back to life, then stopped adding the synthetic vitamins to their diets, then watched them drift back into the sinister sicknesses that the vitamins had conquered so swiftly. The one hope for their permanent rehabilitation was high protein, high vitamin, high calorie diet.

"But we aren't raising food enough in America for everybody to have that kind of diet," I interrupted.

"Of course not," said Tom.

Then the medical searcher that he really was, the pioneering scientific famine fighter, flared up in him. No sarcasm about the silly plowing under of corn or the slaughter of the little pigs. No jibes at the New Deal's bungling efforts to re-distribute the necessities of life. No communistic sharing of scarcity. Tom brought out more case histories and records. "Look," he said, "here are people kept on the bad diets most of them had been on all their lives, that led to their breakdowns.

"Now look," he went on. "We simply add the right chemicals that those diets lacked. We don't change the diets at all. We just keep adding those chemicals. They maintain these people at higher levels of vigor—on diets that are terrible—than they were on their original deficient diets."

"But those new chemicals themselves are mighty expensive," I said.

He pointed out that, once these people could work, they could begin to buy more of the essential protective foods—meat, milk and eggs.

Tom said not to worry, the chemical industry's production technique was getting them down cheaper and cheaper.

"They'll get to be dirt cheap, finally," he said. "Just give the nutritionists a chance to spot and map every chemical food deficiency. Then we'll enrich cheap food with some of these essential chemicals—and it'll be almost as cheap as the cheapest, deficient diets are now." Even so, Tom said that this enrichment would only be one step toward better health.

Was he a crazy dreamer or a prophet?

Now it was as if a veil came over his eyes and he looked as if out across an ocean. "There's going to be a murderous food shortage when this war is over," he said. "We've got to hurry to find practical ways to fight the famine that's coming."

He reminded me of all the politicians I'd known, from the highest to the lowest, he was so different. He was a primitive of the breed that came to the front when pre-historic men were doomed by the descent of the glaciers.

VI

I knew big government men who'd be interested. "It ought to be easy for you to get money for such a development," I said.

Tom smiled but bitterly. He did not think so. The big money was for killing, not for making new life, he explained. I asked whether Mr. Harry Hopkins hadn't said that hunger was not debatable. Hadn't the President himself proclaimed that now we'd have to be physically tough and spiritually strong? Hadn't I just seen how these synthetic vitamins could surge up morale?

Tom looked at me, I thought, pityingly. His wordless shrug asked whether I had any faith in political slogans. Was I so fatuous as to believe there was any government foresight against the looming great hunger?

Then he opened up to me about his hand-to-mouth scientific existence. Just the month before, he'd had to lose some of his workers because he hadn't the money to go on. Then he told me the curious story of how he'd kept his research going. This new type of investigation was frightfully expensive; he had to transport most of his thousands of human subjects from their homes from many miles around to his clinic, and back; he had to pay for their experimental diets, for their stay in hospital, when necessary; it was a different kettle of fish from vitamin research on mice, rats, and guinea pigs.

The University of Cincinnati (where he was an associate professor of medicine), like all universities, had to budget its expenses carefully. All they could do was to pay his modest salary and he was mighty grateful to them for allowing him a yearly nine months' leave-of-absence to come down here to do his famine-fighting research at the Hillman. The willingness of the University authorities to grant such a leave of absence was unprecedented.

"How have you raised your money?" I asked him.

It turned out he'd wangled the money by a sort of glorified panhandling, five hundred dollars from this friend, a thousand dollars from that multi-millionaire. He'd been granted five thousand dollars from this and that wealthy foundation; and additional thousands from chemical manufacturers—you understand not to boost their products but to test them, with no strings attached, but letting the chips fall where they might. Much of his time was spent flying about the country, begging dribs and drabs of research money.

He'd been able to turn out his unquestionably enormous amount of work because he didn't need much sleep and had a wonderful team of youngsters working with him and because he was a bachelor not having to waste much time on social diversions. His research—for all its promise for mankind's future—was on a frayed shoestring. He worked, expensively, under a looming cloud of bankruptcy. He

might have done differently if he hadn't been, scientifically, so un-
compromising. The big directing men of science, the big committee
men who run American science, couldn't harness him. He was polite to them but he wouldn't kowtow—scientifically—to the boys
of the upper scientific echelons.

It struck me that Tom was a scientific mendicant friar who was
worshiping God according to his own conscience and was going to
have his own say on the way to find and to feed the world's chemical
hunger, though, mind you, he was tolerant of how other searchers
did their work.

This was all sufficiently striking and new to me but what has
stuck with me most vividly from those hot 1940 August days in
Birmingham was Tom, *the doctor.* I remember standing by listening to him talking to a little woman, Daisy Jones. Nicotinic acid
had brought her up out of a nervous despair. She'd got a job, rehabilitated. She had remained on her deficient diet—but the synthetic vitamins had maintained her new strength. Then—according
to Tom's stern science—without her knowing it those vitamin tablets
had been replaced by tablets looking exactly alike, but vitaminless
—"placebos" the doctors call them.

"I'm slipping, Doctor," said Daisy, "I'll have to give up my job.
Why doesn't the medicine help any more?" she asked.

Her relapse when the nicotinic acid was withdrawn had told Tom
what he needed to know—namely, that the wonderful uplifting effect of this chemical hadn't been merely psychological. In a low
voice he gave orders, for Daisy, to an assistant. When she'd gone for
her new prescription (nicotinic acid again) Tom said: "You see,
we know now that nicotinic acid is the determining factor in
whether she can work or can't. She'll stay on her job all right."

It was a chemical sureness about human fate that was new to me.
Tom hadn't told Daisy she'd soon be all right again. The way she
looked at him told of her absolute faith, not in the man but his
medicine. The way all these rejuvenated people looked at Tom
reminded me of the awed faces of those poor people in Lhermitte's
great painting as his poor people looked at the man standing in the
doorway of their poor cottage. . . . With this difference that here

in the Hillman there was nothing of the supernatural and Tom was only a human being, a physician. . . . Yet their devotion to Tom—just as it showed in the awe of those people in Lhermitte's painting—was religious. It's this feeling of hundreds of those people that I remember, much more clearly than the structural formulas of the brilliant laboratory science that was at the bottom of their transfiguration. On the plane back to Wake Robin I pondered how I'd never seen a doctor quite like Tom Spies.

He differed from other physicians in the revolutionarily scientific yet simple means he was using to lift so many so high from so far down in despair. Would he be able to transmit this science to all doctors, finally? Why not? He was in the highest standing not only in scientific but even in political medical circles; hadn't the leadership of the American Medical Association told me, *tête-à-tête* at lunch the April before, that this work of Tom Spies was among the most important medical discoveries of the past twenty-five years?

Yet Tom was ahead of his time. He was a lone wolf. His science threatened to blast the medical superstition of the general adequacy of three meals a day. He might be safe so long as he was operating in the deep South where the poor whites do not get those meals and are expected to be chemically famished. But already there were hints that his new science was picking up cases of chemical starvation among supposedly well-fed folks, even on Park Avenue. What would happen when that new science began to challenge the ancient nutritional notions of the doctors of New York, Chicago, and San Francisco? What if these new synthetic vitamins escaped from the control of the doctors and got into the hands of the plain people? You didn't have to be a prophet to foretell trouble for Tom Spies.

That day going back in the plane to Wake Robin I made up my mind to find out what made Tom Spies tick, to check the reliability of the impression he had made on me and to follow the events that were sure to occur when his science collided with some doctors who might consider that he affected their peculiar prerogatives.

＊≫＊ ≫＊ ≪＊ ≪＊

*That night it was hot and quiet as we looked down on
the lights of the city. For days Tom had shown me the
nervous terror of many chemically starved people. He
had astounded me by the way he could chemically make
them brave. He made me see visions. "What's the difference between this Birmingham fear and fear in Boston or San Francisco? How much of all this psychoneurosis is chemical?" I asked him. "How'll we know
till we test for it, chemically?" asked Tom.*

*This year the nation was getting set to mobilize.
"How many of these scared psychoneurotics will they
find?" I asked. "We don't know," said Tom. "We do
know they're a major economic burden now." "Could a
survey be made with these pure chemical vitamins
you've got?" I asked. Tom answered: "Of course."*

*"Why don't you agitate for them to start it?" I per-
sisted.*

*"Who'd be interested?" Tom asked, with a faintly
bitter smile.*

≫＊ ≫＊ ≪＊ ≪＊

CHAPTER IV

Famine-Fighter's Progress

≫ ≪

WHEN I first began watching Tom Spies at his famine fighting, he was only 38 years old. How had it come about that he was so far out in the lead in the discovery and cure of chemical starvation? The answer is simpler than you'd think and is not primarily concerned with science. When Tom was a boy in knee pants in Texas he showed a special human characteristic that determined his way of life and his fate. The mother of one of his playmates died of pellagra *and this shocked him.*

Each succeeding year he kept on being shocked when a number of neighbors went demented and died of pellagra, the origin of which was then inscrutable excepting that it was known to rage in its deadliest form among the very poor. Tom could only then be called exceptional because these disasters seared themselves into his memory. Then at Harvard Medical School his professors displayed to his class a severe case of pellagra supposedly rare in New England. Again Tom Spies showed himself to be slightly different from his fellow students. He went to the library and learned every fact of the first, original, now classical account of pellagra by the 18th Century Spanish physician, Gaspar Casal, who described the sickness under the name *mal de la rosa.* Again, in his first year as a tyro doctor (he was 28) he took a somewhat unorthodox course, for young doctors that is, when confronted with the duty of treating his first desperately sick pellagra victim. This was at Lakeside Hospital, Cleveland, Ohio; the pellagrin was a drunkard and as is common with far-gone sots he had little or no wish for food, just booze, so he was deep in a nutritional tailspin.

For this far-gone member of the human rearguard, young Tom was sure there was hope. For pellagrins it was no longer as it had been in his boyhood in Texas. By now the great Joseph Goldberger had proved that a lack of meat, milk, eggs, fresh vegetables caused pellagra, and Goldberger taught that meals rich in these foods would not only prevent it but ought to cure it. Tom now conducted himself in a manner not characteristic of run-of-mill medical internes—who almost certainly would simply have prescribed Goldberger's good meals for this drunkard and called it a day. Night and day Tom personally stuck at this derelict's bedside. He pled, he cajoled, he force-fed him Goldberger's supposedly curative diet. In forty-eight hours the drunkard was dead of pellagra.

"His dying was naturally a shock to me," reported Tom Spies.

This conclusion was not scientific, yet it set Tom apart from young graduates from the most highly scientific schools of medicine. In those schools the science of why people die dominates the science and art of how to keep people alive. Then too, for most young medical men there are grades of shockability by deaths—depending upon the economic, social, and moral rank of those who die.

Who could be less important than this drunkard?

For Tom this old soak's death was an enigma challenging Goldberger's complete conquest of pellagra; and Goldberger (himself just dead) had prestige as the world's greatest famine fighter. Now Tom Spies showed how shocked he was by his failure to save this one no-account life. He stayed up nights, digging through Lakeside Hospital's case records to trace the fate of those severe pellagrins who should have been saved by Goldberger's famine-fighting science. What he found was disturbing. The records showed a death rate of 54 per cent of all severe pellagrins admitted. This hadn't caused a stir probably because most of them were drunkards, and who cared? Now Tom wrote letters, bothering hospital record-keepers all over; and in the nation's leading institutions he found approximately the same mortality among God's forgotten.

Tom then had a hunch which was scientifically simple yet difficult to translate into experimental action. Maybe the quantity of curative agents in Goldberger's diet was enough to prevent pellagra, but not to cure it when it was really bad. What would happen if you fed them more, fed them plenty, fed them super?

Before he could even start to test this notion Tom bumped into a difficulty that ought to have defeated him. Scouting around in Cleveland's skid rows, he could find plenty of drunks; and a fair number showed the sinister three D's—dermatitis, diarrhea and dementia—of pellagra; but he had a terrible time getting these threatened people into the hospital. Maybe the news of so many being carried out feet first had spread among them via the underdogs' grapevine.

Tom devised an unorthodox method of herding pellagrous inebriates into the hospital to test his experimental mercy. Though these were the days of the reign of Andrew Volstead, Tom bribed them into the hospital with the promise of hooch, free hooch, all the hooch they wanted. It was not only illegal but even seemed unscientific, because wasn't this a special, an alcoholic pellagra that was dooming them? Wasn't it different from the pellagrous malnourishment of southern poor folks? Wasn't, for example, the frightful pain of neuritis, common among these drunkards, caused by alcohol, not by lack of vitamins?

If they'd just *eat* what he gave them, they could have all the booze they wanted, Tom told one desperately sick souse after another. All they wanted, even two bottles a day if that was any inducement, though, mind you, he measured exact amounts they took. That fetched them in.

Tom set up camp by the beds of one after another of this redfaced, itchy, sore-mouthed, beefy-tongued, diarrheic and demented flotsam and jetsam. The way Tom personally nursed them, dosed them, fed them you'd have thought the life of each one was as precious as that of old Mr. John D. Rockefeller, Sr., himself. (And it was, to Tom.) He cajoled and bribed them with booze and more booze as they gagged at his enormous meals of beef, eggs, milk, yeast, wheat germ and liver. He threw the nutrition book at them.

Dr. R. H. Bishop, Jr., then director of the hospital, remembers the exceptional conduct of young Tom Spies as a physician. "There was an indefinable something about him . . . that is difficult to describe," wrote Dr. Bishop. "This was illustrated time and again as he personally ministered to his patients day and night, sitting by their bedside, encouraging them to take nourishment from his own hands, watchful of every symptom, eternally questioning cause and effect."

Did this about Tom impress Dr. Bishop because of its rarity? Probably. Dr. Bishop concluded his impression of the young searcher in words that were a bit mystical. "It makes you take a man like that on faith, confident that there is an inner strength, perhaps of divine origin, which is denied to many of us."

Whether the source of Tom's strength was divine or merely mundane, he did get the beef, eggs, milk, yeast, wheat germ and liver into his reluctant doomed derelicts. And look. You call it *alcoholic* neuritis that sears their nerves as if with a hot iron? Nonsense. On a bottle-and-a-half of booze a day that agony slowly faded away when he fed them, when he fed them terrifically. You call their disease *alcoholic* pellagra? Moonshine. After weeks of Tom's super-feeding, the flaming butterflies faded from the skin of their faces, the red-hot rawness vanished from their tongues, clear-headedness replaced their goofiness, slowly, painfully slowly. Definitely.

For the success or failure of his experiments Tom Spies set up a criterion that was stark and simple. He'd look at each hopeless one admitted to hospital. He'd mutter to himself: "Brother, do you live or die? Do you walk out head first or do they carry you out, feet first?"

By the end of 1934, Tom Spies had treated 125 severely diseased pellagrins. He had cut the old death rate from 54 per cent down to 6 per cent. He had triumphed over death not so much by science as by persistence. No, not really by persistence but because of the peculiar low threshold of his shockability by any death.

II

Let me hasten to explain that no invidious comparison, in this matter of shockability by death, is being made between Tom and doctors in general. For the somewhat low degree of their shockability by death our doctors do not need to apologize. Standing by the bedsides of people their art and science cannot save, if they were deeply shocked by death after death, by all deaths, then doctors could not go on being doctors. If they're to keep their sense of proportion and their sanity, they must take death in their stride. If they took every death too much to heart they'd destroy their value as doctors. It's no different from a ballplayer who wouldn't last long if he moped too much at a strike-out. What keeps a good ballplayer going is knowing he can't hit them all out of the ball park. So too with physicians. After all, some patients have got to die. You can't save them all.

At the same time I do not apologize, either, for Tom's exquisite shockability by death. His being so disturbed by deaths that were very difficult to avoid—it was this that sent him into a sort of fourth dimension of doctoring, of sleepless thinking, of cutting and trying at the most impractical, outlandish measures that finally (with luck or by happy accident) might make the avoidance of these deaths somewhat easier.

That is the discipline of your true death-fighter. Humanity being what it is, this discipline is not attainable by many. But this may be the reward: with luck or by happy accident, the conquest of these formerly unavoidable deaths may at last become so easy that you can wrap the science of it up in a few pills to put into the hands of those doctors whose profession means simply a pretty good way of making a living. This may finally result in giving a death-fighting routine to those doctors who maintain their mental equilibrium because they can think about getting away for the afternoon's golf game while they're standing at the bedside of a patient in danger of death or in unbearable pain. The reward of the pioneer death-fighter does not come till he makes his life-saving fairly simple and easy for all the doctors.

III

Tom was still a long way from that; all he'd so far done was to prove that if you took perfectly silly pains and trouble, a few people who used to die no longer had to. Even though it was of no general medical significance to save the lives of these drunks who were humanly negligible, just the same Tom's work (which was only a *tour de force* without general medical appeal) now got him a chance in big-time medical science.

Dr. James S. McLester saw Tom's life-saving trick. This distinguished physician had written a book on nutrition and was at that time President of the American Medical Association. He looked at Tom's sensationally low 6 per cent death toll among those pellagrous drunks and could not believe their disease was the same as that of the pellagrous southern have-nots. For many years Dr. McLester had preached that, whether or not the Gold-berger diet was prescribed, the death rate of pellagrins sick enough to have to be admitted to hospital—in the south—was terrific.

Dr. McLester showed scientific spirit. He invited Tom Spies to come down to Hillman Hospital to prove whether he could keep doomed pellagrins out of the grave in the south the same as he'd done in Cleveland. His chief at Western Reserve University, Dr. Joseph T. Wearn, agreed with Dean Alfred Friedlander and Dr. Marion A. Blankenhorn of the Medical College of the University of Cincinnati, that it was fundamentally important to find the answer. Tom was appointed to a post at the University of Cincinnati. Dr. Robert Bishop, head of the University Hospitals of Cleveland agreed upon joint financing of Tom's research with the University of Cincinnati. The Cincinnati authorities showed broad-mindedness by allowing him to work on a yearly nine months' leave-of-absence from Cincinnati, down in Birmingham. Here, in the spring and summer of 1936, Tom tested his super-intensive feeding of 50

pellagrins who were all very sick and most of them at the point
of death.

Only three died and even these three (as the postmortems showed)
had been cured of their pellagra before they died of other diseases,
like cancer, that they had along with their pellagra. Dr. McLester
accepted it that alcoholic and southern pellagra appeared identical.

It was a sad science really. By extraordinary hardship for Tom,
his doctors, and a large staff of nurses, these dying patients went
through a slow resurrection. They couldn't be treated in the wards
of charity hospitals appropriate to their station in life. They had
to be coddled in private rooms for weeks and months exactly as if
they were very important persons which, when you considered their
social standing, was ridiculous or at any rate not very practical.

What was it in these huge meals and this yeast and liver that so
slowly dragged them away from death? Goldberger, when he'd invented his anti-pellagra diet, hadn't the foggiest notion what its
curative agents were, chemically. Vitamins? Probably. One or several vitamins? No answer. Here again Tom Spies stood apart from
rank-and-file physicians. Night and day he soaked up the laboratory
science of organic chemists and biologists just then busy (at the expense of the lives of thousands of rats, guinea-pigs and dogs) trying
to disentangle the confusion of chemical compounds making up the
B vitamin complex.

Tom had so impractically saved those southern pellagrins in
1936. The next year, Dr. Conrad Elvehjem (pellagra the farthest
from his thoughts) was on a detective hunt at the University of
Wisconsin, trying to pin down the precise chemicals responsible for
the growth-promoting virtues of liver extract for little white rats.
From such liver stews he purified crystals of nicotinic acid amide.
Would they increase the weight of his little white rats? Elvehjem
thought yes, though that turned out to be wrong. Nicotinic acid
amide might then have gone to limbo on a back laboratory shelf
to gather dust on its bottle, except that it chanced that a dog in
his laboratory languished from a dietary deficiency disease, called
black tongue. The dog was dying. It so happened that this historic

dog was given crystals of nicotinic acid amide, pellagra still being far from Elvehjem's dreams.

The next day the dog was jumping about in his cage, alive again.

Tom Spies was ready for it. Within two months this scientific news of canine resurrection got to him, at Cincinnati. Wasn't black-tongue the canine replica of human pellagra? Maybe, maybe . . .

Nicotinic acid? It was the chemical child of nicotine, the second most potent of all human poisons. It was known that a cigar butt dropped into a glass of beer as a Mickey Finn could be fatal. Tom went to see the country's most eminent pharmacologists. None of them knew whether nicotinic acid was or was not deadly to human beings but they saw no reason why it shouldn't be. Its seeming safety for dogs meant it still must be tried in men.

So Tom tried it, by mouth, first in a few milligrams and then up and up till huge doses—1,000 milligrams in a day—it did nothing more than flush his face and make his arms and legs itch and tingle. The harmlessness of nicotinic acid was confirmed by test on others.

What nicotinic acid now did to a 65-year-old colored woman seemed as if it couldn't quite be true, though it was witnessed by Dr. Spies, Dr. Clark Cooper, and Dr. Marion Blankenhorn. She had come into the hospital stuporous. Her heart beat fast in a very faint tic-tac rhythm. The whole inside of her mouth was fiery red and her tongue was fiery red, raw and beefy. She couldn't eat and didn't want to eat and for 36 hours refused to try to eat and immediately vomited fluids that were given her. Her state was what is called—medically—moribund. Within 16 hours after her first cautious dose of nicotinic acid she was still alive and the inside of her mouth looked different. Her chart said "improvement detectable in tongue." Within four hours of her second dose of nicotinic acid the fiery redness of her tongue had vanished and its size had returned to normal.

Up till now she had feebly resisted every attempt to feed her. Since her condition showed, in Tom's words, "that she might possibly live if fed, even against her wishes"—she was tube-fed with yeast and liver. Within 48 hours she was sitting up eating a high vitamin, high calorie diet. Tom waited for her to relapse; it couldn't be that speedy, it couldn't be so simple. She stayed well. Afterwards, when discharged from hospital, she walked several miles to her home.

I V

Here was the most fantastic of contrasts, and how could it be true? What had taken Tom weeks of day-and-night doctoring, dieting, nursing at unjustifiable expense could not possibly be reduced to a *"cure"* in 48 hours and for next to no money! Tom's eyes gleamed and he woolgathered, knowing how easily and cheaply chemical industry could turn out tons of nicotinic acid once the big kettles got cooking.

Tom now began trying this new chemical key in the locks of doors that seemed slammed against sanity and life itself.

To Hillman Hospital in Birmingham came a middle-aged woman in what is medically called *extremis*. She was in deep pellagrous dementia, so deep down that return seemed impossible. For weeks she imagined she was being poisoned by her neighbors; she heard monkeys, rats, and cows running around her; she felt bugs, snakes, and worms crawling over her. For two weeks before being carried to the Hillman she had not been able to eat at all. There was a burning in her belly, she explained, "like something red-hot eating her insides out." When Tom examined her, she was slobbering quarts of spittle daily. She tossed about and needed restraint. Her lips were swollen and covered with crusts and her mouth was so sore she couldn't even drink water. Her hands and face were ablaze with pellagra. On her perineum there were foul-smelling ulcers. When Tom asked her questions she only mumbled that people wanted to kill her, and please chase those animals away, they kept bothering her.

By now Tom was far bolder with nicotinic acid than in the beginning; and within 12 hours huge doses of it had quenched the fires in her mouth and abdomen and she sat up demanding food, stating that this was the first time in all the months she'd been sick that she'd felt hungry.

Within 24 hours after the first dose of nicotinic acid she had what the psychiatrists call "insight." She realized she'd been crazy.

Now she smiled. She looked up at Tom telling him she knew she'd been foolish and crazy in the head when she'd felt those bugs and snakes and thought folks wanted to kill her.

Within 36 hours the foul-smelling ulcers that had tortured her were almost completely healed.

Within one week she was eating a ditch-digger's diet, and wolfing it. Within nine days she went home, clear mentally, and in good condition.

Is it any wonder that Tom Spies lived in a whirl of work during this 1937 spring and summer? Here in the cheap crystals of this comparatively simple chemical (child of a deadly poison) lay one difference between life and death, between mental clarity and utter insanity. Now for the confirmation of these events that made the adventures of Alice in Wonderland seem humdrum. Now for the absolutely necessary check experiments that might (who knew?) disillusion him and wreck his not quite rational hopes.

A parade of demented pellagrins now began arriving at Hillman Hospital. With his crystals of nicotinic acid Tom Spies went after their crazy misery by what he called "the direct attack."

These were stern human experiments. As they came into the hospital, note was made of the mental symptoms of each of them and their duration before entry. Then each patient was maintained on a rigidly controlled, restricted diet. For days they were given no treatment. If they didn't improve spontaneously, if they got worse —then, nicotinic acid.

This was Tom's ordeal with one after another of 60 successive pellagrous insane, severely psychotic; and within a period that varied from ten hours to six days all became clear-headed after doses of nicotinic acid. Then the beautiful hunger that accompanied their return to sanity made it possible for Tom to put them on a high protein, high vitamin, high calorie diet that solidified their cure.

While all 60 were acute, severe psychotics—violent and hallucinated or deeply depressed—the severity of their mental symptoms would have caused commitment of all of them to mental institutions. The results of the nicotinic acid treatment were Biblical: the maniacal became calm, the deeply melancholic became cheerful. What was awesome was their clear memory of their actions while demented. They were perplexed. They asked Tom—it was pathetic and heartening: "What made me act that way? I know I was crazy."

Tom could smile. It was the absence—over a period of years—of a fraction of a millionth of an ounce of nicotinic acid amide from the cells of their brains that had finally made them crazy. *It was chemical insanity.*

Beyond this astounding new scientific truth there was a dividend for Tom Spies. He knew that all 60 would have been almost sure to die if left untreated and very likely to die if treated by ordinary methods of the Goldberger anti-pellagra diet because how many doctors could have taken the time, what hospitals would have had the nursing care and money, to super-feed them?

Yes, the treatment of severe pellagra was getting to be a bit easier.

Now Tom plunged into the depths of stern experiment, hinting a confidence in his new science that was strange in the world of experimental medicine. It showed his serene belief in the sharpness of this new tool, nicotinic acid, that so deeply marked the line between mental health and the madness of pellagra. At the Hillman he observed 15 pellagrins who were brought in without mental symptoms. They simply had dermatitis and diarrhea, two of the classical D's of pellagra but not the third D—dementia.

Yet they were all too ill to eat, and he didn't try to make them eat. They were simply given a ten per cent glucose solution. Within a few days ten of the 15 were crazy, not knowing what day it was or whether it was morning or evening and not remembering what had just happened and hearing and seeing things that were not there. For these Tom made a prediction, to wit:

"The acute mental signs and symptoms which develop under controlled conditions should disappear promptly if sufficient amounts of the substance (nicotinic acid) are added to the glucose diet, all other factors remaining constant."

For all the prophecy came true. There wasn't a case among all the now more than 70 pellagrous demented—*when it was acute*—in which Tom and his staff failed to relieve their craziness with nicotinic acid. They kept well on a high protein, high vitamin, high calorie diet. It wasn't so easy when Tom went to mental institutions where pellagrins had already been committed. He did relieve some who'd been mentally sick for as long as nine months. Many patients with other psychoses at the same time suffered pellagrous insanity, secondarily. Nicotinamide knocked out the pellagra. They became more alert; they were tidier; they were no longer bedridden; but they did not come all the way back to mental health because nicotinamide didn't relieve their primary psychosis.

The events of the past year gave Tom to ponder. He thought of the more than 500,000 mental cases in the country's asylums. Of course the insanity of the vast majority of them wasn't pellagrous. Of course nicotinic acid wasn't the answer for them. But mightn't the bulk of mental disease be chemical for all that? Nicotinic acid was only one of the nutrients among all those already tagged or yet to be discovered—that might be necessary for the healthy functioning of the human brain, and for which there might be a hidden hunger.

Tom might well woolgather. What did we yet know of the cause of mental diseases? Aside from paresis, known to be due to syphilis, aside from pellagrous dementia, now known to be due to lack of nicotinic acid—aside from these two, almost nothing was known. Really nothing. Yet, look at these pellagrous insane he had cured. Their craziness mimicked every sort of mental sickness from dementia praecox to manic depressive psychosis. Among his demented pellagrins there had been inventors of perpetual motion machines, and those who thought they were Napoleon, and others imagining themselves victims of persecution, and others who were mute and with masklike faces and withdrawn from contact with everybody.

When these symptoms were pellagrous, and if they had not lasted too long, then nicotinic acid wiped them away like magic.

Tom was not surprised to find mentally deranged poor southern white folks without any pellagrous flame on their skins or in their

mouths and without diarrhea, who just the same had pellagra—
because they promptly became clear-headed after big doses of nicotinic acid. That led Tom to try his magic chemical upon a series
of victims of manic depressive psychosis, on sufferers from hardening of the arteries, on schizophrenics. It was no go. On these, reported Tom, "the treatment was without psychiatric result."

Yet he'd made a beginning. Though he didn't write it or say it
out loud, Tom could whisper, "Insanity can be chemical."

v

In those last years of the 1930's Tom Spies groped and tested his
way through strange medical country. He had to fight his astonishment. As he learned to use nicotinic acid more skillfully and more
boldly in bigger and bigger doses he had to conquer his amazement
at people being brought into the Hillman on litters and getting up
and walking home that evening. Here were cures more lightning-
like than any before observed by man. Like Louis Pasteur and
Robert Koch, 60 years before, Tom now had to adjust himself to
a new kind of medical thinking. Those old pioneer microbe hunters had had to convince themselves (and then the doctors) that
miserable microbes 1/25,000 of an inch long could actually kill a
six-foot human being. But at least those old worthies could see the
assassins through the lenses of their microscopes. Tom's mental hurdle was harder. It wasn't the presence of a microbe that killed his
pellagrins and drove them crazy. It was the absence of infinitesimal
quantities of nicotinic acid, it was the lack of a fraction of a millionth of an ounce of it in the cells of their bodies that meant their
doom.

How could the presence of such negligible traces of one chemical
mean vigor and its absence mean weakness and finally death?

Why had God—and this is asked with due respect—been so stingy
with this nicotinic acid that's so essential to life? Lean meat is one
of the richest sources of nicotinic acid. Yet the beef from a trainload
of cattle yields hardly more than a spoonful of the crystals of this
pure chemical.

But Tom, the practical death-fighter, wasted no time complaining about the feebleness of the amount of nicotinic acid in the best food; he faced it that his southern poor folks couldn't buy that food; he was happy that the industrial chemists could make it cheaply by the ton; he was delighted that a fifteenth of an ounce of it would yank demented people away from the grave and back to sanity. Best of all about Tom Spies was his not lingering over the miracles of those nicotinic acid cures. In the homes of the southern poor people, in the cotton mills and steel mills, in the clinic and on the wards of Hillman Hospital, Tom's sharp eyes, his shrewd questioning, his incessant chemical cutting and trying told him that nicotinic acid was no panacea. A lack of other vitamins (with which the Creator has been similarly niggardly) accounted for the widespread chemical starvation that kept millions in a half-living condition.

More and more Tom had to face it that his chemical miracles were only partial. It became clear that Joseph Goldberger's idea of a single pellagra-preventive vitamin was too simple. Or that what had been lumped under the name, pellagra, was really a spectrum of many diseases, a rainbow made up of different chemical deficiencies. A woman dragged herself, every step a torture, into the Cincinnati General Hospital to Tom Spies. With four other grown-ups in her family she'd been living on the pittance deemed adequate by government leaders who declared that hunger was not debatable, who said no one should starve. They maybe meant starve literally, not chemically; and again they were right about the hunger because she wasn't hungry at all. Nicotinic acid—1,000 milligrams daily—and her inflamed skin and diarrhea vanished; but she had neuritis, too, white-hot pain of it so she couldn't stand the weight of bedclothes on her legs. Now this agony grew worse despite the nicotinic acid that Tom had added to her restricted diet.

Then, plus the nicotinic acid, he began daily injections of 50 milligrams of vitamin B-1, thiamin.

Pain faded; her appetite zoomed; her depression gave way to cheerfulness; within three days she was up out of bed, walking painlessly; in nine days she had gained 18 pounds on a high protein, high calorie, high vitamin diet that she now ate wolfishly after months during which she hadn't cared whether she ate at all.

During these exciting years of the late 'thirties organic chemists were crystallizing one pure chemical vitamin after another out of that vague stew they'd called the B-complex. Alert to the keen cutting edge of these new chemical tools, Tom began trying them on vague chronic famines, curiously complicated chemical starvations that kept people half-alive for years before you could properly diagnose them to have outright pellagra.

A 50-year-old white man in this condition came to Tom at Hillman Hospital. For months he'd lost weight. He didn't want to eat. He complained of indigestion—cramps and diarrhea alternating with constipation. His tongue and mouth burned. He couldn't sleep. He could hardly remember. He had cramps in the soles of his feet and muscles of his legs. His gait was bad and he could walk just a few steps at a time. For years he had noticed that this general breakdown waxed in the spring and waned towards winter. Now at last in 1938 he had come to Tom with all these miseries plus the first actual sore-tongue sign of early pellagra.

In the hospital Tom for some days held this man on the terribly deficient diet on which he had lived for years. Then nicotinic acid and away went the signs of pellagra, yet the man remained miserable. Then injections of thiamin, and his neuritis got better. Then the yellow vitamin, riboflavin, and the little sore cracks disappeared from the corners of his mouth and he felt much stronger. Then huge doses of ascorbic acid, vitamin C—and the signs of scurvy disappeared from his gums. He couldn't see well in the dark; and this defect was conquered by vitamin A. His gait and his walking still bothered him. Vitamin B-6, pyridoxin, and in a few days he could walk two miles. He was still anemic. For this there was as yet no pure chemical bullet—but his blood grew thicker after injections of extract of crude liver. . . .

Here Tom Spies was groping in a new world of medicine. You couldn't call these people victims of a single sickness. For lack of a better name, Tom called it "sub-clinical mixed deficiency disease." Each of these new chemicals fitted its deficiency exactly as a key fits a lock. Tom was a new type of medical marksman accurately shooting each particular chemical starvation out with a definite, chemically known magic bullet.

Tom and his nurses and dietitians were constantly out on scouting trips, visiting in the homes of his victims of chemical famine. He was especially persistent in calling on families of which fathers or mothers had come, sick, to the clinic but not bringing their children. If parents were sick, what about their youngsters? At what stage of life did this chemical starvation really begin? What he found was ominous.

An eleven-month-old boy baby from a pellagrous family was brought to Hillman Hospital, feverish, terribly emaciated and with a chronic and apparently incurable diarrhea. Doctors tried everything from paregoric and the latest milk diets to neo-prontosil. No go. Worse and worse. Downhill and it looked as if on the way out. On the little boy's skin, in his mouth, not a sign of the flame of pellagra. Tom stabbed in the dark, remembering the child's chemically famished father and mother, and added a big dose of nicotinic acid to the youngster's milk.

Within 24 hours that hitherto unconquerable diarrhea had disappeared completely; within a week the baby was on a strong upgrade, on a high calorie, high vitamin diet and went home from the hospital.

Testing these pure chemical vitamins on more and more children, on hundreds of poor white and Negro waifs, it became clear to Tom that this chemical starvation is very often a life-long ailment, starting when children were still nursing at the breast and it might even begin while they were unborn in the wombs of their malnourished mothers.

Tracking down this insidious chemical famine—"pre-pellagra" you might call it—Tom could spot them as a special type of little human being. They were small for their age. They were fretful and easily crying. Though they seemed too tired to play they had such fidgets that they could not rest. They didn't sleep all out like normal youngsters but tossed and turned and frequently woke up, crying. They were mockeries of what ought to be blooming childhood.

This was what was encouraging, yes, stirring, to Tom and his staff of researching young men and women. When they'd determined a child's specific chemical starvations and then began treatment, the transfiguration was blitz-like, much faster than the rapid chemical cures of their fathers and mothers.

VI

On the last day of my stay at the Hillman clinic in Birmingham that hot August of 1940, Tom showed me the eleven-month-old baby boy he had rescued from that nearly fatal diarrhea. His name, Jerry McCoy, sticks with me because he was now such a marvel of rosy-cheeked huskiness, smiling at me.

"How quickly did you notice the effect of the nicotinic acid on his intestinal trouble?" I asked Tom Spies.

"Within an hour," he answered.

I remember the last evening of that first visit to the Hillman clinic when Tom took me for an automobile ride to cool off and we parked for a talk to summarize all I'd seen. It was hot and quiet and we looked down on the lights of the city. I told him how shaken I was by what I'd experienced these past few days. It was a new kind of doctoring. It was a chemical history of the development of disease—not from the cradle to the grave, but from the time these people were unborn in the womb till the time they came under Tom's care as pellagrins. Just a few years before, seriously ill hospitalized pellagrins died, 54 out of every 100. This morning I had talked to Mr. Robert Wharton, President of the County Commission administering Hillman Hospital.

"We pay for burying Hillman patients; it's a county hospital," said Bob Wharton. He looked at Tom with a proud smile. "Well, we haven't had to pay for burying any of this young man's patients, yet."

In the past four years more than 1,500 victims in all stages of pellagra had come to the Hillman clinic. Not one had died.

It was a new kind of doctoring because it was family, not individual medicine. Tom kept digging up about-to-be-sick, half-alive families. He found them when any one actually already sick member of a given family showed up at Hillman clinic. That was the clue. Then when Tom and his staff got out to their company-town hovels or farm-shacks they'd begin their investigation of every member of each family, including the dogs. It was remarkable that, in many of the families from which pellagrins came, the dogs had black tongue; but why not?—they all ate from the same miserable table.

That evening I confessed to Tom that this possibility most of all excited me—this pre-pellagra, this years-long preliminary state of very poor health resembled that of countless millions of half-alive people all over the nation. I kept prodding and probing Tom for a yes-or-no answer. "Look," I asked, "wouldn't the great majority of patients in this state of dilapidation be diagnosed as psychoneurotics in almost any doctor's office? From California to the State of Maine?"

Tom said he didn't know. His group of nervous people weren't going to the doctors in Maine and California. His own experience, right here, was all he knew. "But this will interest you," he said. "Most of our patients, practically all who'd been to doctors, had been diagnosed as neurasthenics or psychoneurotics long before they came to us with full-blown pellagra."

I kept trying to pin Tom down. "What's the difference between Birmingham and Chicago neurasthenia, between Birmingham and New York psychoneurosis?" He couldn't say.

I became excited. Wasn't it agreed that more than fifty per cent of all people coming into doctors' offices had complaints for which no organic cause could be found, complaints that were dumped into this medical catch-all, psychoneurosis? "How do your pre-pellagrins differ?" I kept deviling him.

Tom answered by describing his chemically famished people who couldn't be called definite pellagrins, who had been snapped out of their nervous breakdowns by the new synthetic vitamins. They are tired. They can't sleep. They are, almost all of them, thin. They aren't hungry. They have dizzy spells and their limbs are numb. They have spells of heart palpitation. They are bundles of nerves.

Many are sexually impotent. Though tired, they are restless and cannot relax and are constantly anxious about they don't know what. They are sure something bad is going to happen. They are scatter-brained. They almost all complain of dyspepsia, indigestion, heartburn. They are unstable. At any moment, without knowing why, they may start to cry.

"We mustn't forget that similar symptoms may be seen in many other diseases besides pre-pellagra," warned Tom.

"But let's say we could transplant these people to Chicago and abolish their southern drawls. How would you tell whether they're symptoms of those other diseases or whether their symptoms are nothing but those of your chemical famine?" I asked.

"I'd find out by testing for it. Putting 'em on our restricted diet. Then trying them out with our synthetic vitamins," said Tom. "You've seen it. Don't you understand it? We'd test them, chemically."

I kept coming back at him. Wasn't psychoneurosis brought on by worry, by the strain of life? Didn't it depend on the type of personality?

"Doesn't seem to be so with our pre-pellagrins," Tom answered. He said you couldn't connect their neurosis with a previous worry. No, they worried because they were neurotic. You couldn't lay their nervous breakdowns to their type of personality. Various types of personality all had the same kind of nervous breakdown. No. You couldn't say they became neurotic from conflicts with their environment or frustration of their hopes. These pre-pellagrins were a special kind of neurotic. Their nervous sickness wasn't brought on by the usual causative factors of neurosis.

Usual causative factors? "Don't you mean *supposedly* usual causative factors?" I asked.

Tom said nothing. Here was what was tops about him as a doctor: he was cagey about venturing opinions on subjects outside his personal experience. I sensed that he knew how alone he was in his pioneering. If his science did get to spread out from the Birmingham region to the notice of the big time nerve and mental specialists in the northern cities, would they give it a real try? Their view of the cause of psychoneurosis was not chemical, it was mainly *literary*. Many of them looked for the cause of neurosis in worry, instead of looking on worry as a symptom of the neurosis. Or they might look on it as more or less of a dirty story to be dredged up by psychoanalysis—a story of incestuous feelings of little girls for their fathers or little boys for their mothers. It was getting more and more popular to look for the origin of neurosis in that somewhat nasty (and hypothetical) sub-cellar of the brain called the unconscious. It was getting more and more popular to interpret psychoneurosis in terms of the pseudo-science of Sigmund Freud who has made humanity seem so much dirtier than it actually is.

With so many neuro-psychiatrists doing very well on this profitable system, they'd hardly be friendly to a test of Tom's simple science. I couldn't blame Tom for hedging. Just the same I asked him the sixty-four-dollar question.

"In how many clinics in the rest of the country are psychoneurotics being tested for possible chemical starvation? The way you test them with nicotinic acid, thiamin, riboflavin?"

"Nowhere, systematically, so far as I know," he answered.

"You don't call my question stupid?"

"No, it's pertinent. It's the only way the physicians will be able to find out," he replied.

Then Tom opened up. Now, take this thing called fear. What's the difference between Birmingham fear and fear in Boston or San Francisco? Tom had seen a formerly brawny, now chemically-famished coal miner, who'd confessed, "I'm scared to death. If I see two guys fighting with their fists, it seems to me I'm going to pass out." And this man, before he took sick, had been famous himself as a brawler and an amateur prize-fighter. The synthetic vitamins had given him back his courage. It was notable how this hidden chemical hunger broke down morale. "These people seem to live under an overhanging danger. When they see two automobiles passing they expect them to crash," said Tom.

Then we talked of the President who a few years before had become a national hero by telling us that the only thing we had to fear was fear itself. Now he was our leader in a time when fear was no longer national but worldwide, this 1940 summer. We were getting ready to mobilize. How many millions of these scared psychoneurotics were we going to find? How many would break down under the strain of combat?

"We don't know how many," said Tom. "We do know they're a major economic burden now."

"Couldn't a survey be made with these tools the chemists are giving you?" I asked. Tom believed investigations should be made.

"Then why don't you ask them to start it?" I asked.

"Who'd be interested?" Tom asked, with a faintly bitter smile.

VII

What made Tom Spies unique as a physician was his being so close to the organic chemists who were right then making the deepest physiological discoveries in medical history. Together with biochemist Robert R. Williams, Tom had just published a book on the B-1 vitamin that was the first statement of what amounted to a scientific revolution. The chemists had no sooner tested their new pure vitamin crystals on rice-birds, rats, and dogs than Tom Spies was hot on the trail trying them out on his sick people.

He admitted he owed everything to chemists like Bob Williams. Tom was simply the testing hands of the products of the masters of the chemical stills and kettles; and in the case of the master vitamin B-1 (now called thiamin) he was reaping the reward of the more than a quarter of a century of chemical failure that climaxed in its final synthesis by Bob Williams in 1937. Tom told me how the saving of a humble life had got Williams started.

Back in 1912, this lean, iron-jawed, bespectacled small man with the quizzical eyes had begun his hunt for the precise chemistry of this thiamin without which we now know that life is impossible. Though Williams was no physician, only a chemist, what began his hunt was his own experience of a medical miracle. One morning he sat on the earthen floor of a hut where a Filipino mother was holding her dying baby in her arms. The child was gasping, blue-faced, on the way out with infantile beriberi. Towards the baby's open mouth Bob Williams reached a medicine dropper and drop by drop into its mouth he let fall a crude extract of rice bran. It contained, chemically, God alone knew exactly what. It was a crude chemical mixture, seemingly too weak to have a rapid effect and Williams knew it had to be quick or this child would be gone. Hour after hour Bob Williams plied that medicine dropper. First it was only that the baby was still gasping. Then it was that there was no longer such a lifeless glaze over the baby's eyes. Hours later it was the fact that the baby's color could no longer be called blue—this kept Bob sitting there, intent, plying his medicine dropper.

At last the child breathed naturally, and then cried, and was actually hungry, and that religious moment set Bob Williams off on the chemical trek across the years that had now ended in thiamin, the B-1 vitamin. Williams is first to admit that he was only one of a chemical army and that he never would have trapped it alone. To mention (Williams himself says) all the names of all the searchers would be to call the roll of at least half the mature biochemists of England, America, France, the Netherlands, and Japan; and it's doubtful whether the chemical identification of any other substance in biochemical history cost so much time, work, and mental sweat. Yet in the end it all narrowed down to Williams. To support himself and his family he was a chemist in the Bell Telephone Laboratories that had no interest whatever in vitamins. Every night and every week-end in his backyard garage laboratory for years Bob lived his real life that climaxed in his being able to tell the world's industrial chemists exactly how to put together this combination of carbon, hydrogen, oxygen, nitrogen and sulfur now known as thiamin.

For this Bob Williams has not yet got the Nobel Prize.

And yet (Nobel Prize Committee, please take notice) no other organic chemical among the known millions of organic compounds quite equals this B-1 vitamin, thiamin, in the profundity and universality of its essential action. This master key chemical is present wherever there is life, within the living cells of all plants, all animals so far investigated. It is the without-which-no-life for microbes, worms, flies, beetles, birds, snakes, fishes, elephants, and men. Thiamin is the key chemical of an enzyme system without which no living thing can burn glucose, the master fuel of the fire of life. Thiamin helps carry oxygen that alone keeps nerve and brain cells working. Without it we couldn't move a muscle, think a thought, or go on living.

But now that we know of it, why shouldn't we take thiamin for granted the way we do water and sunlight that are just as necessary to life? Thiamin rates all this rhetorical fuss because all living things exist on a borderline of thiamin hunger. In natural foods this B-1 vitamin is present in tiny bits of hardly more than one part in two millions. Nature fights to make enough of this master key chemical to keep life going. This sinister scarcity of thiamin was worked out by the laboratory martyrdom of thousands of pigeons and rice-birds. It was now clear, too, that on the best diets most people live on a hairline separating just enough from not quite enough vitamin B-1.

Bob Williams, the army of biochemists, and the chemical engineers deserve our remembrance for their trick of making limitlessly what God had put so stingily into food, with a resulting only so-so humanity. The chemical production of the first gram (thirtieth of an ounce) of thiamin had cost more than a million dollars; and now within three years the engineers of the stills and kettles had already got it down so cheap that Tom could begin to use pounds of it to salvage the wrecked lives of hundreds of people who had next to no dollars at all. Nicotinic acid and riboflavin (as well as thiamin) were vital chemical cogs of the machine made up of the molecules within the nerve and brain cells. Nicotinic acid and riboflavin, too, were almost as scarce as thiamin in good diets—and these vitamins too could now be manufactured limitlessly.

These last years of the 1930's in Birmingham, Tom had found that God could be kindly as well as niggardly. God had so arranged it that nerve cells—after they'd been wrecked by long starvation for these vitamins—began clicking healthily again when you poured these pure chemicals into a sick human body. Not adequate doses of them. Not what the scientists of the National Research Council estimated were optimum doses. No, Tom's trick was to shove in huge doses—that was his science in its boiled-down simplicity. In the blood those huge doses of vitamins seemed to build up a high chemical pressure that drove those vitamins into the sick body cells.

He left all the abracadabra of complexity behind in the laboratories of the chemists when he held his thousands of chemically famished people down to the bad diets that had made them sick, then socked them with enormous doses of these chemicals to make them better. I could feel scientific opposition looming for Tom the way you can feel the low barometer that foretells a storm. His science didn't have enough big words. "What are you really trying to do?" I had asked him, after midnight of that last memorable Birmingham evening.

He'd answered quickly. "I'm finding out what makes people weak and how to make weak people strong," he said. Wasn't such simplicity a bit too terrific?

It didn't bother the poor southern people whose lives he was salvaging. But what about the searchers of the Rockefeller Institute, Harvard, Johns Hopkins? Most of them made their scientific reputations by cultivating complexity. Toward their looming objections Tom Spies walked somnambulistically. In Tom I felt a low-keyed fanaticism. Deep down he was sure that the outright pellagra of southerners, the beriberi of oriental millions, the sprue fatal to tropic myriads—that these were only exaggerations of the mysterious feebleness of much of humanity. These outright ills were caricatures of a submerged chemical hunger that made many of us (and especially as we grew older) the half-alive creatures that we really are.

To show this to the doctors all over, that was Tom's coming crusade. These were the stakes for which he was willing to gamble. His blue chips were the synthetic vitamins. These chemicals essential to life might well be a deeper discovery than that of microbes causing sickness and death. Would the doctors follow him?

⫸ ⫸ ⫷ ⫷

CHICAGO, ILLINOIS   OCTOBER, 1940

That night after the meetings were over, Tom and I took a long walk north along Lake Michigan in the raw, damp northeast wind. Tom said these meetings would mark the beginning of the greatest step forward in public health—the beginning of mass nutrition to lift mankind's vigor. We saw visions and were full of hope. Live or die was our motto.

Within three months after that, Tom had his first serious trouble. Attempts—some of them subtle and some pretty raw—began to be made to discredit his work and even his character. Was it that he was a bit too vigorous in his fight to lift human vigor? Should mankind stay half sick for the benefit of the doctors? Or rather for what their business agents believe is for the benefit of the doctors?

⫸ ⫸ ⫷ ⫷

CHAPTER V

Famine-Fighter's Ordeal

>> <<

IN 1940 it seemed possible that Tom Spies might be getting ready to lead the doctors on a new life-building adventure. It was hopeful, yet sad. The doctors were about to test the power of the new synthetic vitamins to bring better life at the moment the world's rulers were organizing the bloodiest shambles in human history. This would surely be followed by the downright starvation and chemical famine of still more millions.

Would our doctors then be able to rebuild what the political leaders were going to tear down?

In the new science of nutrition, Tom's was already a name to conjure with. In the broadest sense he was a teacher. At a meeting of the Postgraduate Medical Assembly in Chicago there was a large lecture room for the doctors and when Tom told them about fighting the hidden hunger of pellagra hardly a chair was empty. It was his lantern slides that did his best talking. He spoke in a low tone, relaxed, without gestures. He showed vivid color photographs—before and after—of inflamed mouths, faces and eyes rapidly healed by vitamins. He showed before and after portraits of wizened children who became robust after vitamins, and pictures of down-at-heel grownups, strong again.

I heard Tom talk to several hundred physicians at their annual clinical conference in Michigan. Few of them had ever seen an outright case of pellagra or beriberi but his pictures held them intent. Then they rose and really applauded him. It was clear that these northern doctors sensed it that these visible horrors of pellagra in the south were only an exaggeration of much of the vague, sub-surface ill health of their own patients in the north.

Between the lines of Tom's lecture they seemed to sense new chemical hope for many of their own sick people. After the meeting it was stirring to see the doctors crowding around Tom questioning him.

"It's always that way," he told me. "It's wonderful how they grab for it, they're hungry for it."

Conservative despite his missionary spirit, Tom never told the doctors that this chemical famine might be nationwide. Yet I knew that he was already dividing his hunger fight into three lines of attack that would ultimately carry the battle into every doctor's office. Does starvation for vitamins and other essential chemicals lower our resistance to microbic disease? Does it cause enfeeblement and even signs of premature old age in children? Will these starvations explain not only nervous and mental diseases in grownups but also the great killing degenerative sicknesses of the blood vessels that strike at the hearts, kidneys, and brains of millions of us in our prime?

In this triple drive Tom believed he could help. To try to answer these questions he knew he would need unheard-of sums of money for clinical research. To many a professor in his medical school research tower Tom's financial requirements seemed megalomanic. Hints to this effect didn't fret Tom at all. It was a research project on a scale as yet never attempted in the history of medical science.

To all small minds and spirits Tom's plans were grandiose. He had a way of walking right through the objections of lesser men. He explained his coming financial needs coolly:

"We've got to arrange," he said, "for poor people to come to the clinic and keep on coming and if necessary to stay in the hospital without expense to them."

This was no business of a few thousands of dollars a year to feed and house mice, rats, and rice-birds. It meant, eventually, millions of money. It meant what no medical school, even the richest, had at its disposal because of shrinking endowments.

For the past seven years this quest for money has disturbed our sleep. It has exposed both of us to character assassination. It has lost us supposed friends. It has resulted in many rebuffs for one success. Tom has exasperated me by his inordinate demands for money, money, money, and I have exasperated him by making believe that for the moment he surely had enough. Yet for me this money hunt has been worth all its headaches—for one especial reason. At the start of it, I believed men having any connection with medical science must inevitably become ennobled by this contact. I believed they were made more honest than the common run of men by their closeness to the hunt for truth. I've come out of this experience, realizing that men working in the field of medical science are human, all too human, and some of them in a not very pretty sense of that term.

II

At the beginning of our campaign, we were young and hopeful. In the late summer of 1940 we were granted an audience by the president of one of the great eleemosynary foundations; and this president may justly be called one of the most successful medical money-raisers of our time. In these days when humanity's yearning towards brotherhood is being expressed more and more by mass interest in medical research, the foundation's president is a man of significance. He is a blend of genial mixer and deadpan negotiator. He is immaculately groomed, usually wearing a boutonniere in the big-city style. He has precisely parted smooth brown hair, cool eyes and the jaw of a fighter. His memory is elephantine, his logic diabolical and his mental reflexes are usually three jumps ahead of you. He is the third toughest man (in the sense of his not letting personalities stand in the way of his ultimate aims) that I've ever met. His intuition for science is good. His interest in the miserable condition of the world's sick people is sincere. In today's bewildering burgeoning of foundations to fight this, that and every other human misery, this particular foundation's president is one of the very top men. He may justly be called a Big Time Operator.

(Following the fashion of abbreviation, I shall speak of the Big Time Operator as the B.T.O.)

To understand what Tom Spies was in for in his quest for research money it is necessary to understand a bit about the way this foundation goes about allocating its immense research moneys. To advise him in his responsibility of expending these public contributions, the foundation's president has set up an interlocking complex of committees. These groups are composed of medical research men, medical specialists, and men high in medical politics. In general these committees are recruited from a new and significant type of medical man. This is the Big Committee Man. (I shall speak of the Big Committee Man as the B.C.M.)

It is not only an honor but a great deal of fun to be a B.C.M. When you have become a B.C.M. you vary the monotonous grind of your research, your teaching, or your medical practice by getting trips (expenses paid) to the more and more frequent conclaves of the foundation. Your duty as a B.C.M. is to give counsel to the B.T.O. who has the ultimate control of the big research money. The counsel that the B.C.M.s give to the B.T.O. is, as nearly as possible, scientific and impartial. But, since B.C.M.s are human, it turns out that their advice to the B.T.O. may at times have an element of expediency. Among the B.C.M.s, science tends occasionally to get mixed up with good old-fashioned log-rolling. Finally, even though in a given instance the counsel of the B.C.M.s is strictly scientific, it can be vetoed on the ground of expediency by the B.T.O. who has the ultimate control of the research money. This demands a certain pliability and flexibility in the scientific convictions of B.C.M.s—that is, if they are to be successful in this new American calling. In other words, if you stick too consistently and too doggedly to your scientific convictions and facts—come hell or high water—you are not likely to remain a B.C.M. for long.

Between the ultimately powerful B.T.O. and his advisory B.C.M.s stand the researchers who need the research money. Whether they do or do not get funds depends to a large extent on the merit of their projects. It depends also to a certain degree on whether the B.C.M.s like the way the supplicant researcher dresses, or talks, or the way he parts his hair, or whether the researcher represents a deserving department of a sufficiently respectable medical school, or whether he is working at one of the big Ivy College medical schools. There is no question that prejudices and whims play a part in the recommendations the B.C.M.s make to the B.T.O. who doles out the research largesse. Is the applicant for research money "regular"? Who are the applicant's sponsors? Are they regular? It's who you know; it's American. It may not be entirely scientific, but it's human.

For better or worse such is the situation, more and more, of today's researcher, especially of today's younger researcher, who had better know his scientific onions, who had better know more than that, who had better know the right people who have the right contacts with the biggest B.C.M.s. The fate of the young researcher tends to be governed by a powerful, inscrutable and unpredictable remote control.

III

So, in the autumn of 1940, the foundation's president honored Tom Spies and this writer with a luncheon in New York. The foundation's president is an excellent listener. Tom sketched his battle plans against chemical famine with a low-keyed intensity that soon wiped away the foundation president's deadpan and brought him to the edge of his chair.

For Tom Spies, the country boy from Texas, that was a wonderful day. Though the foundation in question was not devoted to Tom's field of metabolism and nutrition, the foundation's president —deeply stirred by Tom's needs, plans, and the significance of his work—assured us that a way could be found to make Tom a substantial grant of research money. Tom's mention of the amount he would need for one year for one phase of his work didn't disturb the foundation's president at all. Within one month the foundation's president had activated a sub-committee of B.C.M.s. They proceeded to recommend for Tom the largest single one-year grant in all his ten years of scientific mendicancy. The foundation's president immediately passed the recommendation. Surely the grant would be extended for a term of years, because who can be asked to make a scientific discovery in one year's time? It was all a bit like Alice in Wonderland and, those days, Tom was walking on air, and with this generous financial recognition, what could now stop his progress?

Immediately after this windfall, Tom was invited to Chicago to take part in a conference of scientific, medical, and industrial big shots who were organizing a campaign to enrich the nation's flour and bread with vitamins. Though he was only one of a group of scientific witnesses who testified how life-giving B vitamins had been milled out of our white bread, it seemed to me that it was Tom who best drove home the human consequences of this ruin of our staff of life.

It was not so much what he said, it was the silent power of the lantern slides that he showed, picture after picture, each more terrible than the one preceding it. Feeble children and weak and addled men and women, their eyes, their tongues, the insides of their mouths, their skin—all inflamed, and their faces discouraged and woebegone, all because they were deficient in B vitamins. Then followed other pictures showing these victims transfigured. And each picture accompanied by low-keyed, simple description by Tom the commentator. But it was the pictures, not Tom, that told this story of despair and hope.

I noted the reactions of powerful men in the audience, of Surgeon General Thomas Parran of the Public Health Service; of big George Merck, a prince among vitamin manufacturers; of big Lee Marshall, the tough dean of the country's baking industry. Watching them all, there was no doubt that vitamins would go back into our flour and bread; and there was no doubt that this day Tom did his bit for the vitamin enrichment of the nation's bread that was soon to follow.

That night Tom and I took a long walk in the raw northeast wind along the Outer Drive by Lake Michigan. Tom prophesied that this conference marked what would be one of the greatest of all steps forward in public health—mass nutrition to lift mankind's level of vigor. That night we were full of hope.

IV

For me—always inclined towards hero worship—Tom was one of the medical men of the hour. Within two months after those great days in Chicago, an attempt was made upon the character of Tom Spies.

Before giving details of this raid upon his reputation, I would like to make a few remarks upon the art of character assassination in general. From the point of view of the victim, if a choice could be allowed between physical death and the killing of character, physical death might seem preferable because after you're physically dead you don't have to worry. If you are not a psychotic, a psychopath, or a politician with the hide of a rhinoceros (Tom Spies is none of these), but if on the other hand you are a creative man and sensitive (which Tom is), then the attempted killing of your character may do bad things to you. It did bad things to Tom.

When you are a good man and have been so esteemed by your peers, a charge or a whisper or a low-spoken innuendo to the effect that you are not quite straight and similar figurative stabs in the back are not good for you. They are likely to wobble you, to destroy your faith in yourself, because the creative man, no matter how sure of himself he may outwardly seem to be, is likely to be doubter of everything, himself included.

If enough of his peers begin to doubt a man, he may begin even to share those doubts. And what is sad to see in humanity is the number of people who will doubt a man in whom they formerly had faith. Such doubts may arise from the merest rumor, the most flimsy hearsay, and the former friend, hearing these rumors, often begins to believe them without lifting a finger to prove them right or wrong.

While the assassination of character is a cruel kind of living death for the victim, it is usually pretty safe for the perpetrator. It does not carry with it the possible consequences of physical murder for which you may, if caught, take the death penalty or sit in jail for life. Those who now went gunning for Tom Spies were in no way punished even when their treachery was exposed.

Killing of character, compared to physical killing, is a simple art, demanding no apparatus of guns, knives, or poisons that may become instruments of crime detection. Killing of character can be as subtle as it is simple. It can be done with refined elegance. It may consist of a shrug, or the pointing of a finger at one's head as if to say the victim was once a good man but now a bit screwy, or it may be confined to an almost imperceptible lifting of an eyebrow. In the case of Tom I have seen these various methods sprung at the right moment with damage to his reputation.

Finally, character assassination in the academic world is likely not to bounce back upon the perpetrator, because in the academic world the victim almost never retaliates with a suit for libel or slander. Such legal roughhouse is alien to the manners of the academic world.

This brief essay on character assassination has been prompted by my amazement at watching the process operating in the scientific world where scientific men are supposed to be primarily hunters for truth; and should not the hunt for truth be the most ennobling of all the pursuits of mankind?

V

In the autumn of 1940 Tom Spies had got his first really big grant of research money, after his story had so impressed the foundation's president. We shall call this organization Foundation "A." * The grant was to cover Tom's researches into possible relationship between human malnutrition and resistance to infections. That same autumn Tom made application for another grant from another foundation, which we shall call Foundation "B." He requested this money in support of an entirely different project, namely, a

---

* In the original draft of this narrative the names of the foundations and their executives were mentioned. At the suggestion of Dr. Seale Harris, the grand old man of Southern medicine, and of Dr. Spies, the names of the foundations and their executives are here withheld.

study of malnutrition in children and its possible effect upon their later lives.

Immediately after Tom had applied for this second grant from Foundation "B," the president of Foundation "A" forwarded to me a memo on Tom Spies. It had been written by the medical director of Foundation "A." This memo charged that Tom Spies had applied to Foundation "B" for a grant to be used *for the same purpose for which he had already received money from Foundation "A."*

From the president of Foundation "A," Tom asked the chance to clear his name. He was given the chance, and he promptly cleared it. The medical director of Foundation "A" acknowledged in writing over his signature that he had known Tom's application for a grant from Foundation "B" was for work in an entirely different field and of a nature other than that for which he had got his grant from Foundation "A." The medical director admitted that he had known this before he wrote his slanderous memo to the president of Foundation "A."

It's curious that the medical director was not dismissed from his position; it's still more curious that he did not resign from it. Tom was urged to consider the affair as a regrettable mistake. Tom had lost many weeks of work and many nights of sleep. But now Tom could resume his interrupted researches and all would surely be well. As the months went by, it appeared that all was not well. An aftermath of rumor had grapevined among the B.C.M.s of Foundation "A." Tom had become controversial, disturbing the aplomb with which high scientific matters should be conducted. To some of the B.C.M.s he had become a trouble-maker.

In the summer of 1941 it came time for Tom to make application for a renewal of his first year's grant. Tom and I were convinced it would be renewed without question, but now to our astonishment the renewal was held up. Consideration of Tom's project was taken away from the nutritionists who had passed upon the application as a sound one. Decision on Tom's application was turned over to a super-committee of B.C.M.s, none of whom, curiously, had special knowledge of Tom's field of work.

This super-committee did not turn down Tom's application outright. It simply proposed a drastic cut in Tom's appropriation. Tom refused to accept the cut. He held out for full appropriation or none. Tom got no more money from Foundation "A," and so it resulted that he had to stop his work before ever it had got fairly started. Now new rumors began to flit about—not in writing—to the effect that Tom had not used his first year's grant for the purpose for which it had been intended.

In my simplicity, during the opening years of the 1940's, I was perplexed at this ganging-up upon a man of Tom's stature as a medical researcher. In 1939 he had been given the John Phillips Memorial Award of the American College of Physicians. He had discovered the anti-pellagric power of liver. This had led Conrad Elvehjem to the nicotinamide cure of black tongue in dogs, which in turn had led Tom to save the lives of dying pellagrins with this same chemical. He had uncovered subclinical pellagra in little children who showed no outward sign of the disease. He had shown that psychoneuroses of chemical starvation can be cured by thiamin—vitamin B-1. He had demonstrated that demented pellagrins can be rescued even after they've been admitted to custodial institutions for the insane. He had proved that vitamin deficiencies make human beings vulnerable to attack by certain microbes. He had made it clear that nutritional failure almost never means hunger for a single vitamin. Lacking one, we almost always lack others.

In eleven years of day and night work, Tom Spies had done more than his bit to bring new science from the chemist's kettles and the vitamin hunter's animals to suffering mankind. He had helped to pioneer a new chemical continent in the medical world. He had found chemical answers to ancient riddles, explaining why—sometimes—we're down-at-heel physically and why we're sick and why we die. Why then didn't Foundation "A" go on supporting him?

Looking back on it now, I'm no longer indignant at this attack upon Tom. I'm amused at my own simplicity in thinking that any truly pioneering work should have just, unanimous, and immediate recognition. It has rarely been so in the history of science. I've discussed Tom's case and many similar ones with Charles F. Kettering who remains at the top of all living scientific pioneers I've known. About troubles like Tom's, Boss Kettering is philosophical: the farther a pioneer in science has gone in advance of others, the more his *work* is sound, the more likely is he in danger of attacks on his *character*. According to Boss Kettering, when an ordinary man meets an extraordinary, a new piece of work, he almost invariably shows a reflex of negativity. He is for everything in his own experience and against everything that he hasn't tried. It's simply a matter, according to Boss Ket, of *"I* didn't do it so it can't be so."

V I

After all, Boss Kettering was right to soothe my indignation with his famous gag: "The price of progress is trouble." And in those opening years of the 1940's Tom was making progress despite his detractors. His revelation of submerged chemical famine was striking home to lay people and to thousands of rank-and-file physicians. In the month of the above recorded attempt to blacken his reputation—November, 1940—an article in *The Reader's Digest* told how Tom Spies was giving new life to victims of hidden hunger.

Tom was overwhelmed by nearly fifteen thousand letters and thousands of telegrams. Though malnutrition was then supposed to be confined largely to the south, a heavy majority of these calls for help came from prosperous states like New York, Pennsylvania, and California, and many of them came from supposedly well-fed and undoubtedly well-to-do people. Over a thousand long distance calls—the majority from physicians—disturbed Tom's work. While certain foundational B.C.M.s might doubt him, there was no question that rank-and-file physicians were for him.

Curious cases made it clear that undetected famine for vitamins lurked in unexpected economic levels and certainly was not confined to southern have-nots. Tom encountered a leading physician of a northern medical school who was suffering from eyes so red and ulcerated that he could hardly read or stand daylight. Opthalmologists were baffled. Tom found what he'd first discovered among sore-eyed Birmingham poor folks—riboflavin, vitamin B-2, deficiency. A couple of shots of the yellow chemical and in a week a clear-eyed physician was back at his duties.

An expert in animal nutrition went to Birmingham to learn if the new science might have a bearing on the health of animals other than human. What he saw at the clinic made him forget his original errand. His wife was a severe psychoneurotic. His home was threatened with a crack-up. The expert went back north and substituted pills of pure B-vitamins for the aspirin to which his wife was habituated. His family life became happy.

The use of the synthetic vitamins began spreading out beyond doctors and nutritionists. A brilliant young chemical engineer in the north, absorbed in his work, paid no heed to his diet. He developed sores at the corners of his mouth and his eyes burned so he could hardly see; he was convinced that his employers were trying to rob him of the credit of a new chemical process he was developing; he told them so and they fired him. Back home, jobless and in despair, he chanced upon the popular story of Tom's vitamin treatment of nervous and mental troubles. He hurried to the drugstore and came back loaded down with vitamins. He took big doses of B-complex; he took huge doses of various synthetic B-vitamins such as nicotinamide. In a week his melancholy began lifting; in a short time he was back at work, outlook normal.

He made a pilgrimage to Birmingham to report his experience, to state his belief that there were many thousands of young scientific and other mental workers who were mis-eating themselves into hidden hunger. He thanked Tom. "I had become a real crackpot," he said. "If it hadn't been for those vitamins, I'd either have been put in an institution or committed suicide."

Tom Spies was concerned about this self-treatment that bypassed physicians. Vitamins aren't harmful, Tom knew. But the earliest symptoms of chemical famines aren't confined to chemical famine. The earliest symptoms of deadly diseases such as TB or cancer may mimic those of chemical famine. A victim trying to doctor himself with vitamins might waste precious months by not going to a doctor for precise diagnosis and so lose the chance of cure of cancer that might have been possible if he'd immediately gone to the right physician. Like most physicians Tom was against people trying to be their own physicians. Just the same, I believe that physicians could teach their patients to do a great deal to keep themselves well.

Tom never took his science direct to the people but confined his teaching to physicians. Flying many thousands of miles from coast to coast, Tom was a missionary for the spotting and curing of hidden hunger. Of the thousands of doctors to whom he talked, not one had graduated from a medical school offering a course in the new science of nutrition. Tom was a one-man department of nutrition. To rank-and-file physicians he was becoming a medical celebrity.

Tom's progress threatened him with new trouble in the early 1940's. He was a member of the American Medical Association's Council on Food and Nutrition. His own work at Birmingham had proved that vitamin deficiencies are almost never single. If you're sick for lack of nicotinamide, you're also likely to need thiamin, riboflavin, and possibly vitamins A and C. For rank-and-file physicians it would be a laborious and impractical job to try to diagnose vitamin deficiencies one at a time and then by prescription wipe out these single deficiencies one after another for every patient. It would also be tough on the average patient's already overstrained medical budget. What's more, when you poured all needed vitamins at the same time and in big doses into chemically starved patients, the vitamins seemed to act more quickly and powerfully than when given singly.

It was for these scientific and practical reasons that Tom Spies fought for the American Medical Association's approval of multiple vitamin capsules.

Not meaning to, Tom bumped against one of the Association's jealously guarded traditions. For years it had carried on a campaign against shotgun prescriptions, shotgun vaccines, and shotgun gland preparations. Doctors should diagnose one disease at a time and that meant treating it, usually, with one medicine. One disease, one cure—if any. Now shotgun vitamins loomed as a new threat to what the Association's authorities considered to be medical science.

On the other hand, Tom's scientific evidence indicated that in general doctors treating vitamin deficiencies wouldn't be scientific unless they did use the vitamin shotgun. This had a great deal to do with the Association's final approval of multiple vitamin capsules. This in turn made today's great vitamin industry possible. And this began to put vitamins within the reach of almost everybody.

Today, looking back at Tom's fight for multiple vitamins in the early 1940's, the scuffle seems merely amusing. Yet, though today there is no longer any question of the scientific correctness of Tom's position, in the early 1940's his championing of multiple vitamins did him no good with the leadership of organized medicine.

For the subtle opposition which developed to the continuance of Tom's work, may there not have been an economic angle? For organized medicine's leadership could the reasoning have been as follows? Since vitamins are not in general harmful, it was probably going to be impossible to limit their sale to prescription by doctors. Might this not mean business getting away from the doctors?

Might the consistent taking of ample vitamins by the public bring it about that many of the public would have to visit the doctors less often?

After all, the duty of the leadership of organized medicine is to keep doctors treating as many sick people as possible. The organization of the doctors is certainly based primarily on *cure* of disease, not its *prevention*. That is the province of health departments. Now before you can cure a person, that person has first got to be sick. The more people there are sick, the more you can cure, and the better off are the doctors.

VII

Whatever the explanation, Tom Spies was without question regarded as dangerous by the leadership of organized medicine. In the early 1940's various efforts were made to close down the Hillman Hospital Nutrition Clinic in Birmingham. During these dark days certain men banded together to keep the Hillman clinic alive and to keep Tom working. These men in their simple way (of course you'd hardly call them qualified to judge because none of them bore the degree of M.D.) believed that Tom's research was important for the life and vigor of mankind. This small group of men incorporated as a non-profit body calling itself "The Spies Committee for Clinical Research."

This was a turning point in Tom's life. It must have been pleasant to feel himself in a lodge with a few straight-shooting men who would fight for him. First there was Lee Marshall, a rock of ages. He was America's biggest baker, chairman of the board of the Continental Baking Company, key man in getting vitamins back into the nation's bread. He worked with so little lost motion that he could run his company during the war and at the same time serve as the Director of Food Distribution of the War Food Administration. Lee sized Tom up: "He's had to spend too much of his time raising his own research money. It's our job to make him financially irresponsible."

Lee brought in his friend, James S. Adams, then president of Standard Brands, the big food company. To both Marshall and Adams it was plain that Tom's research might do a great deal for their companies, but to both of them this was a secondary consideration. Marshall and Adams knew that Tom was a pioneer in a new science that was going to mean the difference between vigor and feebleness and life and death, for millions of people. Marshall and Adams shared a simple faith in America's glory, production, and how can you produce with half-alive people? Finally, both of them shared another American characteristic: they both had a pretty deeply covered streak of sentiment about the way Tom's science brought hope and life back to human underdogs and a stronger future for half-starved children.

Jim Adams had a further ambition. It was to take control of research money out of medical and scientific politics. Jim Adams and Lee Marshall were the nucleus of a body-guard of first-rate, public-spirited men whose names would go a long way to keep the Hillman Hospital Nutrition Clinic alive.

Of course this lay bodyguard would have been unable to guard the clinic from medico-political sharpshooters had not the lay bodyguard been in turn guarded by a Medical Advisory Council of physicians and chemists of the very highest rank in the field of nutrition. Dr. R. R. Williams, Dr. W. H. Sebrell, Dr. C. G. King, Dr. Norman H. Jolliffe were scientific men with whom the most implacable and adroit of Tom's medico-political adversaries would hesitate to get gay. This council assured the trustees that Tom's work must go on at all costs and this brought it about that the Hillman Hospital Nutrition Clinic stayed open.

VIII

As against the leadership of organized medicine who was sorry that Tom could remain at work in Birmingham, there were thousands of people—from rich and quality to poor and no-account—in the Alabama hills who were happy Doctor Tom (so they all called him) could care for them. In the old days in very bad cases of pellagra more than 50 out of every 100 died of it. During the war years 35,959 patients were admitted to Doctor Tom's clinic in various stages of malnutrition with not a single death from what Tom now called "nutritive failure." It wasn't only that the chemical treatment was now really powerful, it was that they knew about Doctor Tom and came to him—almost all of them—long before they were ready to die.

During these war years in Birmingham, Tom made a mighty experiment. Better than arguments it answered organized medicine's leadership who believed he was getting too big—medically—with his vitamins. With his nutritionists and nurses he combed through more than 5,700 malnourished people, many of them black, but more of them white. He got down to 893 so sick they hadn't worked for many months and most of them not for years.

What ailed them? Not TB or syphilis or leukemia or diabetes

or nephritis or heart disease or any other standard chronic sickness. All these were ruled out by complete and drastic clinical and lab diagnosis. What was wrong with them? Their complaints masqueraded under symptoms of many digestive, nervous, and mental ailments, all ruled out by Tom's skilled medical screening. They couldn't be called pellagrins. They were more or less the type of down-and-out forlorn you can find in any doctor's office, nation-wide.

They'd lost weight and strength but couldn't eat. They fidgeted, yet they complained of an awful tiredness. They had burning pains and tingling in their feet; they could hardly sleep. They couldn't concentrate. They scared easily. They were gloomy. They were, all of them, good only for the physical and emotional ashcan.

Two hundred and sixty-eight of this rearguard of 893 men and women were so far gone when they got to Tom's clinic that he couldn't risk putting them on his base-line diet which, in a few days in hospital, would bring out marked physical signs of malnu-trition. Into these emergency cases went life-saving measures—huge doses of synthetic vitamins and anti-shock treatment—right now.

For the rest, Tom and his staff put them on the base-line diet for a few days; then as one sign after another of their complex of chemi-cal starvations became clear, they were socked with big doses of the various synthetic vitamins. It was what Tom called a thera-peutic test; it was simply a try-it-and-see test to determine which vitamin began to reverse what sign of chemical starvation.

In these war years not one of the 268 who'd come to the Hillman as life-and-death emergencies passed away. All rose from their beds and went home walking. In those years all the rest of the total of 893 climbed quickly or slowly out of their weakness. Tom's try-it-and-see therapeutic test spotted their chemical starvations just as microscopes and blood tests ferret out deadly microbes. If vitamin deficiency was there, those test doses clicked like new chemical keys opening rusty chemical locks.

Such was Tom's diagnosis and beginning treatment of nutritive failure.

Then the Hillman famine fighters began what is a new and little practiced phase of medicine. It is still a prevailing condition that physicians and surgeons have done their job when patients have been treated, haven't died, and have made their way home as best they can—marked "improved"—from their doctor's office or the hospital. Of course many are improved so that both they and their doctors can say they are cured. Many remain in a condition where the doctors congratulate themselves on the fact that the patient is still alive and the patient doesn't know quite whether he wishes he is alive or dead. It was this phase Doctor Tom now tackled with these nutritive failures.

It is the new phase of medicine—rehabilitation. That means no longer being a burden to your family, being strong enough to earn your own and your family's bread and butter; it means getting up out of bed in the morning raring to be up and at 'em. This was Tom's stern test for real cure—he wouldn't settle for less—among these 893 who hadn't been able to work for many months or years.

It was a dogged business. While the first improvement of most of them was dramatic, so that they quickly got from horizontal to vertical, in most of them their chemical famine was very deep. It wasn't satisfied in a few days, not to the point of rehabilitation. These people were now fed high calorie diets rich in protein, vitamins and minerals, large doses of synthetic vitamins, yeast and liver extract to get in all B vitamins known and unknown. They were fed and fed and fed and at last all of these 893 finally got back to full-time jobs. *Under their own steam* they got them because now at last they wanted to work and couldn't keep down their human instinct to work so that they found themselves jobs as miners, steel-workers, ship-builders, mechanics, farmers, cooks and housekeepers—and among them were 41 young men who had been invalids and were now fightin' enough so that they were accepted for unlimited service in the armed forces.

That wasn't enough for Doctor Tom. After the 893 had got to work his staff kept following them all up, feeding them, and finding out whether they kept working. All except the boys who were out of reach because they had gone away to the Army.

Besides this rehabilitated 893 there were thousands of people in the Alabama hills who'd been still able to work, dragging themselves round, now really working thanks to what the Hillman clinic had done for them. Doctor Tom now had become a legend to the Negroes and poor whites, to the poor white collar workers, storekeepers, professional folks and to the big industrialists. One Negro congregation renamed its church "in honor of the memory of Doctor Tom." But Doctor Tom wasn't dead! No, but it was in honor of his memory alive or dead and forever.

Birmingham's citizens, led by their industrialists, subsidized the Hillman Hospital Nutrition Clinic—it was the first community nutritional project in America. In 1944, more than 2,000 doctors, nurses, chemists, and nutritionists came from all over the nation to Birmingham to watch Tom's war on nutritive failure.

Top southern industrialists, Messrs. Thomas W. Martin, John Porter, and Hugh Comer joined Tom's bodyguard as trustees of the Spies Committee. Hugh Comer (he looks like a southern and handsomer Abe Lincoln), president of the famous Avondale Mills at Sylacauga, Alabama, recognized Tom as a new power in the fight of the south to lift itself up by its economic bootstraps. "We consider the work that Tom Spies is doing . . . of inestimable value," wrote Hugh Comer.

"It would break my heart to see Tom Spies moved out of this country," wrote Mr. Comer, "and I am delighted beyond measure that he has had a part in our life around the foothills of Alabama. . . . Bless his fine heart."

Here was a new ally. When an industrialist whose mills are a medical, nutritional, economic model for America—north or south, with a phenomenal record of low absenteeism and a wonderful record for high production during the war—thinks that way about Doctor Tom, who can harm him?

Who in the U. S. A. or the foreign scientific world had heard of Hillman Hospital before its famine fight stirred doctors and scientists from all continents to make pilgrimage to the hopeful hurly-burly of Tom's clinic?

Even so, there was still powerful medical opposition to Tom. When a man is the missionary of a religious thought (which Tom essentially is) even his most devoted supporters (as the trustees of the Spies Committee undoubtedly were) can find time to work for him only now and then, intermittently. At the same time it seemed as if certain of the enemies of that religious thought were working daily to discredit it and to tear its originator down. Evil is more persistent than good and were it not for that, humanity would long ago have built a permanent Utopia.

Now it seemed there might no longer be room for the Nutrition Clinic at Hillman Hospital. The authorities of the University of Alabama were going to have other uses for the space, for the wards, for the beds where Tom had been finding out how to put life into thousands of sick people. It seemed that this space was going to be needed to teach medical students.

IX

While vitamins were becoming more and more scientifically respectable and significant, at the very same time certain leaders of organized medicine were violently denouncing the growing commerce in vitamins as disreputable, wasteful, and quackish. Thousands of scientific papers were proving that vitamins are the indispensable chemical sparks of the metabolism—the sum total of all chemical changes—of our bodies. Over and over it was proved that many people, even on well-balanced diets, show signs of vitamin deficiencies. This being true, why then shouldn't people in general supplement their diets with vitamins—to make sure they'd have enough of them?

While medical "authorities" told the people that they could get ample vitamins and minerals from a well-balanced diet, nutritional scientists—who were respected by the aforesaid medical "authorities"—demonstrated the difficulty of getting a surely ample supply of vitamins in a so-called well-balanced diet. Vitamins are hard to preserve in the storage and transit of food; vitamins were lost in cooking; diets were improperly selected in respect of vitamins because of nutritional ignorance or lack of money or wartime rationing.

To test the availability of a well-balanced diet that would give us all our needed vitamins, Dr. Robert Harris of the Massachusetts Institute of Technology conducted an experiment. With the permission of 71 families in New York and Boston whose choice of food was better than average, the doctor took plates off their tables and analyzed the food for vitamin and mineral content. Only 7 per cent received all the nutrients advised by the National Research Council for optimum health. Only 21 per cent got what is called a protective intake of vitamins and minerals.

The medical "authorities" tried to counter the Harris experiment by giving wide publicity to another experiment, at Duke University. Here a group of medical students who were supposed to be living on a well-balanced diet were given small vitamin and mineral supplements. After a brief time they reported that they didn't feel any better despite the extra vitamins.

The leadership of the American Medical Association announced that the Duke experiment "proved that normal people on average diets of the type studied do not benefit by extra vitamins." The spokesman said he believed this evidence applied to the vast majority of Americans with their high standard of living. Yet the diet on which the Duke students lived was not an average but a superior ration. And furthermore, who could say that a diet adequate for young husky students would be adequate for millions of older Americans? No one could say it. It had not been tested.

At the same time there was a highly authoritative—remember that word "authoritative"—medical report that all was not nutritionally okay with the vast majority of normal people on average diets. Nobody would question the authority in nutritional science of Dr. Norman Jolliffe and Dr. H. C. Sherman of New York City. Nobody would question the medical respectability of Dr. James S. McLester, the same who originally invited Tom Spies to come down to Birmingham, Alabama. These three savants pointed out that there is malnutrition and malnutrition.

"Some types of malnutrition" (like pellagra, scurvy, and beriberi) "are strikingly obvious to everyone; some are apparent only to the physician who looks for them; and some are vague and elusive even to the careful observer using the most specialized techniques."

About the prevalence of these three degrees of malnutrition our three savants made an estimate. "If the first group (malnutrition strikingly obvious to everyone) is counted," said they, "the prevalence will be recorded as low—almost negligible.

"If the second group is counted (apparent only to physicians who look for them) it will be recorded as high.

"If the third group is included (vague and elusive even to the careful observer using the most specialized techniques) then the rate will be sufficiently high to occasion genuine concern," warned our three savants, though they did not (and could not) specify how high the rate should be before we got worried.

Amid this confusion of medical counsels the vitamin industry boomed upward to reach a gross of more than $200,000,000 in 1944. Apparently, despite the warnings by the American Medical Association leadership that the vast majority of the American people didn't need them, the American people were swallowing vitamin pills and capsules with growing enthusiasm.

Against this new custom the leadership issued a ukase, to wit: "The average American on today's diet needs no vitamin supplement. The use of reinforced bread takes care of most of his deficiencies."

For this flat statement there is no clinical evidence. Also, alas, the American people were eating less and less bread. Also it is true that the people who are poor and need vitamins most usually get the least and those who need them the least get the most.

To the support of the leadership came the then president of the American Medical Association. "Certainly," said the president, "the people of this country are not in such a state of malnutrition as to require the use of $250,000,000 worth of vitamins."

To the aid of the leadership and the president came a famous professor emeritus of physiology. "All of us know," said this professor, "that the vitamin prescription has gone out of the hands of the doctor and is in the hands of the quack, and the maker of vitamin pills and what-have-you; in other words, in 1944, the vitamin pill business is now a major part of patent medicine quackery."

But were the rank-and-file physicians of America promoting quackery? About 70 per cent of all vitamins are sold either by prescription or upon recommendation of doctors; and nearly 75 per cent of the over-the-counter sales of vitamins are registered by those brands advertised exclusively to doctors by companies promoting products only through doctors. *And not by deplorable radio advertising direct to consumers.*

Who was right in this strange argument as to whether or not we should take vitamins in addition to those in our food? Were the rank-and-file doctors being victimized even more than the public? In 1943 the physicians wrote an estimated 43,000,000 vitamin prescriptions.

It's true that the rank-and-file doctors had more than the advertising of the vitamin industry to support their vitamin enthusiasm.

"All the evidence from numerous surveys over the past ten years to the present, among persons of all ages, in many localities," announced the Food and Nutrition Board of the National Research Council, "is without exception in complete agreement that deficient diets are widespread in the nation. . . . All the data from numerous surveys with new methods among persons of all ages in many regions are entirely in accord in showing that deficiency states are rife throughout the nation."

The National Research Council's board estimated that some degree of malnutrition hits about 75 per cent of our population.

The American Medical Association's leadership and president were correct when they pointed out the low prevalence of outright pellagra, scurvy, and beriberi in America—but did that mean that we are only a mildly malnourished nation? What about the widespread subclinical deficiency disease that Tom Spies, Norman Jolliffe, Henry Sebrell, and other pioneering famine-fighting physicians were finding to be at the bottom of much of our lack of vigor?

Wanting the truth, would it be fair to accept the National Research Council's estimate of 75 per cent of us being to some degree malnourished? What actually is the prevalence of this subclinical malnutrition that lurks like the ice-berg eight-ninths of it, maybe, under the surface? I asked Tom Spies.

He simply answered that nobody really knew how much of this subclinical deficiency disease there was. Unless we had plenty of physicians trained in the new science of nutrition to find and report these conditions, how could we know? In all of America we have only a handful of such doctors. In the middle 1940's no medical school had a department of metabolism and nutrition where medical students could get this new knowledge.

I asked Tom whether the $250,000,000 vitamin business was a hoax upon the public, and whether the rank-and-file doctors were quackish in their recommendation and prescription of nearly 70 per cent of all the vitamins bought by the public.

Tom thought not. Nor was he at all excited about this supposed victimization of the public and the rank-and-file doctors. "It has got many people's health regained," wrote Tom, "and it would be difficult to convince me, irrespective of how big the business was and how much money was made from it, that it was a waste.

"I don't see how you can tell it was a waste," Tom went on in his customary mild style, "until we know how much is needed in the way of vitamins in this country. We don't know at present. We must remember, though, that the poor do not get as much as the well-to-do."

What Tom wrote made sense. "Wouldn't it be better," he asked, "to err on the side of protecting the health of the people than to err on the side of allowing deficiency diseases to develop to the stage where all physicians could recognize them?"

It was not the least of Tom's merits that he was willing to err to keep people healthy. It was obvious that Tom Spies was looking ahead to the time when nutritional science would be the foundation not of curative but of *preventive* medicine. This is where Tom was ahead of the traditions of those who guide the apparent economic interests of the doctors through the American Medical Association—the doctor's union. It is still the dominating tradition in these circles that medicine is mainly curative. If a lot of people weren't a little bit sick, how were the doctors going to live?

And anyway (this was a favorite taunt of those who dominate the doctor's union) wasn't the vigor that people *thought* they got from vitamin pills and capsules, purely imaginary? Wasn't it purely psychological?

To this objection it wasn't Tom Spies but Rhea who had an answer. Rhea, my wife and co-worker, pointed out that, among those who raise animals such as chickens, pigs, and cattle, there is no objection to maximum vigor for their birds and beasts. Farmers want maximum egg and milk production and as much pork and beef for as little money as possible. It is universally considered an aid to vigor, growth, and functional activity of chickens to super-charge their diets with vitamin D and riboflavin. Ditto for pigs with iodine, vitamin D, and nicotinamide. Ditto for cattle with vitamin A and irradiated yeast. Rhea urged that certain animals are now being found deficient even for the vitamins they make in their own bodies, even when they're fed the best balanced diets. Vitamin C, for example, is now given to bulls and cows to increase their fertility. Nature has inscrutably not let them make quite enough of it for maximum reproduction.

"When animals show this higher and definitely measurable vigor as a result of adding vitamins to their routine diets, can we say that this is the result of the effect of vitamins upon their imaginations?" asked Rhea in her quietly devastating manner.

Looking out many mornings over the blue of Lake Michigan and lying wakeful many nights, pondering over Tom Spies and other medical pioneers, it became clear that the deeper the discoveries they tried to bring to general use, the more medical authorities consider them to be mavericks—an unbranded animal, not a member of any herd.

This late 1941 summer marked a turning point in our life among the doctors. We cut loose from association with those considering themselves medical authorities. From then on we determined not to recognize medical "authority." From now on out we tried to follow only the authority of the facts to the full extent of our power to get at them.

What happened during the following years, to Tom Spies, was in one way encouraging. It proved that a discoverer doesn't have to remain a maverick permanently. This disturbing question remained: If you stop being a maverick will you make any more discoveries?

CHAPTER VI

Famine-Fighter's Vindication

≫ ≪

IT was this battle of the vitamins that gradually made us understand Tom's significance as it is likely to be estimated by historians
of the future. Tom's job was the diametric opposite to that of
Joseph Lister who some seventy years ago had a tough time teaching doctors that Pasteur's microbes were something which, when
you get them, make you sick. Now Tom was trying to get it across
to physicians that vitamins are something which, when you *don't*
get them, make you sick.*

It's easy to see why Tom's job was tougher than Lister's. It seems
weird that devastating, even fatal, illness can be produced by the
absence of something. Microbes are murderers, visible assassins.
How can the absence of anything be murderous? It's mentally
tougher to deal with negatives than with positives, to think of
sickness as caused by what is *not* there than by what *is* there.

Tom Spies had a chance to be regarded in the future as the
Lister of nutrition. Lister had been derided by the medical authorities of his day. They denied the existence of disease-producing
microbes. Or, granting that microbes did exist, they asserted they
must be harmless because they were so enormously little.

Tom's missionary job was truly tough. First he had to teach
doctors that vitamins, by not being there, made people sick. Then
he came bang against a body of medical "authority" asserting (and

* We thank the nutritionist, Dr. Bernard Oser, for this condensation of the
meaning of vitamins into the vernacular.

needing no evidence because of "authority") that vitamins were there, in plenty, in the average American diet.

When Joseph Lister performed his operations in a carbolic acid spray, and when his patients then didn't become infected and didn't die, it was a clear-cut demonstration of the power of antisepsis to fight microbes. But when Tom made physically down-at-the-heel people more vigorous by vitamins, the "authorities" liked to point out that it was only psychological—disregarding Tom's rigidly controlled experiments. What encouraged Tom was that more and more rank-and-file doctors listened to him and not to their "authorities." What saved him from despair was his keeping on working.

He was now in the middle 1940's fumbling towards the test of an essential chemical, a new vitamin, the effect of which the highest "authority" couldn't ascribe to the recipient's imagination. Tom was experimenting with a synthetic chemical, the effect of which could be measured exactly on human beings. Just as animal husbandmen measure the effect of already known vitamins on the productivity of pigs, chickens, and cows—by weighing and measuring and counting. Weighing, measuring, counting—these are the nemeses of authority. In the face of accurate weighing, measuring, and counting—let liars beware.

This hoped-for new vitamin that Tom was testing, built human blood. If it really built human blood you could count and measure the increase of the human red blood cells. Would this essential chemical relieve pernicious anemia, that, before liver shots, had been 100 per cent fatal? Would it restore the dangerously thin blood not uncommon in expectant mothers? Would it zoom up the blood of anemic malnourished—there were millions of these. Might it save the lives of countless victims of sprue, a major curse of the tropics? Might it check the anemic decline of old age? If it did, it would be a first vitamin victory over the mysterious waning of body-building chemical forces dragging us downhill from life's prime.

The hunt that had led up to this possible vitamin blood-builder had begun 21 years before when Dr. George R. Minot, of Boston, in his private practice (it had seemed too crazy to try in a medical school) fed tremendous meals of liver to certain doomed victims of pernicious anemia. The results got the Nobel Prize for Minot and three fellow Americans.

These historic patients had come dragging to Minot with faces tinged a faint yellow, waxy, giving you the creeps because it was as if they were corpses, walking. Their illness had sneaked over them as an insidious languor; their bodies were flabby rather than wasted; their lips and tongues seemed bloodless. It had been the fate of all similarly sick that, as their blood grew thinner and thinner, they got more breathlessly tired to the point of torpor—in which they all at last passed away. Such (slightly paraphrased) is the poetic description by a stern and handsome old English doctor, Thomas Addison, who was as excited about discovering, diagnosing, and precisely describing a new disease as he seemed uninterested in finding its cure.

It wasn't that the old gentleman wanted these poor devils to die; it was simply that he was deeply dubious about anybody's ever being able to find anything to save them. In this, Addison was a precursor of famed Sir William Osler, Baronet, whose curious nihilism about cures impregnated two generations of America's doctors with the deadly superstition that the more fatal the sickness, the more impossible to heal it.

Minot just fed poor pernicious anemia devils liver, cooked and raw, and then more liver. It would have been unbearable . . . excepting that one after another of these as good as dead persons began to see a faint pink flush come over their faces and to feel energy conquering their languor. To people with blood ten times thinner than it should be, to wretches too far gone to swallow, Minot rammed fresh, pulped liver through a stomach tube when their breathing was so faint he could hardly detect it.

In a week they were sitting up clamoring to eat; in less than two weeks they were wanting to get up and walk. Minot had added a bit of new science to that of the Book of Deuteronomy where it's written that "the blood is the life." He had proved there is life in liver; and now a simple experiment told him that what liver did was to stir up life hiding deep in the marrow of the bones.

When these poor pernicious anemia people were nearly bloodless and close to dead, and when Minot drew a bit of marrow from inside their bones (bone marrow is where blood is born) his microscope showed him the secret event leading up to these tragedies. There was a sit-down strike of the megaloblasts; these are the giant cells of bone marrow that make red blood corpuscles. The sick marrow swarmed with megaloblasts, too many of them, but absolutely refusing to pour out the red blood cells fundamental to life.

When his liver-feeding dragged these doomed people out of the valley of the shadow, again probing their blood and their bone marrow, through his microscope Minot saw resurrection; billions of new red blood cells swarmed out of the bones into the blood; they were blue-networked cells, reticulocytes. Swarming in the blood they brought the great news that the bone marrow megaloblasts had signed a new contract and gone back to work.

This pernicious blood sickness is only one of the anemias where bone marrow can't make blood. The same disaster happens in sprue, in many a pregnancy, in the majority of cases of very severe pellagra and in the malnutrition of old age. To distinguish these anemias from the far less serious anemia due to lack of iron, the dangerous anemias of all these conditions are stamped with a medical trademark. In all of them the red blood cells are large in size despite their perilous smallness in number. So, in the medical jargon still designed to keep understanding of his ills away from the man in the street, these blood failures are dubbed "macrocytic" (meaning large-celled) anemia.

Would liver rescue the uncounted sufferers from other macrocytic anemias as it so spectacularly saved pernicious anemia victims?

This question brings Doctor Tom back into the story. He was one of the first to try to find the answer. In 1935 (still at his job of saving the lives of those drunks in Cleveland) Tom found that the majority of his desperately sick pellagrins, in addition to their inflamed skins, tortured bowels and addled brains—also suffered from this macrocytic anemia. Then six years later he brought dying pellagrins back to life with nicotinic acid. Then he ran onto a clue. He observed that the nicotinic acid cured most of the pellagra—

excepting its neuritis, a soreness of the corners of the mouth, and its anemia.

To rebuild their blood to rehabilitate them back to work he had to feed them liver or give them shots of liver extract. It turned out to be the same for the sprue of the tropics, for the anemia of pregnancy and for the large-celled anemia of malnourished old age. Very well. Liver is an almost universal blood-building elixir. But what, chemically, was this life in liver? It was more than idle curiosity that made Tom ask this.

The liver treatment is crude; liver shots hurt many people so they stop co-operating; liver shots made many allergic so it was next to impossible for them to go on with the treatment without which they could not live; liver shots were a terrifically complicated chemical mixture, a variable soup which, according to the vagaries of its cooking, was sometimes powerful and at other times feeble. Though, mind you, liver extracts were a wonderful remedy. But at the same time you had the right (in view of the fantastically advancing organic chemical technique) to ask for something more exact, more elegant, something the precise chemical structure of which you could write on the blackboard, something you could fabricate one hundred times out of every one hundred, just so, in your stills and kettles.

For 20 years from the brave days of George Minot, millions of dollars and the day and night toil of the world's best scientists had failed to find the anti-anemic chemical magic bullet hiding in liver, the compound that puts blood-building force back into bone marrow. Toward the end of the 1930's and in the early 1940's a gleam of hope—but no better than the light of the firefly—began flashing off and on in scores of laboratories. Vitamin hunters were toying with a powerful, yet impure chemical. Tested, it was found necessary to the life of microbes, to the existence of laboratory animals; and without it baby chicks couldn't grow—and wait, without it, baby chicks *couldn't make good red blood*.

Dr. Roger Williams (brother of famous thiamin-Bob) and his associates at the University of Texas named this not-yet-but-almost pure chemical "folic acid." Because they found it in foliage—such as the leaves of spinach. But it hid in many other foods, in mush-rooms, soybeans, kidney, yeast and, yes, in small amounts—in liver.

It is a scientific curiosity that for years the very fact that this folic acid was found in raw liver, steered physicians away from the notion that it could be a weapon against certain of the deadly macro-cytic anemias. The race to get at the exact chemistry of folic acid seemed a scientific wild goose chase. Some extracts of liver that con-trolled pernicious anemia were almost completely devoid of the folic acid that liver contained naturally.

It was a highly contradictory business. This almost-pure folic acid, from liver, enriched the blood of baby chicks; but liver ex-tracts, though enriching human blood, had no effect on baby chicks, and contained practically no folic acid.

II

With a faith in this impure folic acid that seems to this day un-explainable, a team of sixteen chemists and vitamin hunters at the Lederle and Calco Divisions of the American Cyanamid Company kept stewing, cooking, distilling, adsorbing, precipitating, and at-tempting to crystallize for the precise chemistry as if it were some chemical holy grail. I asked the brilliant Hindu medical scientist, Dr. Yellapragada SubbaRow why they stuck at it. "Well," said Sub, "this not pure folic acid was absolutely essential to the lives and growth of more than 500 kinds of microbes; no laboratory animal could live without it; we knew we were after an essential chemical."

Essential to mankind? Maybe. They didn't know. They hoped so. It was faith. The Cyanamid folic hunt was an adventure that could not have gone on in any university; it was a prime example of the shift of medical research from ivy-walled colleges to industry. En-couraged by Mr. William B. Bell who is curiously one of the most conservative and at the same time one of the most optimistically progressive Americans I know, the executives of American Cy-anamid poured thousands, then hundreds of thousands and finally millions of dollars into the chase for this chemical will-o'-the-wisp that doctors were pretty certain could not control human macrocytic anemias.

There was not that kind of money, there was not so great a crew of top-ranking chemists and vitamin hunters to be found in any ten colleges.

It was a gamble. What was Mr. Bell's justification to his stockholders? It was the intensity of his faith in his research men who believed that a chemical so absolutely vital to microbes, rats, mice, and monkeys must hold a key to the lives of men.

And yet, even if this research team did succeed in trapping folic acid pure, even if it did turn the chemical trick of synthesizing it cheaply in kettles, so what? If its virtues were confined to building blood and stimulating growth in baby chicks and other animals—and if it showed no such precisely specific power in human beings—those dollars would have gone down the rat hole.

At last, in August, 1945, this team of seemingly hare-brained scientists reported the synthesis of pure folic acid out of coal, salt, petroleum, lime and air. The event was considered so momentous that the publication in the periodical, *Science,* was signed by sixteen authors. These were the sixteen scientists who had put the work of their hands and brains into this curious adventure; their names, thus published, were their spiritual wages; the publication gave them all a dubious immortality.*

At the moment of publication the word "dubious" seemed in order. Before it was synthesized, doctors had tested folic acid concentrates on human pernicious anemia. They mixed these concentrates with gastric juice (which pernicious anemia patients lack) using the exact amount of concentrate in which folic acid is naturally present in liver. It built no red blood in these sick human beings.

And now, when they had determined folic acid's exact chemical structure, when they'd crystallized it, synthesized it—again, so what?

* The authors of this now historic paper were, in alphabetical order: R. B. Angier, J. H. Boothe, B. L. Hutchings, J. H. Mowat, J. Semb, E. L. R. Stokstad, Y. SubbaRow and C. L. Waller of Lederle Laboratories; and D. B. Cosulich, M. J. Fahrenbach, M. E. Hultquist, E. Kuh, E. H. Northey, D. R. Seeger, J. P. Sickels and J. M. Smith, Jr., of the Calco division of American Cyanamid.

Crystalline folic acid was found in the ridiculously small amount of only one-tenth of an ounce in one ton of fresh liver.

III

That same month of August, 1945, Drs. T. H. Jukes and Stanton Hardy of Lederle Laboratories sent a smidge of still extremely rare and precious crystals of folic acid down to Tom Spies in Birmingham. He was the man to try it. Tom would carefully try any pure chemical, and for this test he had what seemed a far-fetched justification. Tom had detected a rise in the number of white blood cells —not the red blood cells—in malnourished patients to whom he had given folic acid when it was in its still impure, concentrated form. Again, so what? It's the *red* blood cells, not the white blood cells, that are the fatal lack in human macrocytic anemias. Such was his illogical jump-off into the unknown with the new synthetic crystals.

In his gamble he was out of the logical groove. He seemed really irrational. Powerful liver extracts control human anemias but in those very extracts there is little or no folic acid!

Here was his unorthodox reasoning, the kind of left-handed thinking (found in no textbook) that so often makes the difference between sticking in a logical rut—and discovery. Tom stayed awake nights, talking it out to himself.

"What if there isn't any folic acid in liver extracts that control human anemias?

"There is folic acid in the original liver from which those extracts were prepared.

"Maybe, in purifying the liver to get one cure, the chemists had thrown away another.

"Maybe there was more than one anti-anemic chemical in natural liver.

"If there is more than one anti-anemic chemical in natural liver, maybe one of them is folic.

"So let's try it, in great big doses."

That was the way Tom jumped out of the groove of textbook logic. For twenty years the entire medical world had been hypnotized by the notion that the only possible anti-anemic chemical was the one—still chemically unknown—that hid in liver extracts.

In November, 1945, Tom Spies reported that folic acid had red-blood-cell-building power parallel to the most powerful liver extracts when the folic was tested out on eight human beings severely sick with macrocytic anemia. Unlike liver extracts (given by shots) the new chemical was taken by mouth. By the end of the year the yellow crystals had built good red blood in 26 out of 27 victims, *including five suffering from deadly pernicious anemia.*

Tom, who had been sleepless from doubt, now stayed awake from excitement. It was fantastic what small doses of the new chemical stoked up terrific blood-building power in sick bone marrow. A 75-year-old man was brought to Hillman Hospital with severe diarrhea, breathless and with a sinister pallor with his red blood cells down to half their normal number. To give the new folic acid its severest test, to rule out any accidental effect of blood-building food, for a week Tom held the deeply sick man on a high carbohydrate diet, with no liver, no meat. Then the treatment started, simple, just a few milligrams of folic acid—surely not enough to help a mouse or a baby chick—given daily by mouth.

In four days the old man mumbled that he felt some better.

His tongue and his mouth had been so sore that he could hardly eat at all and that fourth day he ate enough food for two hard-working men. Was it psychological, was it his imagination as all vitamin-knockers would surely say? Tom's microscope now proved that the old gentleman's feeling of new strength wasn't fooling him. The megaloblast giant cells, that had been on strike refusing to make new blood, began a back-to-work movement deep in the marrow of that old man's bones. It was out of this world the way this daily few milligrams of folic acid gave those reluctant, slow-downing megaloblasts a chemical kick in the pants so that they began pouring out reticulocytes—young red blood cells—in hundreds of billions out of his bone marrow into his blood; in a couple of weeks these wisps of crystals of synthetic folic acid gave him quarts of good rich red blood.

It was epochal. Here was a new member of the family of vitamins that, for the first time in medicine's history, produced an effect on one of the most basic functions of the human body—blood-building—an effect that you could count, that you could precisely measure, under your microscope, in exactly so many millions of red blood cells per cubic millimeter of blood. It was historic. It was a vitamin of exactly known chemical structure in super-tiny amounts triggering the building of enormous quantities of blood, measurable.

As for the old man, all this didn't matter at all. In a short while he went back home. What mattered to him was that he now wanted to go back to work in his garden, and did. "When I first came here," he said, reporting back to Tom for a check-up, "I was nothing but a burden to my family and I thought it was time to die. But this little bit of yellow medicine has sure put life back into these old bones."

That winter Tom Spies and his research team found that life may hang not by its proverbial thread but by a few crystals of this new yellow chemical. They went to Havana, Cuba, and in collaboration with some of the leading physicians at the Calixto Garcia Hospital, in a ward furnished them by the University of Havana, they faced six men and three women marked for death by tropical sprue.

These were all bags of bones looking like just-living Nazi or Commie concentration camp victims. They suffered devastating diarrhea; when their food was given them, often within an hour it was in the bedpan. The mucous membranes of their mouths and eyes were so pale that they looked like what they almost were, dead people. They were sad and incessantly weeping. Their faces were dead-pan and when they turned their heads or raised their hands it was in slow motion. None of them any longer cared whether they lived or died. They were empty of energy and had almost no blood at all.

How could folic acid save them? Tom Spies took a stern decision. Before treatment began, he kept them for days on a meatless diet (meat might build *some* blood) to be sure that it was folic acid that helped them if in their extremity anything human could help them.

This base-line diet brought them even closer to death. Then began the test—at first in big doses—folic acid crystals by mouth.

The first flicker of returning life came within two days when their mask-like faces lighted up into just the hint of a smile. That day the dreadful colicky pains left their bowels. There was a drying up of their life-sapping diarrhea. On the fourth day their upsurge of energy made them actually want to get up out of bed and walk; and some of them did. Their joy at their return to life was shown by their gratitude to Tom, the other doctors and nurses. They begged to be allowed to help nurse and care for other sprue victims, not yet treated. Within a week they were all up and about the ward, helping those not yet saved.

These events revealed a power in the little yellow crystals that was beyond scientific measuring and counting and still more mysterious than their ability to make new blood. This upsurge of energy appeared *before* Tom could count any blood increase under his microscope, before the pouring of the young reticulocytes out of the bone marrow, before the marrow's manufacture of billions of new red blood cells—which didn't begin till the fourth day of the folic acid treatment.

What was unearthly, as this fight for life unfolded, was the way Tom found he could cut down the daily doses of folic acid, down to only a few milligrams a day. These tiny amounts of the yellow chemical (with no meat or liver in the diet, mind you) so zoomed the hitherto negligible appetites of the victims that within a few days they were demanding extra helpings of food. All gained weight, several of them spectacularly, one of them 30 and another 37 pounds in two months' time.

All nine of them lived and went back to work and have kept on earning their livings, all these nine who had been about to die.

Maybe the Book of Deuteronomy had it wrong, or only partly right, about blood. True, the blood is the life. But folic acid makes blood; but deeper than that, the yellow chemical before it starts making blood fans the dying spark of the flame of life, of that sum total of the chemical changes in the body known as metabolism— of which blood building is only one phase. The beginning resurrection of those dying Cubans within 48 hours of the first doses of folic acid reversed Deuteronomy. The life is the blood.

About Tom's discovery there was practically no controversy, and attempts to run this new science down would have blown up in the detractor's face because the results were measurable, arithmetical, unarguable. Confirmation and extension of the new knowledge of the blood-building power of synthetic folic acid piled in from Dr. W. J. Darby and Dr. E. Jones of Vanderbilt University, Nashville, Tennessee; from Dr. C. V. Moore and his co-workers at Washington University, St. Louis, Missouri; and from Dr. C. A. Doan and his associates at Ohio State University, Columbus, Ohio.

It seemed that these little yellow tablets of the new vitamin in every way paralleled the power of liver shots over anemias—with one important reservation: liver shots were still needed to combat the nerve degeneration that often occurs in pernicious anemia in addition to the fatal thinning of the blood. It was disappointing that folic acid only half controlled pernicious anemia.*

On the other hand the wide range of action of these little pills (hardly a tenth the diameter of a dime) against various anemias was astounding and applied to possible millions of sufferers where pernicious anemia only involved thousands. Folic acid built red blood in pregnant women who were anemic—and that meant a better start in life for their unborn babies. For sprue, the first spectacular Cuban life-saving was confirmed by Dr. Ramon Suarez at the School of Tropical Medicine in Puerto Rico. Folic acid in every way equaled and possibly even surpassed the action of liver in building blood and controlled that devastating diarrhea—and this meant hope for tropic millions from Port of Spain all the way round the world to Bombay. For pernicious anemia victims, allergic so that they cannot tolerate liver shots, a small dose, one or more pills daily of folic acid by mouth, keeps their red blood cells at high levels, comfortably and safely. A final and unexpected promise of the new yellow vitamin is its power over the anemic decline so frequent in people in the prime of life and in the older years. A few

---

* In 1948, Tom Spies announced the control, not only of blood building, but also of nerve degeneration by the new vitamin—B-12.

years ago this downgrade in blood production was considered inexorable; the cells in the bone marrow were probably just getting
tired and old along with the rest of the body.

But now these supposedly washed-up and permanently decrepit
megaloblasts were rejuvenated—by daily doses of folic acid so small
that the yellow chemical couldn't be traced in the body after the
patient had swallowed it.

Here was the significance of this blood rejuvenation, as Tom
Spies dreamed it for his future hunting. If this reversal of supposedly worn-out tissue can be accomplished with a definitely
known chemical for blood-building cells—why not look for other
chemicals to antidote the ageing of other cells in the human body?

IV

About folic acid Tom dared to write in superlatives almost never
found in the drab chronicles of science. Within a year he had tested
the yellow chemical's power on 217 anemic forlorn. "The results,"
said Tom, "were so incredible that time and again I could hardly
believe my eyes." The news spread worldwide as a sort of sad little
antidote to the earth's post-war misery and sorrow; and in the past
two years observations by many scientists in many countries have
confirmed the power of folic acid in many thousands of sufferers
from macrocytic anemias.

In medical history it is doubtful if any life-saving weapon has
jumped so rapidly from discovery into worldwide use. While folic
acid was still under experimental test on animals at Lederle Laboratories and while Tom's eyes were wide, watching the upsurge of the
young red cells in the blood of those first anemic patients, the
Calco division of American Cyanamid was ready for mass production of pounds of the magic chemical—within a couple of months
of its first synthesis of a few milligrams of the yellow crystals. Dr.
Wilbur Malcolm, Director of Lederle Laboratories, explained this
discovery-to-production transition unheard of in the academic
world. "You see," said Malcolm, "in our institution, research has
to pay its way."

Back of the speed of the spread of this hope for the world's anemic millions there was a characteristic (not yet widely developed among industrialists) outstanding in Mr. William B. Bell. It was an impatience with suffering and death. He had the heart and the nerve to pour Cyanamid's millions into folic acid production and to support Tom's clinical research really fully and adequately. It was a new power of discovery linked to vast facilities for production —now found only in big industry—that made this possible. Vitamins as big business were deplored by certain of the top men of medical politics, you remember. I wonder if those first Cubans doomed by sprue but now healthy and working, and other formerly thin-blooded, listless thousands now strong again after folic acid, I wonder if any of these would complain about vitamins being big business.

v

It was clear that the Cyanamid chemists and vitamin-hunters had given Tom a new chemical bullet to add to the multiple vitamin capsules that were becoming more and more powerful (shotgun) weapons in the hands of the practicing doctors. Tom was careful to warn physicians that folic acid was no panacea. Only exact laboratory tests can determine the type of anemia from which people suffer; and though folic acid is the enemy of nearly all the major macrocytic anemias, it's no cure-all. Against anemia accompanying the blood cancer called leukemia, it is powerless. Nor does it correct "aplastic" anemia, a rare, curious and complete breakdown of the blood-building cells of bone marrow.

But a new use for multiple vitamins (reinforced by folic acid) in the hands of physicians is now looming. Just as there is a good deal of pellagra, sub-clinical and under the surface of apparently so-so health, so there's anemia unsuspected by people or their doctors. A test of the blood of so-called "normal" people has revealed this interesting condition. One-fifth of a group of people, so tested, were walking around with red blood cell counts well under the "normal" of 4,000,000 per cubic millimeter of blood. Folic acid—and these counts shot up to 4,400,000 and even higher.

Beyond their power to build blood, the yellow pills hint another possibility of adding to human vigor. Millions of liver shots are given yearly for weakness and run-down condition and these injections often raise the energy of patients underpar but with no sign of anemia. Before ever his microscope showed a new building of blood, Tom had seen folic acid fan the fire of life in his desperately sick patients. Might the yellow chemical, for many merely underpar people, sometimes replace the present liver shots that so notably boost their vigor? (Not always, mind you, for it is likely that many still unknown life-building chemicals are hiding in liver.)

And might multiple vitamins—now strengthened with the new folic acid—not only prevent macrocytic anemias but raise the energy level of human beings a bit higher?

VI

Surely Tom Spies was safe now from annoyance by organized medicine's highest command? He had crowned his many famine-fighting triumphs by bringing folic acid to the doctors to give new blood and strength to anemic millions. Adding this major feat to that of the nicotinamide control of pellagra, there surely would no longer be any danger of his losing his workshop, of his having to leave the hopeful hurly-burly of his beloved Hillman Hospital clinic in Birmingham, Alabama? Or so I thought, when the folic acid discovery was adding to his fame, in 1946.

What then was my surprise, in 1947, to read in the *Birmingham Post* that a group of Birmingham leaders had just appeared before a standing committee of the Senate of the State of Alabama, demanding a senatorial investigation as to why Tom's nutrition clinic was about to be evicted from its quarters in Hillman Hospital.

Written notice had come from the authorities of the Medical College of the University of Alabama to the effect that the space occupied by the nutrition clinic would from now on be needed for the teaching of medical students. For his famine-fighting research Tom now had literally no place to go. For many years now he had been doing that clinical research nine months out of every year at

Hillman Hospital, each year on leave of absence graciously granted him by the University of Cincinnati where he was Associate Professor of Medicine. He couldn't go back there for an all-year-round famine fight. The Cincinnati authorities would be glad to have Tom come back to teach medical students, but it had no laboratory space available nor any beds for his patients.

This dazed me. Could it be possible, at the top of his stride as a medical researcher, that Tom was finished? Well, in the 1870's many of the big powerful authoritative medical men had sneered at Joseph Lister, but he'd always been able to go on working. Could it be, in the 1940's, in our supposedly scientifically free and enlightened America, that the war against true medical pioneers was more savage and subtle? It seemed that everything was set to make Tom scientifically homeless.

In a way the boldness of Tom's enemies demanded my admiration, or it would have, had those enemies worked in the open. How did they dare to make a scientific orphan out of this man who was by far Alabama's most famous medical investigator? He had received citation from the Medical Association of the State of Alabama for his scientific discoveries; and the spokesman on this occasion adopted Tom, the Texan, as a native son of Alabama. He had received the Gold Medal of the Southern Medical Association. Who among all medical researchers in the entire south could equal him? Now he had no place to go.

I pondered the resourcefulness of Tom's enemies. They were about to succeed in evicting him from his workshop in the face of a recent public expression of esteem of the overwhelming majority of the physicians of Birmingham and Jefferson County. For ten years the doctors of the region had been sending sick people to Tom's clinic. For ten years those doctors had been watching more and more mysteriously sick people coming back home stronger and more hopeful. All that time more and more of these doctors had come to the clinic to look over Tom's shoulder, to try to learn to use his famine-fighting science. On April 18, 1947, this year of Tom's threatened eviction from his clinic, these doctors had presented Tom with a testimonial scroll.

It is here presented as evidence that the rank-and-file of American doctors recognize medical originality, even when it arises in their own bailiwick.

"Among the many physicians who render skilled medical care to the people of their communities, it is given only to the rare and gifted doctor who approaches genius to contribute a discovery which truly advances the practice of medicine. We, the physicians of Jefferson County, feel singularly fortunate to have among us Tom D. Spies who twice in a decade has thrust forward medical frontiers—in 1937 with the demonstration that nicotinic acid is curative of pellagra and in 1946 with the successful therapeusis of the macrocytic anemias by folic acid.

"The hundreds of malnourished who have been restored to health and gainful occupations bear testimony to the effectiveness of Spies' work in nutrition, all of which is conducted among the underprivileged without financial remuneration to their benefactor.

"The discoveries of the efficacy of nicotinic acid and of folic acid have climaxed a multitude of contributions which together have marked Dr. Spies as a great figure in American medicine today and have established him as a world-wide leader in the field of nutrition.

"These accomplishments have brought Dr. Spies well-merited recognition in many quarters and have served as a source of pride, gratification and inspiration to his fellow physicians. Yet, they have in no way altered Dr. Spies' plain personal qualities, his sincere friendliness, his helpfulness when consulted, and his simple modesty. Lest it appear that Dr. Spies is a prophet with honor save in his own country, we the undersigned physicians of Jefferson County, of Alabama, who have witnessed his great work and his greatness, place our signatures below to express deeply our appreciation of and affection for Tom D. Spies in acknowledgment of his contributions to mankind and his character as a man. We are humbly privileged in so doing."

Why did Jefferson County's doctors publicly pay Tom this type of tribute?—it was like a eulogy reserved for characters who have passed away. Was it that they knew that Tom was in danger of losing his clinic? I do not know. It could be. "Lest it appear that

Dr. Spies is a prophet with honor save in his own country," that's the way the Jefferson County doctors began the closing sentence of their testimonial.

Of 328 Jefferson County physicians who were approached for their signatures, 322 signed the testimonial. Not more than a half dozen declined to join their fellow physicians. This declaration of the rank-and-file physicians of Jefferson County certainly did the medical profession, as a whole, the highest honor. It showed that, *no matter where the opposition to Tom might come from,* they were ready to go on record that Tom Spies was a fine investigator and a selfless man. All honor to these Jefferson County doctors.

Long ago, when a youngster in medical school, I had been thrilled by the late Dr. Victor C. Vaughan's tribute to the medical profession as the only one of all the professions that was working to destroy the reasons for its own existence. For more than 35 years I had seen isolated, individual doctors working with that aim, but never organized medicine as a whole or in any notable part. Now here were these Jefferson County physicians backing Tom in his fight towards a disease-free mankind, towards a state of human vitality and vigor where doctors would be less and less needed . . .

The testimonial to Tom was presented in April, 1947. The closing of the clinic still threatened in June. Unable to help Tom in Birmingham in any way, I retreated into philosophy that is the solace of those powerless and incapable of action.

The explanation of Tom's troubles was really simple. It was just that the political power in the hands of certain representatives of organized medicine didn't look upon the medical profession as working to destroy the reasons for its own existence, didn't have a vision of science transfiguring humanity. Of course it was too bad that organized medicine's highest command could not be convinced of this simple truth: the type of work Tom Spies was doing would take no work away from the doctors for a very long time. Because the more is known of the chemistry of the human body, the higher the standards of vigor and long life we will set for ourselves, and to attain to these standards it will require the full-time attention of even more doctors than those who are trying to patch us up as they have to do now.

Now philosophical, now in no sense a fighter, I purged myself of indignation over Tom's apparent coming fate. It is not that these representatives of organized medicine are evil. They would all deplore the persistence of sickness and suffering; they would go on record as deploring it just as clergymen are boldly against sin. It is simply that the vision of certain of medicine's highest command remains somewhat limited. It is just that they haven't got beyond knowing that, so long as plenty of sickness and suffering exist, there'll always be plenty of remunerative repair work for surgeons and doctors. Not yet having raised their sights towards the vision of mankind's possible chemical transfiguration and not realizing the enormous amount of medical work it would need to bring this about, certain men of medicine's highest command were alarmed (unduly) at Tom Spies as a portent of an age when a chemically supercharged humanity might have less use for the doctors. Politicians of whatever sort, if they are to be successful, are not interested in change; they are interested in the perpetuation of their power.

VII

Now in June, 1947, in Birmingham, Alabama, it became evident that Tom had friends who were not powerless, as I felt myself to be. An informal committee of Birmingham citizens had indeed inspired a state senatorial investigation into the coming closing of Tom's clinic. The citizens' committee wanted to know just who was trying to do what to their Doctor Tom. Why was his clinic to be closed when they all knew that his clinic had made their city a Mecca for the world's nutritionists and doctors? The leader of the citizens' committee was Mr. Hugh Comer, fighter for a higher level of life for all southerners, white and colored.

The senatorial committee had investigated and now all was serene. "There was peace today between Spies Clinic and the Medical College of Alabama," reported the newspaper. "The Medical College has agreed that Dr. Tom Douglas Spies' Nutrition Clinic may continue to occupy its quarters (in Hillman Hospital) for an indefinite period of time."

It was made clear that this indefinite period of time meant a period of years. The Dean of the Medical College of Alabama went on record that "the Medical College recognizes and fully appreciates the value of the work of the Nutrition Clinic and will provide all possible assistance."

Tom's vindication had been won by his own region's physicians and lay citizens. The doctors who had signed the testimonial knew that they were defending a modern Lister. The citizens' committee knew that Tom was really the prophet of a new south.

Here was Tom's analysis of the tragedy of the persistence of the low southern level of living, an infamy that still divides America:

"The south is a region that has suffered from poverty, ignorance and ill health," said Tom. "Where there is sickness, there is bound to be low income, for the diseased person cannot do a good day's work. Where incomes are small, there is less tax money for schools; low standards make for general ignorance in matters of personal hygiene and nutrition; in turn, worst health follows.

"The best way to break that vicious circle," Tom finished, "is to improve public health and the best way to improve public health is to improve nutrition."

For ten years Tom had been proving that; so the doctors and citizens of Alabama did not allow him to be kicked out of Birmingham.

As this is written, Tom Spies is carrying his famine-fighting science to the north, to Chicago. Keeping his beloved Hillman Hospital work at Birmingham, Tom has just been appointed chairman of a new Department of Human Nutrition and Metabolism at Northwestern University Medical School. It is the first of its kind in any medical school in the nation.

At one of the preliminary conferences leading up to this historic event, Northwestern's Dean, J. Roscoe Miller, took fire and flashed a question: "After all, what *is* medicine but nutrition?"

That query was the exact parallel to another, asked by Charles F. Kettering 35 years ago as he puttered with a stuttering, pounding little single-cylinder engine (he called it his guinea pig) in a dingy tobacco warehouse in Dayton, Ohio. In those days gasoline was gasoline and all motors were short-lived and feeble.

"Isn't the fuel you feed it as much a part of any motor as its valves and pistons?" asked Boss Kettering.

The experimental answer to that revolutionary query led to the long-lived, largely break-down-proof packages of super-power that have leveled mountains for motorists and helped airmen to conquer the sky.

Now at Northwestern University, tinkering chemically with human engines infinitely more complex than any motor made of metals, Tom Spies is making bold to spend the rest of his life, and long may he live, to begin to find the answer to a question that's the same as Boss Kettering's—with the added significance that the food you feed human beings is not only fuel for human energy but is also the material that fundamentally determines the soundness, sturdiness, and long life of the human motor.

Around Northwestern University's new Department of Nutrition and Metabolism, President Franklyn Snyder and Dean Miller plan to build the first National Nutrition Center. The University has affiliated with Tom's old bodyguard, those industrialists and other citizens who formed the Spies Committee for Clinical Research in Tom's dark days in the early 1940's. That committee has promised a research budget of $150,000 yearly, for five years. A building to house a combination hospital-laboratory has been purchased.

Here Tom and a staff of physicians, chemists and nutritionists will make a new chemical attack—a search for the still unknown or missing or inadequate chemical cogs in the machinery of human metabolism. The fight will be directed at those chemical derangements of the human body that strike at the hearts, kidneys, and brains of millions of us in the years that ought to be only the beginning of life's prime.

When I remember back over the seven years of work with Tom Spies, what stands out about him is his mysterious magnetism that has attracted the powerful brotherhood of doctors, chemists, industrialists, and plain citizens now pledged to see to it that his work will not die.

I believe that this devotion of so many men to the work of one man has been stirred not so much by admiration for the researcher that Tom unquestionably is, but more by a feeling of awe at another of his qualities. That trait is best summed up by McClellan Van Der Veer, Chief Editorial Writer of *The Birmingham News*, who has stood by Tom through his troubles.

"Tom's work is not only a cold quest for knowledge, but grows out of an imaginative understanding of suffering people," says Van Der Veer. "Knowing the frustrations, failures, agonies and deaths of people, never forgetting them because he keeps on feeling them, Tom is completely possessed by the will to work on."

In the seven years that I myself have known Tom, I have never heard him speak of spiritual questions, and so far as I know he belongs to no religious sect or denomination. Yet, he has his own church in his heart. To paraphrase Count Tolstoy's words, "The kingdom of God is within him." He knows how disease and death arise from chemical famine that's in great part due to the curious niggardliness with which nature has put vitamins into mankind's food. For this I have criticized the Creator. This Tom does not do.

Tom's feeling for our tragically imperfect world of mentally and bodily half-alive humanity is best summed up in the quaint words of the great Dutch artist, Vincent van Gogh. Even more than Tom, Vincent worked ahead of his time. Like Tom, he was raw to the suffering around him. Like Tom, he was never cynical. "I feel more and more," wrote Vincent in the days of his deepest suffering when he was painting his way furiously towards his present immortality, "that we must not judge God on this world, it's just a study that didn't come off. What can you do, in a study that has gone wrong, if you are fond of the artist—you do not find much to criticize—you hold your tongue. But you have a right to ask for something better."

In his own pioneering towards a transfigured humanity, that's all Tom is really asking.

VIII

Now that all is harmony for Tom Spies in Birmingham, now that he has become head of the most modern and probably the most scientifically significant department of one of America's most splendid medical schools, now that he has reached this pinnacle of medical respectability at the very doorstep of organized medicine's leadership (which is also situated in Chicago) it would seem on the surface that Tom Spies is out of all danger.

And yet I wonder if he is not now in the greatest danger of all his adventurous working life? From those early days in Cleveland when he saved the lives of those no-good drunken pellagrins, through all his famine-fighting adventure up till now, Tom Spies has been an unbranded animal, in short, a maverick, a member of no herd. All his work has been mental and physical exercise against heavy resistance, the best kind of work to sharpen the brain and harden the muscle. Now that he has been vindicated, he will have to fight a subtler enemy than any he has ever met. That is, medical and scientific respectability. His new danger is that he may try to be respectable (totally respectable medically and scientifically) and a maverick, at the same time.

I would not blame Tom Spies if he would not want to be a maverick any longer. What happens to your genuine medical maverick takes a great deal out of you. Is it because no man can stand being a maverick for too long, that almost no men have made more than two medical discoveries? Since these thoughts were set down, Tom Spies has shown he is still a maverick. He had just proved that the new vitamin, B-12, controls combined system disease, the terrible nerve degeneration in pernicious anemia that is not conquered by blood-building folic acid. And really it doesn't matter whether he remains the remarkable maverick that he has been. What mystifies me and heartens me about Tom is that this tough man from Texas is so gentle.

PART THREE

THESE MEN ARE RUGGED

Who'd ever heard of such a project? Here were a pair of young doctors, saying it might be possible to cure early, contagious syphilis in one day—in contrast to the 12 to 18 months continuous treatment declared necessary by the authorities.

This fantastic proposal for a mass test of a one-day syphilis treatment might never have been tried excepting for Herman N. Bundesen. The Chicago health commissioner was not authoritarian. Without having put new science to test, he would not declare against or for it.

"I don't know and I know I don't know but I'll damn well find the fellows who do know." That was Bundesen's motto. He truly hated death and would test any new weapon that had a chance to defeat it.

The Man Who Hates Death

≫≫ ≪≪

HOW, in chronological succession, can you coherently tell about the simultaneous amazing occurrences in a ten-ringed scientific circus? What happened in Chicago in the summer of 1942 began to point (though it took several more years to get the outline clear) towards a developing progression of this life among the doctors. It is more a progression of intensity than a progression in time. This insight dawned while I watched, against a somber background of world-wide mass-murder, the work of Herman N. Bundesen, Chicago's rough-and-tumble death-fighter.

That summer of 1942 drove it home to me that while there was Bundesen (or men like him) there was hope, and it seemed there would always be Bundesen.

Then 62, he was shaggy-browed with grizzling hair but with the build and bounce of a young middle-weight boxer in top condition. The activities of this human hurricane would seem to have needed the energy of a dozen men. He had already driven Chicago's maternal, newborn, and infant death rates below those of any large city in the world, yet he was dissatisfied so long as any mothers and babies died at all. He had made deadly, milk-borne infections practically non-existent in the city; he was getting set to beat diphtheria and whooping cough deaths down to zero; he was writing (yes, himself writing) a health column that went to almost 500 newspapers; he was directing the medical organization of Chicago's civilian defense.

Now in addition to all that in the summer of 1942, Bundesen

took on a new battle. Its objective—not merely to control but to wipe the curse of syphilis out of his rowdy and sinful city.

It was fortunate for Dr. Bundesen that he never minded being thought ridiculous by many of our most sedate and most highly respectable public health authorities, because circumstances surely conspired to make this new effort seem silly. In Chicago syphilis was not only rampant, but threatened to become more so. Hundreds of thousands of newly mobilized soldiers and sailors, disporting and relaxing in the city's taverns and honky-tonks, were attracting to Chicago thousands of women, many of them infected. The patriotism of the city's more respectable women threatened them, in turn, with danger from newly infected sailors and soldiers. The fundamental immorality of war, its looming hint of future death, incited a general sexual wildness and multiplied chances of infection.

To begin to eradicate syphilis, Bundesen knew he'd have to ferret out a majority of all those suffering the disease in its contagious form; and how could he discover a majority of all cases of this especially secret sickness that lurked in a tenderloin (professional and amateur) that had become essentially city-wide?

Tough epidemiologist that Bundesen was, let us grant that he could smoke out the majority of contagious cases. But he would then have to break the chain of the spread of the sinister sickness, not necessarily by curing, but by suppressing the infectiousness of these people.

But how could Bundesen—or anybody else—presume to attempt this? The standard treatment, to knock out syphilitic contagiousness, demanded at that time at least 12 months of continuous, weekly shots of arsenic into the arm veins and bismuth into the bottoms of those infected.

It was no secret that this system—in any campaign to wipe out syphilis—was impractical, yes, futile. The treatment was too long, too uncomfortable, too painful—so that hardly more than 25 out of every 100 victims could be persuaded to stick with it till they were no longer spreaders of the contagion.

So, in his aim to drive syphilis out of Chicago, Herman Bundesen could be sneered at as quixotic, or worse still, utopic. To break the chain of the spread of the evil sickness, you'd have to knock out its contagiousness, not in months or a year, but in weeks or better still, in a few days.

"We must suppress all infectious syphilis quickly, safely, and kindly," said Bundesen.

But in 1942, the available intensive treatments that gave some promise of such rapid action had none of them been proved safe enough to be used routinely, in the necessary mass attack upon the disease. To be used at all, a special hospital would be necessary. And Dr. Bundesen had no such hospital.

To acquire an existing ancient, unused, down-at-heel hospital, to remodel it, to equip it with the requisite complicated apparatus, to hire the doctors, nurses, and special technicians needed to begin these new intensive treatments and (perhaps) make some sort of mass intensive treatment practical, would demand $1,000,000 to start with and close to $1,000,000 yearly thereafter. To ask the Federal government for this money (when its policy indicated that money was needed mainly for killing our enemies rather than curing our own soldiers) was like asking for the moon.

He began what authorities deemed impractical and impossible, not by genius, not by magic, but only because of the intensity with which he hated sickness, insanity, and death. He did not conjure up this now historic campaign as one brings a rabbit out of an empty plug hat. He only put into action a system of death-fighting that was uniquely Bundesenian, which can only be understood if we go back to the beginning, and retrace the successive steps of the hard way (the only way he knew) by which Bundesen has learned to fight needless death.

II

If he had tried to, Herman Bundesen could hardly have picked out a more hopeless city than Chicago when he started what was then pretty much his one-man war against death, as the city's new health commissioner, in 1922. Microbes were the least of his enemies; what he fought was the infamy that life was dirt cheap in Chicago.

The city's milk, rotten with bovine tuberculosis, was kept that way by an obstructive law. Spread of syphilis and gonorrhea was encouraged by competing gangs of hoodlums who, under Chicago's system of free gangster enterprise, organized chains of brothels. At the point of their gats and tommy-guns they discouraged public health efforts to clean up these pest holes. Chicago's infant death rate was nationally notorious; the fate of mothers in childbirth was entirely in the hands of individual doctors and strictly none of the health commissioner's buisness.

Herman Bundesen—the city's first health commissioner rising from the health department ranks and not a political appointee—would hardly have got his job if Mayor Big Bill Thompson had realized Herman's highest qualification, namely, that he was just a shade tougher than the characters responsible for Chicago's lamentable health record.

He was a graduate from Chicago's gutter. As a tow-headed eight-year-old he'd escaped down a spout from the Chicago Orphan Asylum. As a street gamin (his two best pals later served life terms for murder) he lived by peddling papers and earned meals by work in tough saloons.

One day he snowballed the plug hat off the venerable head of Bishop Cheney of the Reformed Episcopal Church. Instead of bawling out young Bundesen, the Bishop complimented him on his marksmanship and invited him to Sunday School. Herman accepted, his tongue in his cheek, with a project of stealing from the coatrooms; he stayed there to catch his personal religion. It was a white-hot determination to devote his life to the sick and dying.

From then on he worked at every dirty and menial job. In the gutter university of Chicago, Bundesen got the hang of the strong-arm technique of gangsters, developed an uncanny ear for the double-talk of politicians. He learned to understand the pathetic yearning of miserable people to whom strength and life is denied.

He went to Northwestern University and then to its medical school; and there, as a volunteer, he helped fill his belly by free meals in tests of food preservatives that might or might not poison him after he'd eaten them for months. As an orderly he earned his six-by-ten, windowless room, rushing bedpans in the old Wesley Hospital. He became a prosector, cutting up cadavers for anatomical demonstrations. Over bodies in the morgue he was bitten by hatred of the consequences of medical neglect and by hatred of death, not yet conquered.

III

His slogging upward gave him a philosophy which was to the effect that, having come this far up from the gutter, he'd be at home in the gutter if fate sent him back to it. He stuck to this discipline, which helped him to live regardless of consequences.

After graduation he spent three years as a doctor in the U. S. Army and cut his eye teeth as a sleuth against death by ferreting out the method of spread of a typhoid epidemic at Fort Russell, Wyoming. The life of a soldier-doctor in peace time was too dull for him and presently he was back in his brawling and beloved city of Chicago as a part-time civil service epidemiologist in the city health department and part-time practitioner of medicine. Here his detective work—challenging all possible paths of infection to every last case—cut Chicago's typhoid death rate sensationally and this got him appointed Health Commissioner in 1922.

His first fight was against connivers, who were keeping Chicago's milk deadly with bovine tuberculosis. This plague, spread by milk, infected the glands, rotted the bones, bent the spines of thousands of Chicago's children. In Chicago's leading milk-producing county 87 per cent of the dairy cattle were tainted; and a curious state law had intimidated previous health commissioners from even starting to eradicate the disease from cattle.

Former health commissioners had achieved pasteurization of up to 90 per cent of Chicago's milk, hoping to head off the deadly TB bugs that way, even if the cows were infected. Yet, more and more youngsters were crippled. Why?

Bundesen turned detective and discovered that the city's sup-

posedly well-pasteurized milk hadn't even been tested for TB. He
ordered his lab men to test both raw and pasteurized milk. *Both*
were deadly. What was wrong?

"I don't know and I know I don't know but I'll damn well find
guys who do." For the first time he applied his now famous motto.
He called for U. S. Public Health Service experts. Scandal: out of
Chicagoland's 245 pasteurizing plants (just as in the rest of America though this was not known) not one was operating in a way
that would kill TB microbes in milk.

Now, with the government behind him, he was ready to slug it
out with the anti-eradication connivers. He faced a showdown. To
frustrate government attempts to eradicate bovine TB, by killing
infected cattle—indemnifying owners—an Illinois law had been
passed that actually prohibited health officers from TB-testing dairy-
herds. Bundesen called in dairymen, milk-producers and politicians.
He explained (he had a gift of small vivid words) that pasteurization was not keeping TB death out of milk, and exactly why.

Then he bombed them. "Gentlemen," he said, his voice rising to
a roar, "I give you 18 months to clean up your herds. After that—
not one drop of milk—from *any* untested cow—comes into Chicago!"

Most of the dairymen co-operated, and the fantastic number of
400,000 milk cows were slaughtered. At the same time a group of
die-hard producers and politicians got set to "get" Bundesen. The
day before the deadline, when no more milk from an untested cow
could come into Chicago, they let it be known that, tomorrow, the
state anti-testing law would be invoked against Dr. Herman Bundesen. He'd be enjoined, he'd be in contempt, and then . . .

Chicago's rugged good Samaritan called in the reporters. He
told them how his own little boy was infected with bone tuberculosis.

"I'm sick of carrying young Russell around in my arms while he
watches other children playing," Bundesen said. He explained how
pasteurization had failed. "That's not all—it's happening to thousands. I'm going to see that every drop of milk that my own six
kids and all Chicago's children drink is safe and pure—*if I have to
go to jail to do it!*" he roared.

The hubbub, city-wide, was terrific. The next day not a drop of milk from an untested or tuberculous cow came into Chicago. The politicians knew they'd make a martyr out of Bundesen by jailing him. That year, 1926, bone tuberculosis began its down trend in Chicago, till today it's a medical curiosity. That year, fighters for TB eradication encouraged, marked the beginning of the nation-wide conquest of bovine TB, so nearly complete today.

That same year every one of the 245 formerly futile pasteurizing plants was put into really effective microbe-killing operation and this brought an unlooked-for life-saving dividend. Bundesen had cleaned streptococcus and other deaths out of milk along with tuberculosis. Chicago's infant death rate, one of the highest in the nation, took a sensational tumble. In 1927, five hundred fewer infants under one year old died than the number dying in 1922.

In 1927 Mayor Big Bill Thompson fired Bundesen because he had refused to include political literature with information about baby care that he sent to all Chicago mothers. Indignant, the Chicago *Daily News* awarded Bundesen a $1,000 prize as the city's most valuable citizen. The city council—unanimously—tendered him a scroll of appreciation. He ran for coroner of Cook County and was elected by a majority of more than 1,000,000—the most enormous in the county's history to this day. In 1930, with Anton Cermak mayor, Bundesen had his old health commissioner job again.

Bundesen had made cow's milk safe for babies; then he learned that among infants breast-fed the death rate was far lower. A survey by his nurses revealed a scant 20 out of every 100 Chicago mothers breast-feeding their youngsters. The reason? A strange commerce, but legal and hardly assailable.

Chicago's birth lists were daily published in the newspapers. Patent baby-food firms used these to send door-to-door canvassers to Chicago's mothers, explaining how much more freedom they'd have if they didn't breast-feed their babies. Bundesen showed the city council the comparative breast- and artificial-feeding baby death rates and got a regulation passed suppressing publication of all birth lists. Four baby food firms offered Bundesen fifty cents per name—and 50,000 babies were born yearly in Chicago. He laughed in the would-be bribers' faces.

Where the canvassers used to go, he now sent health department nurses, teaching mothers proper breast-feeding. In a few years the city's percentage of breast-fed youngsters jumped to 90—and in the early 1930's Chicago's infant death rate had dropped to less than 50 per 1,000 children born alive, below that of any other large city, far under the national average.

IV

There for three years the proud record stuck. Top healthmen tried to comfort Bundesen, telling him he had reached the "irreducible minimum" of deaths. He raged at this phrase, as mere conversation. "Who's murdering the babies who still are dying?" he demanded. Again, detective work. A breakdown of the death toll showed that 70 per cent of infants under one year old, who died, died before they were one month old; *and the day of birth was the most deadly of all.*

Bundesen believed he was hot on the scent now. In poor homes served by De Lee's famous Chicago Maternity Center, newborn deaths were at a rate less than half that of Chicago at large.

Bundesen accused himself savagely. "That means that Dr. Joseph B. De Lee, my own teacher, knew how to lick this child murder," said Bundesen. "Why haven't I learned what he taught me? What have I done? Nothing. *I'm* the killer."

He didn't have to be that tough on himself. Newborn death had not been the responsibility of any health officer in history. Now he faced trouble. That terribly high death rate of the first day of life hinted at, though it did not prove, bad obstetrics. But nobody had better monkey with doctors presiding at childbirth—that was strictly the doctors' bailiwick.

Again, by Bundesen's men, breakdown of the newborn death toll. It seemed as if the doctors might have an excellent alibi. Prematurity—that was the real culprit. Among 1,300 premature babies born yearly in Chicago, almost 700 died. Nobody to blame. Just poor little unfortunates too unfinished to live.

Well, he'd see about that. Bundesen issued a regulation—one of his series of famous regulations of dubious validity. Every premature birth must be reported to the Board of Health within one hour! Impossible, objected his staff members who knew hospital red tape, and doctors. "Fine," said Bundesen, "let's do it anyway."

For every premature birth, doctors and nurses rushed out from the health department (God pity anybody who slips up) to make sure that oxygen, incubators, and breast milk were available. So in 1935 Chicago's baby death rate tumbled again, still further below that of the nation, and 300 new lives were saved compared to the figures of the years before, that year in the city. Sure, you can lick the deadliness of prematurity, but what was this? Bundesen's gray eyes, narrowing, squinted at a totting-up of death certificates signed by the city's doctors that year. It showed one of the highest *premature* death rates ever recorded.

It was at such moments that Herman Bundesen became dangerous. "Something's screwy. What *is* killing them?" he asked. Then he answered himself, glaring at his experts. "We don't know, and we don't know we don't know, and that includes the doctors. So we just write down prematurity."

He himself took the rap for accepting such death certificates. It was at times like these that doctors, nurses, technicians, secretaries, all the more than 1,000 employees of the health department walked as if on eggs when they went into Bundesen's office. "What's killing them?" Bundesen asked everybody. "You don't know. I don't know. But I'll damn well find the fellows who do know. Or I'm still the killer." The staff walked on tip-toe as if fearing their boss would include them in his guilt.

Again sleuthing. At Chicago's Lying-in Hospital autopsy records —not a very large series it's true—hinted that bad obstetrics might be the culprit. But who would dare to go into that one—with Chicago's doctors? Bundesen would dare to. Before daring to, he took out his oldest (and most characteristic) motto and dusted it off, getting ready for action. "Never step on a man's toes if you can step on firm ground without stepping on his toes," Bundesen would begin his slogan, politely. "But if you can't step on firm ground without stepping on his toes, *then step all over his feet if necessary.* BUT ALWAYS STEP ON FIRM GROUND," roared Bundesen.

Firm ground for his coming knock-down-and-drag-out test with the doctors? Firm ground was autopsies. Mass autopsy of little babies dying the day they were born? Ridiculous. Parental sentiment against it. Many morticians opposed, naturally, because autopsies hindered embalming. Bundesen tackled the undertakers first. Not the most eminent morticians who might be expected to co-operate, but instead, he called in certain notorious recalcitrants. He began blandly. Regrettable. It was revealed they had violated long established health laws. They'd been moving bodies without Board of Health permits. Their premises were unventilated, dangerous to health.

"So, gentlemen, you will have to clean up or we will have to close you up," said Bundesen.

"Gosh, Doc—"

Then also a vivid little lecture on the horror of the newborn dying and the hope of finding out why, by autopsies.

Now a chorus from the morticians. Why, if it was proper sanitation in their establishments *and* autopsies that he wanted, why, certainly. They'd sell it to the parents! And they did.

It was a technique historic and unique in any death fight. It was strong arm. It was Chicago underworld. It was Bundesen. It was his secret of instant action. Instead of waiting for the best undertakers to educate all undertakers, the recalcitrant undertakers (enthusiastic through the new fear of God in them) became Bundesen's missionaries.

At the same time, Bundesen talked personally to every mother whose newborn baby had died. "We don't know why, but autopsies may tell us," he told them. "What we find may mean life for your next baby, safety for babies of thousands of mothers. By helping us find why your baby was taken away, you may give it a living monument," he said. For mothers too poor, out of his own pocket he bought little grave plots and even monuments for the babies.

In the mid-1930's, from next to none, scientific autopsies jumped to the unprecedented figure of over 80 per cent of all Chicago's newborn dead. Bundesen would regret to have to step all over anybody's feet. But here was the story the autopsies told. Seven out of every ten dead newborn were found to have died from causes other than those written by the attending doctor on the death certificate. And the leading cause of death was cerebral hemorrhage, and cerebral hemorrhage most often resulted from obstetrical interference—"meddlesome interference," Bundesen said grimly—with what should have been normal childbirth.

Bad obstetrics—that was a killer.

v

It was none of Bundesen's business, said some. It was no health commissioner's business whether a new baby (or its mother) lived or died. It was the business of the attending doctor. It was not even the public's business. Weren't all doctors doing the best they could? Were they? asked Bundesen. Presently, it was announced that a Maternal Welfare Committee had been organized, jointly by the Chicago health department and a group of the most distinguished obstetricians and gynecologists of the city. It was more than coincidental that these latter gentlemen were proud of their very low maternal and newborn baby death rates. Jointly with the Chicago Health Department the group of expert doctors proposed to police possibly needless newborn deaths.

Again Bundesen issued a regulation. Instantly any newborn died, it was required that the news be flashed to the city health department. All facts gathered were laid before the Maternal Welfare Committee's and the health department's doctors. If their cold analysis determined a baby's death needless, then that death was marked on the record of the attending doctor, and, if it occurred in hospital, then it was charged to that institution.

Dr. Bundesen was bland, explaining it to the city's doctors. The regulation required that, *for any difficult birth,* the attending doctor or the hospital authorities must call in expert consultation.

Dr. Bundesen was suave, explaining that in only a minority of childbirths is there danger. Indeed, the great majority of mothers would deliver safely without a doctor, and if there was danger of complications, any doctor could detect that peril early, and now the new regulation advised (it could not require), but it very firmly advised, the doctor to call expert help the moment a childbearing mother seemed in trouble in her travail.

It was amazing how the large majority of Chicago's hospital authorities and doctors enthusiastically accepted this public prying into what had been their historic and traditional prerogative.

Very soon after the new regulation requiring expert consultation was issued, one prominent hospital refused point-blank to live up to hospital regulations. Into the institution swarmed Board of Health inspectors. Incidentally, they found health laws flouted: ceilings too low; cross-connections between sewage and water supply; in the morgue the janitor was making ice cream for patients; no drain in the morgue. In short the institution turned out to be a general menace to the health of the sick people who went there and by firmly established ordinances Commissioner Bundesen had every legal right to close the hospital down and he promptly did.

Bundesen smiled. "We didn't close the hospital because they wouldn't require obstetric consultation," he related. "We suggested to the hospital authorities, before the place was allowed to re-open, that they should live up to all the ordinances—*and* institute expert consultation in all complicated childbirths."

It flashed city-wide over the hospital and medical grapevine that Bundesen never meant just maybe. The medical and hospital co-operation on the new regulation became enthusiastic, and, quickly, as good as unanimous.

The importance, to mothers, of the difference between having just any doctor or an expert doctor—in complicated childbirth—was soon revealed in the city's newborn death rate. In 1936, Chicago's death rate for infants under one year old was hovering around 40 per 1,000 live births. By 1940 it had tumbled under 30, almost entirely because so many more newborn were living. Herman Bundesen had come a long way since 1922 when 4,500 Chicago infants under one year old died yearly. Only 1,500 were dying now, despite a greatly increased number of births. The better obstetrics that saved newborn babies was saving mothers too; the city's maternal death rate had fallen below half that of the nation at large.

In 1942 Chicago's newborn death rate fell so low that, if all communities had equaled it, America would have been saving 20,000 infant lives yearly.

VI

That same year (he was 60 now) Bundesen began the boldest and most advanced of all his battles against death. That 1942 summer, as I've said, he gave me the understanding of a rising intensity of life among the doctors, this intensity measurable by the speed with which new science can be put to use to fight death. Watching Bundesen now, it seemed as if here at last was a man definitely concerned about whether people—I mean masses of people he didn't know—lived or died. Nobody can estimate the millions who have needlessly died with science right here right now ready to save them. Because who cared? Because so what? Now this 1942 summer, Chicago's rugged health commissioner set about the extreme opposite— to save people before the weapons were really ready. Even so, the new weapons did seem an advance over the impractical ones with which he'd been trying to fight syphilis for 20 years.

During these years he'd tried to make up for bad tools by Bundesenian violence. In the middle 1920's he had dared to close up Al Capone's elegant brothel, The Four Deuces, which housed Al's reigning female favorite. Bundesen found her infected, forcibly detained her and began treatment. He seized Al himself; under detention he subjected the great man to a blood test. Strangely, it turned out negative. Al had to be released, and shortly thereafter the doctor who'd taken the test became suddenly prosperous. Bundesen admits he slipped up. But so did Al, for had he not outsmarted himself that way, he might today be living in Florida or Alcatraz, in good health.

Later a gunman stepped up to Bundesen, stuck a gat in the commissioner's face and pulled the trigger. Misfire. "That was the last time I've been scared," he relates. "My number hasn't come up."

Bundesen's forays were annoying to the city's hoodlums, rather than effective against syphilis spirochetes, and Bundesen knew it. In the late 1930's, a bold, gay and in some ways even rougher and tougher death-fighter than Bundesen, was detailed to help the commissioner against syphilis in Chicago. This was O. C. Wenger of the U. S. Public Health Service.

"My idea of heaven," said Wenger to Bundesen, "is unlimited syphilis and unlimited means to attack it." Bundesen had to admit that the first of Wenger's two celestial requirements was right here in Chicago, now.

"Lissen, Herman," said Wenger, "you can't start this till you get a 'Q' Hospital—I mean Q for quarantine—and then let me dig up all the broads and janes and molls and we'll stick 'em in there and treat 'em—no matter how long—trust me, I'll keep 'em amused—so we'll cure 'em and break the infectious chain."

With a vengeance the two of them set out to make Chicago the first city in the world to become truly syphilis-conscious. They polled a huge sample of over 100,000 Chicago citizens asking them if they'd have their blood tested—for free—in confidence—by their own doctors or the health department—and got a roaring 99 per cent "YES!" The two of them were like a pair of mischievous boys concocting off-color divertissements. Wenger organized parades of thousands of W.P.A. workers who clogged traffic in the Loop and carried banners, defying syphilis—FRIDAY AUGUST THE 13TH IS AN UNLUCKY DAY FOR SYPHILIS—and marched to the City Hall where Bundesen bellowed a terrific denunciation of the sinister, sneaking, slithering spirochete. What made this ruckus truly uproarious and genuine was that neither Bundesen nor Wenger were concerned with the moral angles of their crusade.

"If we only had our Q Hospital," one of them would say, "we'd clean these dolls up and get 'em back into service."

As for everything else, Bundesen had a motto about syphilis. "It's up to the church and home to keep them good, it's up to the police to keep them straight, it's up to us to keep them CLEAN"—

he'd roar that last word with such emphasis that it was plain it wasn't his fault if a girl was a blasphemess or even murderess so long as she didn't harbor the little corkscrew microbes. Their campaign was historic in the sense that here were two men who didn't go on the theory that the fundamental way to prevent syphilis was to prevent sexual intercourse.

Then came the war and, crafty tactician that he was, Bundesen jumped at the chance for the Q Hospital. To generals, admirals, senators, congressmen and the Vice President Henry A. Wallace, the commissioner told of the frightful dangers, real dangers to him. Hundreds of thousands of boys of the armed forces, raring to go, full of you-know-what, in deadly peril from thousands of damsels— willing because they were venal or because they were patriotic. He displayed silhouette pictures of a poor little 13-year-old lassie (a real case) who, in all innocence in the sense she didn't know she was giving it, had started an epidemic of syphilis that quickly involved 33 men innocent in the sense that they didn't know they were getting it. *"We must make this city safe for our sailors and soldiers,"* he said.

He alarmed the generals and admirals; shuttled by plane and train between Chicago and Washington; bellowed arguments at the astounded and always gentle Surgeon General Thomas Parran of the Public Health Service; blandished handsome and placid Mrs. Florence Kerr of the Works Progress Administration; hypnotized the great General Philip Fleming of the Federal Works Agency; captivated Vice President Henry Wallace into becoming head lobbyist and leg man for Chicago's desperately needed Q Hospital. For which Bundesen in 1942 got the unheard-of sum of $1,000,000—because he desperately demanded it.

So, on a November, 1942, day, raw with a mixture of sleet and rain, the Vice President of the U. S. A. stood bare-headed before an audience of some thousands of people drummed up by the health commissioner to stand in the street in front of the old Wesley Hospital (where Bundesen had once been an orderly). Over a nationwide hook-up the Vice President dedicated the Chicago Intensive Treatment Center. Who that saw it can forget the high

Navy and Army brass, sitting on the platform, blue-faced and shivering?

Bundesen proclaimed that here, gratis, all the infection of the secret tens of thousands of spreaders of syphilis would be suppressed —quickly, safely, kindly. All acquiesced to this bold statement, accepting it under the spell of the fury of Bundesen's enthusiasm now at an all time peak in his furious life . . .

All accepted it, that is, excepting certain of the most highly authoritative VD experts of the nation. From these arose a wail of protest. To make people non-infectious with massive doses of arsenicals in a week? Possibly. But how many would die from the treatment? To treat infectious syphilis by artificial fever plus arsenic and bismuth in a single day? But how many would burn to death in the fever cabinets? To make this one-day cure—noisily, sensationally, and utterly prematurely heralded by de Kruif in *The Reader's Digest*—routine? Ridiculous! To *experiment* upon thousands of unsuspecting citizens? As good as criminal. And the leadership of organized medicine warned grimly that the new hospital would be closed if one American was subjected to experiment.

Looking back, it must be admitted that these fears were not without some justification. The five-day arsenical drip treatment, unquestionably powerful, did have equally unquestionable perils. The one-day fever-chemical treatment at this moment had only been tested on 54 infected syphilitics, of whom one had died. To make routine application of these highly experimental weapons upon all Chicago's infected? Impossible. The old commissioner must be slipping.

Now the old commissioner became grim. The one impossibility Bundesen knew was to try to break the chain of contagious syphilis by the orthodox, 18-month-long treatment that was all his critics then had to offer. Their "standard" treatment was so painful and uncomfortable that you lost more than 70 per cent of your patients before they lost their syphilis. His back to the wall, Bundesen reached around for a slogan. "Let's try the impossible—now," he begged. He took comfort in the ironic slogan of his faithful friend and advisor, Boss Kettering: "If it hasn't been done before, it's no use to try it."

Now the old commissioner became strategic. With the counsel of the leadership of the American Medical Association, Bundesen announced that the fearsome perils anticipated in the Intensive Treatment Center would be mitigated by an Advisory Committee chosen from physicians and scientists of the highest distinction. Here he took advantage of the American belief—partly sound and partly superstitious—that if you have a sufficiently distinguished committee, and follow their advice, all will be well. It was to be the duty of the committee to make decisions concerning policies and procedures . . . and types of treatment to be employed . . . "so that they would be as effective and safe as possible and would have the scientific backing among the nation's leaders in the field of venereal disease."

No, the old commissioner was hardly slipping. His committee was not only distinguished, but honest and open-minded. For 11 years Charles F. Kettering, famed "Boss Ket," had watched his engineering and medical collaborators perfect a safe and comfortable fever machine, the Kettering hypertherm, in Dayton, Ohio. He had observed its safer and safer fevers boost and speed up the syphilis-fighting power of arsenicals and bismuth. For a long time another committee member, Dr. Paul A. O'Leary of the Mayo Clinic, had been fed up with the impracticability of the 18 months' cure as a weapon with which to wipe out syphilis.

"You're sitting in the golden chair now, Herman," Paul told Bundesen. "Don't give up if a couple of cases go wrong."

By the end of 1943, almost a thousand of Chicago's dangerously infectious men and especially women (the spreaders) had gone through the one-day fever-chemical treatment. Almost as many had completed massive arsenical therapy given in ten days.

By the end of that year Bundesen was showing VD experts and public healthmen from all over the nation and from allied countries through his Intensive Treatment Center; and all admitted that it was phenomenal. In small cheerful rooms were ten fever cabinets,

one to a room. Here—in a smoother and constantly safer routine—
patients with contagious syphilis underwent the one-day treatment
devised by Drs. W. A. Simpson, H. W. Kendell and D. W. Rose
of Dayton, Ohio. The fevers were supervised by Kendell, one of
the world's shrewdest fever doctors. The comfort of the patients
was constantly built up by Engineer E. C. Sittler who with Boss
Ket had invented the hypertherm.

The visiting scientific and medical firemen (who had expected
to see patients writhing and moaning in torture chambers) were
astounded at the prevailing quiet and calm. The patients lay in the
hypertherms with head outside, naked body surrounded by circu-
lating warm humid air. A temporary heat of 112 degrees in the
machine brought their fevers up to a steady 106; thereafter that
temperature was maintained at 106 by a cabinet temperature actually lower than that of the patient's body.

The attending nurses, like airline stewardesses, had been especially picked for good looks, happy personalities and were highly
trained technically. They told their patients stories, played radio
music, cajoled them through their six-hour ordeal. They were vigi-
lant; their fingers were never far from the pulse at the patient's
temple, their eyes were constantly on the dial wired to a rectal
thermometer that told the patient's temperature within a tenth of a
degree. It was engineering fused with medicine for the mass treatment of disease, for the first time in history.

VII

"We'll suppress infectious syphilis quickly, safely and kindly,"
that had been Bundesen's challenging motto and many had sneered
at him.

How can you get patients to enter a hospital *voluntarily?* In the
early stages of this disease they don't usually feel sick enough to go
to a hospital!

Yet here is the Center, running at capacity, and nobody has been
shanghaied or dragooned into coming. It's Bundesen again. It's

the pay-off of his years of teaching Chicago's people that their seemingly trivial early symptoms may mean incurable insanity or heartwreck later. It's more than mere education. At the Center all patients, instead of being shoved around as anti-social pariahs, are treated with kindness rare in the lives of most of them. In the preliminary period during which they're elaborately checked to make sure they can stand the treatment, they play table tennis, read in an excellent library, see feature films, hear lectures on venereal disease, attend church services of their own choosing, black and white all mixed together, and curiously not stirring up race problems despite their propinquity. Their food is excellent.

"It's because here they're treated like sick people, not sinners," said Surgeon General Thomas Parran as he finished a tour of inspection. "No, they're treated better than most sick people," he said.

Bundesen was like a savagely kind father to the young doctors and fever technicians working day and night to make their treatment safe as well as rapid and powerful. They got off to a bad start: among the first 69 cases, two patients died after the one-day treatment. A staff member tried to alibi. "We tried everything—"

"The hell you did," Bundesen interrupted. "You didn't try coming to me the moment you saw you were in trouble. They didn't die suddenly, did they?"

No was the answer. "Then why didn't you come to me. If I can't help you, it's my fault. *I'm* responsible for these lives."

Vigilance tightened. One of the deaths was found due to undiscovered TB which flared up under the artificial fever. Now all candidates for the one-day treatment were expertly chest-filmed. Out of the next 1,317 patients, two died. The safety of the treatment was becoming comparable to that of most major operations. Now all candidates receive complete check-ups, including electrocardiograms and elaborate blood chemistry tests. Now close to 2,000 in succession have undergone the one-day treatment without a single death.

In 1944, Chicago was cited by the War Department as the safest of any large city in America, in regard to sources of syphilitic infection of troops. The various types of intensive treatment were beginning to cut down Chicago's syphilis. Bundesen kept prodding the young doctors of the Center now to get out of the groove of the one-day, fever chemical, or any other treatment. When the penicillin cure of early syphilis sent the medical world into a furor in 1943, the staff of the Chicago Intensive Treatment Center—Bundesen instigating and finagling it—procured huge amounts of the then still frightfully expensive yellow magic.

"If it's better than our one-day fever chemical or our ten-day massive arsenic treatments, we'll be the first to acknowledge it. But, goddamit, let's get busy and try it," said Bundesen.

Now the Chicago venereal disease control program and the Intensive Treatment Center were actually becoming scientifically respectable. Dr. Paul D. Rosahn representing the Committee on Medical Research of the Office of Scientific Research and Development— this was the top scientific brass dominating science during the war— came from Washington to give Chicago's VD fight a rigorous inspection.

"May I say in all sincerity that the Chicago venereal disease control program under your direction is doing an outstanding piece of work and that in my opinion its organization and staff can be pointed to as a model for others to emulate. May I congratulate you and all those who serve with you," wrote Dr. Rosahn to Dr. Bundesen.

Then came a compliment that pleased the beaming commissioner even more, though its source was lowly. Word had grapevined through the Chicago underworld that the Chicago Intensive Treatment Center was a sure source of "safe" girls. A group of young men paid a visit to Dr. Worley Kendell, the Center's director.

"We believe in keeping clean, Doc," said their spokesman.

Kendell, with his kewpie smile, congratulated them. What could he do for them?

"Won't you furnish us with a list of the women leaving the Center—a sort of little black book, listing the women discharged as being free from disease?"

Dr. Kendell, though flattered, was sorry he couldn't do that. Especially in the case of syphilis, all patients treated had to be followed for months and as long as a year, check-up after check-up, before the doctors could be sure they were no longer dangerous to others.

The group of would-be clean (if not moral) young men retired respectfully. Then presently it was noticed that, whenever a girl left the Center, carrying a grip, several young men would approach her, offer to carry the satchel, invite her to have a cup of coffee, then try to get her address. This was stopped by detailing a policeman outside the hospital.

From 1944 through 1947 the Center's young death-fighters tested many types of penicillin treatment—from small doses of 300,000 units given by round-the-clock injections over ten days to giant doses of 25,000,000 units dripped into the patients' arm veins in one day. They groped their way toward treatment fantastically rapid, safe and powerful.

Testing their growing array of weapons on thousands of cases of early contagious syphilis, and following their cases rigorously, post-treatment, by November, 1947, they were able to present fundamental facts to Herman Bundesen.

They were now sure that artificial fever boosted the power of arsenic and bismuth so that you could give a safe and pretty effective treatment in one day.

They discovered that artificial fever similarly boosted the action of penicillin, so that you could give a still more highly effective fever-penicillin treatment in seven days.

Now Chicago's VD control officer, Col. Ted Bauer, and Drs. George X. Schwemlein and Jack Rodriguez of the Center's staff put their youthful brains together. They went to Bundesen.

Why not throw a real punch at contagious syphilis? Arsenic and bismuth kill the spirochetes of syphilis. Penicillin halts their multiplication. Fever boosts the power of arsenic, bismuth and penicillin —all three. Why not make it four-barreled?

"Why not?" asked Bundesen. "If your advisory committee says yes."

The result is making history. All previous systems of treatment they had tried had shown failure rates of from 15 to 30 per cent against contagious syphilis. That is to say, within a year there was a relapse of that percentage of cases, after immediate apparent cure. In the cases that relapse there is either a return of positive blood test or a return of symptoms and signs of syphilis, or both. If there is no relapse of any kind after a year's follow-up, the probability of relapse is very small.

The results of the new four-barreled fever-arsenical-bismuth-penicillin treatment will be of interest to all who scoffed at the possibility of completing treatment of early, contagious syphilis in one day's time. Previous systems, safe enough to be practical, have shown failure rates ranging from over 15 to 30 per cent. The Center's fever-arsenic-bismuth-penicillin cannon has broken that barrier. Its failure rate is only 13 per cent in a series of 139 patients observed for a year or more.

The treatment takes a total time of 30 hours.

Herman Bundesen, smiling, says he'll settle for that as being fairly close to one day. He adds that this is coming pretty close to knocking out early, infectious syphilis in a quick, safe and kindly manner. He points out, still smiling, that only 2 out of 141 patients were unable to complete the six hours of fever that is part of the treatment. Bundesen continues to smile, but blandly, at what's happened at the Center in five short years.

"When we started, about 70 per cent of patients under the then 'standard' system, ran out on the treatment while they were still infectious," says the old commissioner. "Now at the Center 98 per cent get complete treatment actually more powerful than the system that took 12 to 18 months to complete—and then usually wasn't completed."

But Bundesen keeps irritating, taunting Ted Bauer and the Center's doctors to find something still better. He realizes that while more and more syphilis will probably be treated rapidly in hospitals, a part of the disease will surely continue to be treated in the offices of physicians. The boys at the Center have tested (they didn't invent it) a simple penicillin cure for syphilis—one shot a day for ten days—that can be given easily in a doctor's office. It's highly effective—failure rate a little over 15 per cent. Practical? Yes, says Bundesen, if the doctors can make absolutely sure their patients will come every day for ten days.

"When you get them into the Center, then you don't guess, you *know* treatment's completed," says the commissioner. He keeps prodding the Center's doctors in their present testing of a still more powerful 30-hour, four-barreled treatment that just might be 95 per cent effective.* "I know I'm irritating," says Bundesen. "Sure. The way to stimulate is to irritate."

When Bundesen and O. C. Wenger drew their sensational blood-test dragnet through Chicago in 1938-39, its syphilis rate was 7 per 1,000 population. Bucking a rising trend in many large cities, Chicago's rate, in 1947, was down to 3.9. Bundesen's vigilance doesn't relax. Big motograph electric signs over Michigan Boulevard and huge billboards from time to time remind Chicago's citizens where to go to become free—and for free—of the future consequences of the terrible sickness. Col. Ted Bauer has adopted Bundesen's old technique of persuading the undertakers and doctors to help find out why babies were dying. Ted Bauer has mobilized over 10,000 tavern and hot spot owners as assistants to his crack case finders in ferreting out dangerous spreaders of the spirochete.

This super-intensive case-finding campaign now hints the dawn of possible final victory. For, in the past year and a half, the monthly figure of new contagious cases found has dropped from 450 to 270 in the face of more and more intensive efforts to dig them out.

The innocent are benefiting, along with the "guilty." In the last year, only four infants died from congenital syphilis in Chicago.

VIII

It hasn't been easy for Bundesen to watch all the acts in his ten-ringed public health circus. In 1943, while he was guiding the

---

* By increasing the amount of penicillin in this 30-hour treatment, the failure rate now gives promise of being reduced to a low of less than five per cent!

Intensive Treatment Center through its first dangerous days, his entire health department was riddled by personnel going off to the war. He refused to ask for deferments. Diphtheria zoomed upward; 386 cases killed 53 children that year.

"I began giving myself hell by stopping by the Contagious Diseases Hospital, mornings, to watch them autopsy those little bodies," relates Bundesen.

That way he worked himself up into one of his rages. For a week he as good as shut down the Chicago Health Department. For one hectic week, led by Bundesen expostulating, storming, ringing more doorbells than any, his workers (including stenographers and scrubwomen) invaded every house, apartment and hovel in the city. In a week they unearthed nearly 140,000 unprotected children. Then for these—immunization.

Against a nationwide generally rising diphtheria trend, Chicago's rate began falling, till in 1947 it came down to 26 cases of diphtheria and only three deaths, and in 1948 to 13 cases and one death—that of an adult.

Benevolent despot over the city's life-or-death, Bundesen is building a working model for democracy. He is proving that high or low or rich or poor or white or black (and the Negroes have been the ones who really die) all have the same chance for life. For example, for all parents who consent, his department hospitalizes all known whooping cough afflicting children under one year old. Heretofore, among babies with whooping cough considered sick enough to be taken to hospital, the death rate has been close to 30 out of 100.

Last year in Chicago out of 287 children hospitalized—with special nursing, oxygen, hyper-immune serum, and transfusions freely available—two died.

Today, all these deaths, trending toward zero, are the glimmer of hope of tomorrow's disease-free humanity. Yet Bundesen's battle is surpassed in the mystery of its relentlessness by the personal indestructibility of this strangest of the men I have met.

IX

On a near-zero day in December, 1947, all firemen had been ordered out of a Chicago warehouse wrecked by an explosion. Five
dead. In the ruins one man was pinned down, crushed and moaning.

"*You* can't go in there," shouted the Chief Fire Marshal to Bundesen.

With morphine, then blankets, Dr. Bundesen crawled to that
man under heavy flooring that was slowly sagging. The fire marshal and the chaplain went in with him to the dying man but
Bundesen wouldn't let his doctors and nurses follow him, though
they begged to go along with him. In disasters, in all such very
dangerous corners, this is Bundesen's rule. It's one reason for the
devotion of his underpaid, hard-bitten army of 1,300 doctors, nurses,
and health workers. He explains why he has to do it. "They're the
health department, not Bundesen," he says. "They're what has made
Chicago the spearhead in the death fight."

X

Chicago's rugged good Samaritan was 65 when he took that chance
to try to save one forlorn man. Now he is 66 and at an age when
most big businesses and foundations forcibly retire their executives.
This year, 1948, Bundesen is starting a new and dangerous battle;
it's to begin the wiping out of Chicago's pulmonary tuberculosis.
Till now the white plague has not been his health department's
responsibility and he is fighting an evil far more sinister than the
TB microbe.

This fight demanding the full-time work of an ordinary mortal
is only one among the old commissioner's increasingly complex
campaigns. Why does he take on more work? "Because," says Bundesen, "it's fun, so it isn't work." Then too, it's shame for his city.
TB is one of the few remaining deaths where Chicago compares
very unfavorably to the nation at large.

Running low on emergencies, he gaily creates new ones. "We

have a serious epidemic," he told me recently. "Now what?" I asked, having seen nothing about it in the newspapers.

"It's our epidemic of old codgers," he said. "We've pretty well licked infectious diseases. That's piling up an enormous population of past middle-aged people. They used to die from infection. Now many of them go on, existing, mostly useless, only half-alive."

Bundesen is hot on the trail of new science hinting that in part, at least, it's hormone and vitamin deficiencies—maybe lifelong— that cause the degenerative diseases striking at our hearts, brains, and kidneys, especially our blood vessels. He has spent thousands of dollars of his own money experimenting to try to extend the productive vigor of a hand-picked group of Chicago's leading citizens.

Bundesen is his own most promising guinea-pig. His tanned skin is almost as smooth as that of a boy, with only faint wrinkles round his dangerous yet kindly gray eyes. He seems super-charged. After next to no sleep in a night's death-fighting emergency, I've seen him get to the office early, eyes red-rimmed and face sallow, then have watched the color change to a red-brown glow as the day's work thickens around him.

Today Bundesen has more wallop than he had 12 years ago when I first started working with him closely. "Sure, why not?" he asks and laughs. "We didn't have today's advances in organic chemistry then." He gives us a motto: "Let's grow younger together."

He has a private explanation of the world's present miseries. "At least a part of what's ailing the world is that folks have got old too quick and smart too late," he says with a fierce gleam in his wise old eyes. "It's too complicated a show for the young punks to run. And by the time us old codgers are beginning to understand it, we haven't the energy to stand up to the young jerks who are trying to take over."

In his new fight to extend the prime of life, trying to put the insight of Bernard Shaw's *Back to Methuselah* into practice, he's far out ahead of any health commissioner in the country. And he's laughed at, medically. And that doesn't bother him.

XI

Though his energy seems miraculously not to ebb, though he is certainly not growing old too quick, Bundesen is growing smarter, maybe it's more accurate to say wiser. In the old days he was a prodigious public speaker, proud of his power against death, proud of his energy, ambitious for power, even political. Today he lives by his favorite motto: "You can get anything done if you don't care who gets the credit for it."

Now he appears publicly only when it is necessary in line of his duty as health commissioner. He becomes more and more legendary in Chicago and this is not strange. In Chicago (where politics are neither pure nor gentle) Bundesen with only a brief interlude has served for 26 years as health commissioner under five mayors—Republicans and Democrats, though his job is traditionally intensely political. He is a living legend in Chicago. Bankers, educators, hotel doormen, taxi-drivers, waiters, street cleaners, all smile and say, "Hello, Doc," and smile with affection when they see him. Best of all, he's known to Chicago and the nation's mothers: 12,000,000 copies of his famous book, *Our Babies,* have helped them raise their children.

When I first knew him there was more than a touch of Pollyanna in his philosophy but this has largely disappeared. "Do I love these millions of mothers and children? Of course not. How can I?" he asks. "Let parents love their own children and vice versa. Why do I fight for them? Because I hate death. Why do I hate it? That I can't tell you."

This is his mysticism.

Healthmen may stand in awe of him, but they do not in general adore him. A high dignitary of the British Ministry of Health recently told him: "Many American health officers say they admire your results, but do not like your methods."

"I don't like them, myself," said Bundesen. "But goddammit, they're the only methods I know that will get the results."

Then he smiled, self-critical. "You see," he said, "I've never been able to disagree without being disagreeable."

He has become more and more of a lone wolf.

Rank and file doctors have so far not set Bundesen up as one of their heroes, though the more honest and better informed among physicians will admit that, in their individual fights for the lives of mothers, babies, and children, Bundesen has certainly helped the rank and file of doctors in their proud lowering of death rates. Again it is because the doctors do not like his methods. To stimulate them, he has had to irritate too many of them.

XII

While he confesses his inability to love humanity, while he is confident that the secret of his persistent vitality is chemical, I personally believe there's another reason for his apparent indestructibility. It is his magnanimity. A woman has just been brought into his office, crying. She has syphilis that has been refractory treatment. She has lost one baby despite prenatal therapy. Pregnant again, she has now refused the new and far more powerful treatment that may not only save her child but cure her. Bundesen tells her its new magic in little words. He gives her a five-dollar bill and a box of candy. He sends her to the hospital in his own car. This time her baby will have a 98 per cent chance to be born healthy.

That for me is Herman's quintessence. He may not love them but is mighty kind to them. It's that last effort against the last death of the least of people. That's Bundesen.

"We can't *eradicate* diphtheria," members of his own staff tell him. "It's scientifically proved that—"

"All right. But if we just keep in there sticking and slugging, maybe we won't even have those three deaths, out of 3,500,000 people, this year, that we had last year," says Bundesen—the man who hates death. Last year, 1948, not a child died from diphtheria in Chicago.

This year death seemed to be getting higher and higher priority. This year there was life-saving scientific news that ought to have aroused the entire medical world but it didn't. The doctor reporting this news was dreamy, yet immensely learned about the sickness and well-known for his reliability. He reported himself to be pretty well convinced that youngsters, susceptible to rheumatic fever and rheumatic heart disease, can be protected against this widespread and terrible form of microbic murder by a simple supplement to an already good diet. If confirmed, this meant we were close to an anti-rheumatic vitamin. If so, this meant a great medical discovery, making the difference between life and death for hundreds of thousands threatened with rheumatic heartwreck. If there was little excitement about the dreamy doctor's report, you could hardly blame the doctors left to take care of civilians; they were too busy to test new science. The thousands dying from rheumatic heartbreak were more or less lost in the shuffle among millions who this year were being "shot for the good of humanity," as Leo Tolstoy ironically put it.

CHAPTER VIII

The Dreamy Doctor

➤➤ ◀◀

WORKING with Herman Bundesen through the sad days of the war had a curiously narcotic effect on me. The intensity of his drive to save one miserable life hypnotized me temporarily and tricked me into prophecy. Herman dazzled me into believing that the splendor of his own emotion against needless death must inspire more and more doctors so that they might combine to become our leaders in a truly intense fight for the lives of everybody. Herman's secret weapon was that he was never ashamed of seeming ridiculous because of the excessiveness of his hatred of death, and that was why he stood alone. He took the promises of life-saving discoveries at their face value. To make as many as possible of these discoveries operative for all who needed them *right now* so that the fewest possible should die, Herman was not ashamed to seem over-enthusiastic, sentimental, and super-promotional.

I remember so well the terrible, scornful going-over Herman got in the spring of 1941, when certain scientists had published reports that the virus of infantile paralysis was discharged from the human intestine, that it was found in sewage, that it could contaminate flies, that apes might be infected by feeding them polio virus. Herman took fire. He argued that these facts, contrary to past belief, made it look as if the spread of this crippler might be like that of typhoid fever, cholera or dysentery.

"If that's so," Bundesen argued to the authorities of the National Foundation for Infantile Paralysis, "then if we pull the sanitation levers way over, the way we do to stop typhoid, then we might stop the coming summer polio epidemic. Let's try it, right now, this summer!"

So, at a conference of a galaxy of infantile paralysis experts (if you can be said to have experts on a disease about which so little is known) Herman laid out the grand strategy and detailed tactics of his plan with passion and gusto. He was grandiose. To make his gigantic field test we would have to mobilize an epidemiologic, virologic, and entomologic task force and it would cost more than two hundred thousand dollars.

From all but two of the scientific men assembled Herman got the ice of a dozen scientific reasons why it couldn't be done. He was voted down overwhelmingly. Privately, to me, the presiding officer of the conference made his finger go up in a spiral from his head which he shook pityingly, this pantomime meaning poor Herman was crazy. Privately, several of the B.C.M.s of the conference came to me, apologizing because they couldn't support such craziness, and pitying poor Herman and expressing their distress that he had allowed his own executives of the Chicago Health Department to be present to witness his humiliation at the hands of the nation's infantile paralysis great men. They did not know Herman. It did not seem crazy to him to propose a two-hundred-thousand-dollar field trial—even if far-fetched—so long as it had even a Chinaman's chance of saving a handful of kids from dying and maiming.

A few years later, with money granted by the local Chicago chapter, *not the central office,* of the National Foundation for Infantile Paralysis, Herman Bundesen did get to direct a study of the mystery of the sneaking of the virus of polio from one human being to another. Herman's epidemiologic detectives were Albert E. Casey, W. I. Fishbein and Frank M. Schabel, Jr. They've found strong evidence that over 80 per cent of children under eight years of age and about 50 per cent of children over eight years of age develop a mild form of polio, 5 to 23 days after intimate contact with a child acutely ill with this disease—provided that contact occurs a few days before or a few days after the onset of the illness in the acutely infected child. Their field studies indicated that intimate contact is responsible for the spread of polio from the infected to the uninfected, and that the virus comes usually from the throat and not from the intestinal tract.

Though aggressiveness like Bundesen's is an American trait in certain walks of life (as among Henry J. Kaiser's wild young men) it is much more rare among those we pay to fight death. Herman's seemingly extravagant intensity was upsetting to the academic and economic aplomb of most scientists; it was disturbing to the bureaucratic ho-hum routine of most healthmen; it was beneath the dignity of most doctors. Herman was primitive. They couldn't humiliate him because he was humble.

"Just show me a guy who has new science that might save a life and I'll go right down to the station to meet him at seven tomorrow morning and carry his suitcase," said Herman. Dozens of times I've seen him do that for men of science before whose magic, like some little boy, he stood in awe and full of faith.

II

While the intensive treatment of syphilis was getting into its stride at Herman's Chicago Intensive Treatment Center, it seemed there might be the chance of starting a fight on another front, against the murder of rheumatic fever that wrecks the hearts of children and grownups. The Metropolitan Life Insurance Company was then opening a nationwide campaign against rheumatic fever and rheumatic heart disease but its authorities were not especially interested in the particular science that made such a field trial possible. The discovery in question was that of Dr. Alvin F. Coburn, who believed that he had found a dietary trick of suppressing rheumatic fever and so preventing its consequent rheumatic heartwreck. Though Herman was already short-handed, never asking deferment for any of his health department staff, watching key men and women go off to war, he would have organized the now possible rheumatic field trial—if he could have gotten Coburn. But this dreamy doctor was in the Navy chasing down hemolytic streptococci in epidemics then raging in Naval activities, and when you're in the Navy in wartime you're in the Navy.

This was a low point of my life among the doctors. At the time Coburn was taken into the Navy in 1942, that left in civilian life in the U. S. A. just one scientific man working full time in the clinic, laboratory, and hospital at the rheumatic murder that kills forty thousand Americans a year and maintains a reservoir of more than a million Americans more or less wrecked with rheumatic heart disease. It would have been out of the question to have approached this other searcher, Dr. Homer F. Swift, in his fastness in the Rockefeller Institute to ask him to undertake such a field trial. Dr. Swift had his own ideas about rheumatic fever and heart disease and they were not in line with those of Coburn.

What made me feel low was that Coburn's nutritional trick would have been a feasible one to test, with Herman's drive and his immense resourcefulness as a healthman, teaming up with Coburn and his unique experience and knowledge of rheumatic fever. Coburn's dietary trick made the time seem ripe for action. (No matter how much you loathe war, which I did more and more, just the same the action that's rampant in war, the brotherhood under danger that's inherent in war, stirs everybody who loves action, and it was making me ashamed of my own inactivity.) Now there was the chance of action against rheumatic terror—for life, instead of against it. The executives of the Metropolitan Life Insurance Company did not seem to share my enthusiasm about Coburn's dietary lead. And I failed to convince the high command of the U. S. Public Health Service—charged with protecting civilian life—that now was the time to act.

Coburn himself? There was plenty of rheumatic fever, right then, in the Navy. Why couldn't he have made his dietary field trial in the Navy on young sailors who would have been under his almost complete control? I do not know. It could be that Coburn's treatment seemed too simple to the high Navy medical brass from whom he took orders. Then again there was a peculiarity about Al Coburn: this tall, chestnut-haired, shut-eyed, drawling South Carolinian was a very dreamy man with a way of bursting into flashes of action and on the other hand with less sense of urgency, less of

Herman Bundesen's fiery impatience, than any searcher I've ever known.

Everything in its own time, Coburn might have replied if I could have talked to him, which I now couldn't. He might have answered that he hadn't even yet convinced the scientific world of his discovery (made many years before) that beta-hemolytic streptococcus, Group A, was the microbe villain that triggered rheumatic fever. Let the diet field trial wait, he might have argued. Let's take a few years off, to find out everything possible about the lurking, the sneaking, the variability in their power of all possible strains of hemolytic streptococcus, Coburn might have said. "Genius is but a greater aptitude for patience," old French Comte de Buffon is supposed to have said. Coburn was super-patient. My own impatience put me at the farthest remove from genius.

So the possible field trial went into oblivion.

What was left for me was to sit, woolgathering out at Lake Michigan through the ten windows of our safe sun house, mulling through scores of thousands of words of notes I'd made over twelve years on Coburn's researches and trying to get the story of Coburn's eighteen years of lone-wolf trailing of the rheumatic mystery down onto paper.

There was an incredibly old-fashioned deliberateness about Al Coburn growing into the natural historian of the rheumatic state that he indisputably had come to be. He had begun as a medical cub at Presbyterian Hospital in New York City in the middle 1920's slowly becoming associated with a disease that, for its inscrutability and complexity, is rivaled only by cancer. He had investigated nine hundred rheumatic families coming to the clinics of Presbyterian and St. Vincent's hospitals in New York City. He had studied more than five thousand patients acutely ill with rheumatic fever in the wards of three New York hospitals. For years he had followed the dreadfully precarious fate of more than seven hundred rheumatic "convalescents"—all with a sword of doom hanging over them—in the Pelham Home in Westchester County, New York. He had said good-bye to three hundred and twenty rheumatic victims at the autopsy table.

"No disease is more unpredictable or with greater vagaries," said Coburn. "So much so that two rheumatic patients are rarely alike in their sickness; so much so that two rheumatic attacks in the same person are rarely the same."

What puzzled Al Coburn was the insidiousness of the rheumatic murder. Only a fraction of the cases could be detected, clinically, before the catastrophic event of their heartbreak. The advanced heart disease of many of his patients escaped his detection till he examined them at autopsy. Many a victim came to his notice with complete heartblock—having had no classical signs or symptoms of the rheumatic fever that ought to have preceded this wreck of the heart.

What was easiest for Coburn to spot was acute rheumatic fever, old-fashioned inflammatory rheumatism. This was a true rheumatic explosion. With high fevers the children, adolescents, and young grownups who were its chief victims were apt to be so sore-jointed that the slightest jarring of their beds was apt to set them screaming with pain. In these, death from heart failure might occur in a few days or weeks. Yet, the actual mortality *in a first attack of rheumatic fever* was not high, hardly more than three per cent. And statisticians who tended to be a bit Pollyanna, constantly pointed out that the death rate from acute rheumatic fever had been trending downwards (no one knew why) for many years since the turn of the century.

What burned itself into Coburn was that rheumatic fever is a disease that usually kills its victims long after rheumatic fever itself is over, or, more accurately, long after many attacks of it are over. For this is rheumatic fever's sinister trait: one attack of it does not immunize its victims; from then on they live under what Coburn called a "rheumatic stigma"; from then on they were liable to new attacks of the torture. This was the viciousness of rheumatic fever: while a first attack damaged the hearts of a low percentage of its victims, subsequent bouts of it were likely to pile up an accumulation of damaged heart valves and wrecked heart muscle.

In his early years of observing and searching, Coburn could do little for these victims of acute rheumatic fever except to quiet their terrible joint pains with aspirin and to soothe their heart pain with opiates, and to ease their overburdened and more and more feeble hearts by rest, oxygen, and digifoline. Meanwhile what baffled him, more and more, was the enormous number of cases of what you might call underground rheumatism that piled up in his clinical records. Here were children who seemed to be simply underpar, or unaccountably tired, and with low fever or no fever, and with mild joint pains or none at all, and some simply lacking appetite and anemic, and others with slight rashes, nose-bleeds, and little lumps or knots under their skins.

They were that way—vaguely sick for a while—then getting a little better, then down a bit again. Each time the electrocardio-grams showed their hearts more damaged, and each time they were more breathless on exertion, with—obviously—not many more years to live.

Then into his rheumatic mosaic, as he called it, Al Coburn fitted terrifying types of the sickness, where the victims had no joint pains and no apparent heart damage, but were bleeding to death, suddenly with massive hemorrhages into their abdominal cavities or into their lungs or drowning in the foamy fluid of a strange microbe-less pneumonia.

Al Coburn's farewells to his patients at the autopsy table taught him the picture of this gradual heartwreck: heart valves thickened so that blood cannot flow freely, or scarred so that blood leaks back in the wrong direction; and at the same time the heart's muscle damaged so that, as a pump, it had much less power, bringing the overhanging danger of congestive heart failure under the least physical strain.

It was all very well for the life insurance statisticians to be opti-mistic over the falling death rates of acute rheumatic fever. The fact faced Coburn that rheumatic fever, whether acute and spec-tacular or underground and no-account, accumulated heart damage *that killed about forty thousand Americans every year*. Here was the curious combination of slowness and suddenness of the rheumatic terror: the majority of more than a million people with rheumatic heart disease show the first signs of it before puberty; yet the majority of those *dying* of rheumatic heart disease, die (many suddenly) after they're twenty-five years old.

There are truly optimistic aspects of this rheumatic mystery. Many of its victims outgrow rheumatic fever attacks, especially after puberty; many escape heart damage, despite repeated rheumatic fever. Looking on the bright side of it, we may bear in mind these cheerful statistics. At the House of the Good Samaritan in Boston, Dr. T. Duckett Jones had charge of the care of 1,000 young rheumatic victims. He followed their fate over ten years. By college age, sixty-four per cent of them were free of rheumatic heart disease or showed such slight traces of it that they could lead normal lives. Dr. Jones could cheerfully point out that, with good care, you have a good chance to outgrow rheumatic heart disease.

But all of these one thousand had had excellent care at the House of the Good Samaritan, and yet, of the one thousand followed up to college age by Dr. Duckett Jones, at the end of ten years, two hundred and forty-two of them would not go to college because they were dead. It seemed that the life or death of this one thousand was in no sense dominated by science but was under the control of inscrutable kismet.

As the 1920's passed into the 1930's Coburn, Duckett Jones, and all other rheumatologists had only the passive defense of bed-rest for the victims of the rheumatic terror. They could not prevent rheumatic fever (though by this time Coburn was getting an inkling of what triggered it). They could not prevent rheumatic fever from damaging hearts. They had a few stray bits of knowledge about the rheumatic terror, it's true. The disease tends to run in families, seems to be a Mendelian recessive, and it seems that the tendency to rheumatic fever is inherited. It's certainly more prevalent in northern than in southern lands. There's much more of it in crowded cities than in the open country. Poor people are vastly more in peril of it than rich ones. And finally the danger of rheumatic fever and possible heartwreck looms especially in late winter and spring.

You may ponder these scientific facts and wonder what good any of them do most victims of rheumatic fever.

Even in his cub days Al Coburn showed himself as distinctly a maverick, medically. He combined two instincts that are rarely to be found simultaneously in the same doctor.

To his youngsters with damaged hearts he was tender as only that rare human being, the born physician, can be. "You love them because they are sick," explained Coburn. When they were too perilously sick even to be brought to hospital, Coburn visited them in their homes. In intervals between their rheumatic attacks he'd go to their homes and take meals with them and their families. He kept telling all of them that they were not really his patients, but his collaborators. He kept exclaiming at the frequently extraordinary intelligence of boys and girls living under the rheumatic stigma.

Coburn may have insisted upon this partly to bolster up their morale, I don't know, but at one time when, without money to go on with his work, he was begging for funds, he stated that he was in a particularly good position to take a final whack at solving the rheumatic mystery because he had five hundred co-workers— all victims of rheumatic fever and heart disease. On their part his hundreds of rheumatic endangered and forlorn youngsters and young people were devoted to this reddish-haired dreamy doctor because they felt his agony at his ignorance about the rheumatic mystery, his honest frustration in trying to cure them.

To this instinct of affection for his suffering ones Coburn added an instinct of curiosity, the cold curiosity of the true microbe hunter. It is the blend of physician-scientist that is truly rare. This ripped him apart, emotionally. Affection for sick people and the icy hunt for truth have nothing in common; indeed, they are antithetical, they fight each other, they have to be insulated from each other. Tenderness to a sick human being tends to blur a searcher's eye; he doesn't want to find out, he just wants to make the human being in pain get better. Sympathy for that sick human being leads to wishful thinking, to your believing you've got something there, a hope of cure or prevention, when you should be coldly doubting.

Trying to be a physician and searcher together, this was Coburn's Gethsemane for many years. It meant changing his priestly clothes of the bedside physician for the laboratory suit of the hunter for facts, facts too often grim and disappointing, then changing back to the clothes of the comforter with a cheerful (and too often power- less) bedside manner.

III

In the middle 1920's Coburn began his scientific attack on the rheumatic mystery with a failure. Nothing seemed more certain than that rheumatic fever must be a microbic, an infectious disease; and yet, like all microbe hunters before him, Al Coburn failed to prove it; he could not transmit rheumatic fever to any animal from mouse to monkey; all seemed immune to it. In the blood of hun- dreds of patients at the height of their rheumatic agony and in their broken hearts at the sad rite of autopsy, he could find no microbe.

It was here that Al Coburn, by the simplest original trick, set himself off from all previous diggers into the rheumatic mystery. Before him all had looked for the microbe while their patients were at the height of their rheumatic fever or heartwreck or dead of the rheumatic heartbreak. Coburn's trick was that he began studying his hundreds of rheumatic patients not only during their sickness, but in those intervals when they were comparatively well.

He hardly experimented, he just watched them. In his clinic and roaming through the tenements among poor humanity in New York's East Side and the Bronx, he asked his patients and their mothers and fathers and brothers and sisters hundreds of questions about the state of their health before assaults of the rheumatic terror. This seemingly random and silly searching gave Coburn the hint of a clue to a curious difference between rheumatic fever and all other sicknesses.

For months he followed the perilous career of a tough, lovable fourteen-year-old Italian boy who had come to the hospital with the hot, swollen joints, the fever and the palpitating heart of a first attack of the rheumatic murder. Questions. Curious coinci- dence—he was hearing the same thing about so many other cases.

Two weeks before the onset of his rheumatic fever, this ragamuffin had had an attack of simple sore throat. Coincidence?

In the strong sun on the roof of the hospital the boy threw off his first attack. In a couple of months he was brought back, half dead with lobar pneumonia, caused by the pneumococcus. He recovered. And there was not a sign of the return of rheumatic fever. Again he came back to the hospital with a severe crop of boils, caused by the staphylococcus. Again he recovered, and there was not the slightest hint of a return of his rheumatic fever.

It was Al Coburn's single microbe-hunting virtue that he kept watching this gamin and then, the following spring, the youngster again suffered a mild sore throat. It was caused by the hemolytic streptococcus. It vanished in a few days. Then disaster—within two weeks he was in the hospital. There was blood in his urine and pain in his flanks and his face was drawn up, wincing, as he tried to be brave against the shattering pain over his galloping heart. He went into high-fevered delirium and in sixteen days he was dead.

Not a microbe could Coburn find at the autopsy that showed the lad to have died of acute rheumatic fever. Surely that transient attack of hemolytic streptococcus sore throat of a few weeks before could have been nothing but a coincidence? Well, maybe.

Poring through the yellowed pages of an old medical journal Coburn stumbled over a curious item. Way back in 1886 an Englishman, Dr. C. Haig-Brown, had remarked that attacks of acute rheumatic fever were almost invariably preceded by tonsillitis—with a symptom-free interval of a couple of weeks between them.

This fragment of fact alerted Coburn, watching hundreds of his rheumatic patients, following them healthy and sick and healthy and sick and dead over months and years. No, it was not coincidence. His enormous piles of medical histories, clinical charts and records hammered a key fact into Coburn:

Regularly, like clockwork, before they came down with their first attacks of rheumatic fever, and with their subsequent relapses, there was evidence that almost every one among his hundreds of patients had suffered attacks of simple sore throat from ten days to three weeks before the rheumatic explosion, with a symptom-free interval between.

The microbe culprit causing that no-account sore throat was the hemolytic streptococcus. With the sore throat's healing the microbe vanished. *During the subsequent rheumatic attack the streptococcus did not come back.* How then could the streptococcus be the rheumatic villain?

In these early days of his rheumatic detective work, Coburn had the good fortune of the guidance of Dr. Alphonse Dochez who had nailed down the hemolytic streptococcus as the cause of scarlet fever. Dochez found it in the sore throats of all patients at the beginning of their scarlet fever. Now here was another clue to encourage Al Coburn. A certain small proportion of scarlet fever patients, after they'd recovered, after the hemolytic streptococcus had vanished, got desperately sick a couple of weeks later. Suddenly their urine turned bloody; their kidneys stopped working; or they writhed with rheumatism that migrated from one of their joints to another; or they became blue-lipped and breathless, their hearts hurting horribly. The very image of rheumatic fever! And if they died, never a hemolytic streptococcus could Dochez find in their kidneys, their joints or their hearts.

Could it be that this sneaking streptococcus, in its first seemingly innocent residence in the sore throat, lit a chemical time fuse to a delayed action chemical bomb that might explode, weeks later? It seemed ridiculous. It was like nothing ever heard of in medicine. It was contrary to all microbe-hunting science—if a microbe kills, it should surely be found at the scene of the crime at the moment of the actual murder!

It was Alphonse Dochez's great and immortal merit that he encouraged young Al Coburn to think the unorthodox, left-handed thought that this microbe-hunting axiom might not always be so.

So, for years, Coburn and his microbe-hunting assistant, Ruth Pauli, stuck at a systematic swabbing and culturing of the throats, month in, month out, year in, year out, of hundreds of their patients who lived under the rheumatic shadow. After three years and more Al Coburn was able to publish, in a most reputable scientific journal, certain facts that were indisputable. Simple sore throat invariably precedes an attack of rheumatic fever and from this sore throat you can invariably fish the *beta* hemolytic streptococcus, Group A. When a sore throat is caused by other microbes, such as the pneumococcus, staphylococcus, or influenza bacillus, that type of sore throat is *not* followed by a rheumatic explosion.

Coburn here described what was unprecedented in all microbe-hunting history. Rheumatic fever was a three-phase sickness: Phase One, mild streptococcus sore throat. Phase Two, a couple of weeks of apparent good health. Phase Three, the rheumatic devastation.

Voices from the scientific back-row heckled Coburn. If the hemolytic streptococcus is the rheumatic villain, why don't most of us come down with rheumatic fever, since at one time or another most of us suffer streptococcus sore throat? Coburn's attempts to answer seemed inadequate. He could say that rheumatic victims are different from the rest of us, that only about five per cent of human beings are *born* susceptible to the rheumatic terror.

But how are they different? Where was Coburn's blood test or chemical test that would show this peculiarity? In short, out of a hundred children, can you, Dr. Alvin F. Coburn, pick the ones who'll come down with rheumatic fever after they've suffered hemolytic streptococcus sore throat? No. Coburn could not pick them—not until after their first attack of rheumatic fever.

To all sensible bacteriologists and pathologists and to rheumatologists (who are all sensible) Coburn's streptococcus theory seemed crazy. For years Coburn's was a voice crying in the rheumatic wilderness only to be met by deafening silence. What kind of an infectious disease was Al Coburn trying to make out of rheumatic fever? By the beards of Pasteur, Robert Koch, and Fritz Schaudinn, this was heresy. In the active stages of rabies you find rabies virus; in the active stages of syphilis your microscope shows you the syphilis spirochete. And here comes this drawling, poetic South Carolinian trying to tell you about a germ disease in which, at the height of the sickness, the germ is not there. This dreamer spins the yarn that the hemolytic streptococcus has been there and gone. In short, the murderer was not there when the victim was murdered. Since this is contrary to all the canons of microbe hunting and medical science, Coburn got the scientific brush-off. He earned the loneliness that let him go on with his maverick searching.

I V

There was a broad and simple thrust to Al Coburn's experiments. It was common knowledge that rheumatic fever and heart disease are more frequent and severe in the northern temperate zone than in the southern part of our country; and in the tropics the rheumatic terror is almost unknown. It was commonly known, too, that the rheumatic danger stalks its victims by far most frequently in the late autumn, winter and early spring. "And it's this time, too," brooded Al Coburn, "when you find hemolytic streptococcus sore throat."

What would happen to youngsters who suffered repeated rheumatic attacks, whose hearts were more and more damaged with each recurrence of rheumatic fever—if you took such youngsters to the tropics during this most dangerous season? Coburn asked this crude experimental question not only on the ground of the statistics of the above-mentioned common knowledge; he was stirred to make the experiment (being a bit of a mystic) by one of his patients, seventeen-year-old Elsie.

Elsie was a child of the ghetto. Dressed like an old woman with a shawl round her shoulders, "she was just a bundle of bones in pain," said Coburn. In succeeding attacks of rheumatic heart disease, at Presbyterian Hospital, Coburn said her life hung by a thread. What impressed Coburn was Elsie's instinct for her physical salvation. If she only could go south, she kept saying, if she could go south she would get better and live.

So, with a pitifully small grant of money that he begged from some kindly rich people in January, 1929, Coburn took Elsie and nine other desperately endangered youngsters with active rheumatic fever and heart disease down to a beach by the sea facing northeast in Puerto Rico. There they lived on the sand in the gentle tradewinds under showers and in the sun. And on this sand in the wind and the rain and the sun, day by day Elsie and all the rest of them got better. As the bronze spread over their bodies the blue left their lips and their hearts beat more slowly and stronger. "For Elsie," wrote Coburn, "life became blissful." No sore throat and no rheumatic fever, with all ten of them splashing in the blue water as they grew stronger and stronger. What had conquered the streptococcus? Al Coburn did not know. He had exposed them to a change "in the cosmic forces of the environment." This was his poetically vague description of this simple and beautiful experiment.

Then Coburn's money ran out. (For more than twenty years he has worked on a shoestring, always at a critical moment going broke.) But this financial crisis was the most disastrous. The money gone, Coburn had to take his ten remarkably recovered human experimental animals back to New York, back to the hemolytic streptococcus that was waiting for them.

Within two months of her return to her ghetto, Elsie had an attack of streptococcus sore throat and—this was really elegant, experimentally—a couple of weeks later a return of shattering heart pain. Elsie called for air, and could hardly breathe. They gave her oxygen, and she breathed better, but only for a little while. Now her heart hurt her so that she begged to be allowed to die and she was granted this final mercy.

"Elsie was a child," wrote Coburn in memoriam, "who seemed to feel and see through everything and everybody, who was haunted by her sufferings only to be made magnanimous and generous, harming nobody, appreciating something in all."

Elsie was one of Coburn's best collaborators and he had her to thank for urging him towards Puerto Rico. "The disease at last won its way," wrote Coburn in his eulogy of Elsie. "However, in the minds of her nurses and physicians will be stamped stronger than ever the conviction that to be a foe of this disease is a privilege."

During the same months, after they had left the sand, rain, wind, and sun, after they had come back to the streptococcus, two more of Coburn's happy band of ten joined Elsie in rheumatic death, and several more had rheumatic recurrences that meant more rheumatic heartwreck.

In 1931 in a scientific monograph, *The Factor of Infection in the Rheumatic State,* Al Coburn recorded all these and many other experiences. Now, especially in England and less so in America, his unorthodox science made rheumatologists and microbe hunters begin to sit up and take notice. Here's what it really boiled down to: no hemolytic streptococcus, no rheumatic fever, no rheumatic heart disease. It was melancholy and highly negative with hardly a ray of hope, except for those few children of the upper economic brackets who suffer rheumatic fever and heart disease, which is notably rare in rich children. For these there now was hope; for such lucky ones it began to become orthodox treatment to send them to sun-swept beaches at Miami, Florida. To Al Coburn, poor man's doctor because this was a poor man's sickness, this treatment meant mockery. What about the hundreds of thousands who could not go? He had made a discovery, only to be frustrated. It was a new and fundamental fact that the "cosmic forces of the environment" foiled the rheumatic murderer. It was real progress that the rheumatic assassin was now—almost for sure—the hemolytic streptococcus. But only an economic crackpot would recommend that America move its menaced rheumatic hundreds of thousands away from streptococcus danger to the Florida gold coast or the happy isles of the Caribbean. It was lucky for present and future rheumatics that Coburn didn't frustrate easily.

v

In 1932 it did seem as if he might have been frustrated permanently because he had come to the end of his tether in the matter of research money. Like all true research mavericks and pioneers, he had spent no time cultivating the big medical money boys. He seemed always to be tackling the wrong people in what he called "this miserable begging." If the world were sane or, more accurately, if the big boys had understood his science, the money should have come rolling in, now that he had so almost surely pinned the rheu-

matic guilt on the hemolytic streptococcus. Columbia University
had no money for this most original of its faculty members; the big
insurance companies didn't seem to think it profitable to support
further pioneering by the man who had almost surely spotted the
cause of one-third of the nation's death from heart disease. Great
foundations like the Rockefeller? They weren't interested.

Why did they all refuse Coburn the research pittance he asked
of them? They weren't malicious; they didn't want rheumatic kids
to go on dying; they couldn't all have been entirely stupid. Knowing Coburn as I do, it could be that they considered him too dreamy.
When he made what in advertising circles is called his "presenta-
tion," he had a way of sucking at his pipe and, head back, eyes
shut, trancing off briefly, then hemming and hawing, groping for
just the right words. He tended not to dramatize the possibility
of the millions of lives his work might eventually save and he certainly didn't hide the grim complexity of the rheumatic enigma.
He refused to cheat by making it seem simple. The moneybags
might well have judged that its solution would hardly come from
such a dreamy man.

In those dark days of 1932 I wrote a story about Coburn's adventures and showed it (before publication) to an immensely rich
man of whom I stood in awe. His millions, his deadpan expression,
his cold gray eyes, all disconcerted me. Mr. Will Keith Kellogg,
the corn flakes king, was a round man, a man of few words, a great
listener whom it was hard to make laugh. When he did laugh, it
was without any expression of happiness but with a hearty shaking
up and down of his abdomen. Mr. Kellogg was a grim dour man
who had just then exploded into immense philanthropy, putting
more than one-half of his vast corn flakes company into the
W. K. Kellogg Foundation which was to aid the health and welfare
of children, Michigan's children having priority.

Mr. Kellogg was famous for having very few human intimates.
On the other hand he was well-known to be fond of Arabian horses
and German shepherd dogs and all kinds of birds. Since (as Ernest
Hemingway says) the human race can be roughly divided into two
general types, humanitarians and animalarians, it seemed to me

Mr. Kellogg belonged pretty much to the latter. It was with trepidation that I tried to interest him in Coburn's heart-threatened children. But when he read about Elsie who came back to New York to die after her blissful recovery in Puerto Rico, tears came to Mr. Kellogg's eyes. For the next ten years the W. K. Kellogg Foundation kept the wolf away from Al Coburn's laboratory door; for this may God and rheumatic children remember Mr. Will Keith Kellogg. These were to be the years of Coburn's deepest thrust at the heart of the rheumatic mystery.

Just as Mr. Kellogg was moved by Elsie's tragedy, he was tickled by Coburn's ascetism. "When I asked Dr. Coburn what he'd need for his personal living," Mr. Kellogg said, "Doc shut his eyes for a moment and finally allowed as how twenty-five hundred dollars a year would take care of him. Pretty good fellow," said Mr. Kellogg, who wasted neither words nor money.

For three years it seemed as if Mr. Kellogg's research grant would promise little for rheumatic children. In his laboratory in the Presbyterian Hospital, in the hospital wards by the beds of dying rheumatic victims, in the slums, Coburn dug up dreary negative answers to his research question.

Some strains of hemolytic streptococcus set off rheumatic explosions. Others didn't at all. Why? No explanation.

What mystery of their body chemistry made only five per cent of children rheumatically susceptible? What was the chemical bug in their machinery for disposing of the streptococcus? He failed to find any blood test to tell in advance: this child is rheumatic and this child isn't. And the hemolytic streptococcus? It was as treacherous, as sneaking, as ubiquitous as it was completely invulnerable to serums, to vaccines, to any chemical ever devised by man.

Then suddenly in the middle 1930's the news of a chemical David against the streptococcus Goliath grapevined from Germany, and Coburn was not too dreamy to become the first physician in the U. S. A. to save a streptococcus-endangered life with the red dye, prontosil.

Before this red magic was under formal experimentation or on sale in this country, Al Coburn wheedled a bit of it out of an

American representative of I. G. Farben. Before prontosil sensationally saved the life of one of President Roosevelt's sons, Coburn used it to rescue a young woman overwhelmed—not by rheumatic fever—but as good as dead with streptococcus blood poisoning.

The moment that Pasteur Institute chemists in Paris found that the streptococcus-fighting virtue of this expensive German dye was to be found in cheaper sulfanilamide, Coburn snapped into action.

If this sulfanilamide could bring human beings, dying from streptococcus infection, back from the grave, then surely it could cure the relatively mild streptococcus sore throat that was phase number one of rheumatic fever.

Again Coburn began by failing. Sulfanilamide did cure the sore throats of his carefully chosen rheumatic youngsters. It promptly terminated Phase One of the three-phase rheumatic cycle. Coburn waited, tense during the two weeks of Phase Two, the "silent" phase between sore throat and the onset of rheumatic fever. Too bad. Despite sulfanilamide cure of the sore throats, bang—rheumatic explosion.

Al Coburn didn't daunt easily. He shut his eyes and pulled at his pipe and came out of his trance concluding that he had failed because he had locked the door after the horse was out of the barn.

He had merely cured those sore throats. He hadn't prevented them. All his kids had had their sore throats for at least a day before he began his sulfanilamide. Before he'd cured them, the streptococcus devils had been brewing their poison for at least twenty-four hours, already seeping into the linings of the blood vessels and hearts of his rheumatics.

Coburn was a great asker of extremely simple questions, a clear stater of problems that can give you an answer of yes or no instead of a muddy maybe. Like Boss Kettering, Coburn knew that a problem well stated is half solved. Very well. *"What will happen to my rheumatic youngsters if I prevent the hemolytic streptococcus from getting into them at all, during the sore throat season?"*

So in 1936 from among his many hundreds of children and young people, marked with the rheumatic stigma in the New York area, Coburn picked one hundred and eighty-four of the worst ones, the ones most susceptible to the damage to their hearts by streptococcus, the ones who had had repeated attacks of severe rheumatic fever and many with already severely damaged hearts. During the dreaded sore throat season from November through May, all were in peril from the accumulating damage of a possible next attack of rheumatic fever, any one of them might snuff out in the heart attack that might follow their next hemolytic streptococcus sore throat.

To all of these one hundred and eighty-four rheumatic children and young people Coburn—under strict medical and nursing supervision—began giving so much sulfanilamide every day, every day from November till June the next year. It was already known that this sulfa could be a two-edged sword; some were allergic to it; some suffered a deadly decrease of the white cells of their blood from it. Sulfanilamide was already known to kill a few, as against the thousands it was saving. If you gave it every day for seven months mightn't its poison become cumulative, finally killing even those who could stand a lot of it for a short time? There was no answer, scientifically, to this question. It was certain, on the other hand, that during the coming sore-throat season many of these one-hundred-and-eighty-four would get streptococcus sore throat and that a proportion would explode rheumatically and that a part of these would die.

When you are intense enough against the cruelty of death, then you gamble.

In 1939 Al Coburn reported scientifically that a small amount of sulfanilamide daily during the sore-throat season protected all but one of his one-hundred-and-eighty-four from streptococcus sore throat *and* rheumatic fever *and* any evidence of rheumatic heart-wreck.

Without sulfanilamide, their chances of an attack of rheumatic fever, in a given season, were one out of three as shown by the prevalence of the sickness in those not getting the new chemical protection.

At last, after thirteen years of failure, here was a break for Coburn and for rheumatic children. The great majority of people getting this daily sulfa-magic had no bad effect whatever from it, a minority had to discontinue because they were sulfa-allergic. Coburn's good news was confirmed by a parallel experiment conducted over the same years at the Johns Hopkins Hospital in Baltimore by Drs. C. B. Thomas and Richard France. When the Johns Hopkins announces that here is a life-saving possibility, all doctors must sit up and take notice, since the Johns Hopkins doctors in those days were usually faithful to the great Dr. William Osler's belief that it is extremely difficult to save any life and that it always will be.

In another than the mere life-saving sense this was a high moment for Coburn. From Irvington House in Westchester County, New York, which takes care of rheumatic children, came additional confirmation that sulfanilamide, daily, prevents rheumatic fever and rheumatic heart disease recurrences. Then the same good news from the House of the Good Samaritan in Boston, where for a long time Coburn's gropings at the rheumatic mystery had not been too greatly regarded. Here was Coburn's triumph—it was the final indictment of the hemolytic streptococcus as the rheumatic villain.

It was just this simple: daily sulfanilamide equals no hemolytic streptococcus sore throat equals no rheumatic fever and no recurrence of rheumatic heartwreck.

Then came the first anti-climax for Coburn. You would say that this sulfa prevention of rheumatic fever was practical, that in the hands of practicing physicians it would work for that majority of rheumatic children who could tolerate sulfa. But now there was ominous news. Sulfanilamide was making children with rheumatic fever worse instead of curing them. Sulfanilamide was killing children with rheumatic heart disease instead of saving them. It seemed disastrous, it seemed to discredit Coburn.

It really did nothing of the sort. It was a prime example of the grim gap that separates a discovery from its use by the generality of doctors, especially if the latter have to sweat their brains a bit to understand it. Any doctor could give such and such a dose of sulfanilamide tablets to a patient with simple middle ear infection and be proud of the cure. It was hardly more complicated than giving constipated old ladies cascara. But out of the scores of thousands of American physicians who might be responsible for the lives of young patients prone to rheumatic heart disease, how many had closely studied Al Coburn's scientific reports? Hardly a handful because they did not subscribe to the scientific periodicals in which Coburn's reports were published. How many doctors had got it through their heads that rheumatic fever is not an infectious disease in the orthodox sense? How many understood that it was a three-phase sickness, and that the actual explosion of rheumatic fever, Phase Three, was only the end result of the victim having failed to cope with the poisons the streptococcus had poured out, weeks before, in Phase One?

To get an answer to these questions I've conducted a private poll among hundreds of doctors—high and low—and have found not more than half-a-dozen who grasp this three-phase machinery of rheumatic fever. This is true up to today, nine years after Coburn had proved it beyond question.

So it came about that, at the end of the 1930's, physicians vaguely understanding that sulfanilamide was in some way good for rheumatic fever, began giving the powerful drug in all and any phases of the sickness. During the height of rheumatic fever sulfanilamide actually made the disease much worse! For some still mysterious chemical reason, sulfas that so beautifully prevent the invasion of throats by hemolytic streptococcus—in short, prevent Phase One— act the opposite when given during Phase Three.

There is no census of the number of rheumatic victims who died from this misuse of the sulfa-drug; and this wrong use of Al Coburn's science discredited the right use of it.

Coburn went his way, dreamy and lonely. He began no crusade to instruct America's medical rank-and-file in the three-phase machinery of the rheumatic state and then to teach them to give rheumatic young people daily sulfa tablets during the sore-throat season to prevent sore throat. Nor was there (nor is there today) any nationwide system of informational or refresher courses that would convey this life-saving news—meaning life instead of death for God knows how many thousands of people—to physicians generally.

Coburn himself remained aloof in uncanny patient watching of the ups and downs of his own New York cohort of poor people stamped with rheumatic doom. Again he took off the clothes of the doctor with the kindly bedside manner, put on his experimenter's coat, and showed the iron of the searcher that he fundamentally was. He asked nature another of his simple questions:

Had these threatened ones been guarded for good from rheumatic danger when, for a couple of seasons, he had guarded them by sulfa-prevention of their Phase One sore throats?

It was more than a stern, it was a potentially deadly, question.

Having asked it, Coburn acted. In the next sore-throat season Coburn discontinued daily sulfa in a group of victims who had been beautifully guarded from the rheumatic terror for three years. The hemolytic streptococcus sneaked back into the throats of a large proportion of them. Of these, a large proportion developed rheumatic fever a couple of weeks afterwards. And, mind you, at this time Coburn had no treatment at all for Phase Three, the explosion of rheumatic fever.

It was a grim way to nail down the strictly temporary nature of sulfa prevention—good only while sulfanilamide was there.

VI

There is this about many true searchers: they are irrationally optimistic. Nothing could show greater misunderstanding of science than those final words of the hero of *Arrowsmith*—"and maybe we'll fail." To be sure you're going to win through to your goal without your knowing at all how you're going to—this is as basic as brain-work, sharp observation, or clever experimenter's hands. Maybe more so. Coburn knew sulfanilamide prevention was a chemical crutch for rheumatic victims, at best. He knew some might be allergic to sulfas. He suspected that hemolytic streptococci might pop up as resistant to sulfa-prevention. He understood that doctors weren't understanding how to use his science. He kept slogging ahead, he kept reading back into older science, looking for straws of new experimental hope.

He asked himself forlorn questions that would make highly-trained physicians smile. Here was a straw, what a slender one! For many, many years practicing doctors had known that aspirin, acetyl salicylate, or its cousin sodium salicylate, quieted joint pains not only in arthritis but in acute rheumatic fever. Highly trained doctors were certain that this effect of salicylates was purely pallia-tive, "symptomatic." It did not strike at the mysterious machinery of the disease, to cure it.

With the reverse idea in his head—it was not rational but emo-tional—Coburn read back to the early 1930's, finding that a couple of English doctors who appreciated Coburn's three-phase diagnosis, had given a not very significant series of rheumatic children not very large doses of aspirin—beginning at the time of their Phase One sore throat and continuing with it daily till after the Phase Three rheumatic fever would be expected to explode.

What was this? Aspirin seemed to prevent a certain proportion of those expected rheumatic explosions.

What interested Al Coburn more than the not very brilliant results of the English doctors was their reason for trying this salicylate prevention. They had based their attempt on a curious scientific fact, established by Dr. Homer F. Swift of the Rockefeller Institute, in a disease that had nothing whatever to do with rheu-matic fever, called serum sickness. This allergy happens to many unfortunate wretches who have been given big doses of serum for, let's say, pneumonia. Let's say that serum beautifully cures their pneumonia. For a couple of weeks they're on the mend. Then they come down with terrific hives and a terrible arthritis that migrates from joint to joint. Some even die of this serum that cured them.

On the old folklore that aspirin soothes sore joints, Dr. Swift gave big daily doses of aspirin right after their serum, and the serum-sickness arthritis was prevented—the aspirin was actually anti-allergic.

It was this that had stirred the English doctors to try to prevent Phase Three, the rheumatic explosion, with aspirin. Now, for an-other reason, it was Dr. Swift's science that excited Al Coburn into his characteristic drastic experimental action. For years Coburn had dreamed it. *Rheumatic fever is an allergic sickness, fundamentally.* For years he had piled up abstruse data involving the hemolytic streptococcus and the blood serum of unfortunates in whom this microbe triggered rheumatic fever. These experiments—of no seeming practical value at all—convinced Coburn that five per cent of people are rheumatically susceptible because they are allergic to proteins of streptococcus. After Phase One streptococcus sore throat, it takes a couple of weeks for the machinery of this allergy to develop, and that's the reason for the silent Phase Two, and that's the reason for the devastating rheumatic explosion, two weeks or so later.

What blocks allergy to serum may block allergy to streptococcus—this possibly far-fetched logical shot in the dark drove Coburn into action after years of allergic dreaming and seemingly impractical dabbling with racks holding thousands of tubes of blood serum (streptococcus antibody) and microbes that represented streptococcus antigen.

Now his attack on the rheumatic terror edged forward into Phase Two of the sickness. He sent out calls to one hundred and eighty-six children and young people on his rheumatic register in New York City. He asked them to notify him the moment they developed sore throat. To the forty-seven who answered his summons for new experiment (and who turned out to have real hemolytic streptococcus sore throat) Coburn gave huge doses of sodium salicylate every day beginning with sore throat and extending through silent Phase Two and for four weeks—well into the period when you'd expect the explosion of their Phase Three rheumatic fever.

The remaining one hundred and thirty-nine who didn't participate were hunted down, just the same, cultured to determine whether they had genuine hemolytic streptococcus sore throat. These were Coburn's human experimental-animal controls.

What now happened far surpassed the forgotten experiment of the English physicians. Of the lucky forty-seven rheumatically threatened young people who got Coburn's huge doses of salicylate daily for four weeks following their sore throat, all escaped the rheumatic explosion *with one exception.*

Of the one hundred and thirty-nine untreated, fifty-seven came down with rheumatic fever that added to the wrecking of their hearts.

Here the iron of the cold searcher came to the surface in Al Coburn once more. Wasn't the sodium salicylate merely *masking* rheumatic symptoms? Rheumatic fever might still be expected to show itself four weeks after the Phase One streptococcus sore throat. So, at the end of four weeks, Coburn abruptly and drastically discontinued his merciful salicylate. Nothing happened. No rheumatic explosions in any of them. It seemed for sure that something new had been added. Salicylate really threw a monkey wrench into the sinister rheumatic machinery, broke up the dangerous allergy. Coburn claimed no originality. It was only that he'd been drastic, giving huge doses. Giving the English doctors due credit, "their results would have been more convincing if they'd used larger doses," said Coburn.

And now—hound on the trail of the rheumatic mystery that he was—his one failure in this brilliant salicylate experiment edged him into a hunch for a future attack on the terror itself, the Phase Three rheumatic explosion. The one patient who had developed the rheumatic explosion despite the big doses of salicylate was a Negro boy of fourteen. He had come to the hospital writhing in the joint pains and with all the symptoms and signs of typical rheumatic fever. Maybe he was refractory to salicylate, even big doses?

Coburn filled this sick Negro boy full of the drug and rapidly and completely his rheumatic fever faded away and did not return. Coburn suppressed his excitement. "This suggested that the boy was not refractory and that, possibly, he hadn't taken his tablets faithfully," said Coburn. No wild hopes of a possible cure of rheumatic explosion of Phase Three when you gave big doses of salicylate, early.

As always and characteristically in his low-keyed manner, in his scientific publication Coburn concluded that his experiment suggested "that rheumatic fever can be prevented by giving large doses of salicylate" during Phase One sore throat and silent Phase Two, daily, for four weeks.

Here at last was a weapon that might be practical in the hands of scores of thousands of American doctors. It was their responsibility to try to guard hundreds of thousands of children and young people from the cumulative damage to their hearts that was likely to follow each attack of streptococcus sore throat, each possibly subsequent explosion of rheumatic fever. It certainly looked practical. Salicylates, even in Coburn's huge doses, were harmless and relatively well tolerated by most people.

Again Coburn's publication attracted little attention. There was no dancing in the streets by doctors. Was it because they didn't understand the phase one-two-three machinery of rheumatic fever? Was it that the disasters from using sulfanilamide at the wrong time made them wary of trying to use salicylate at the right time? Was it that they still failed to hook up sore throat with its subsequent rheumatic fever?

Was it Coburn's own fault, partly? "Every damn thing is your own fault, if you're any good," says Ernest Hemingway. Shouldn't Al Coburn plaster simple phase one-two-three diagrams of rheumatic fever over the land to every medical society in the country? I suppose you can't ask one man to be everything. Unlike Tom Spies with his vitamins, Coburn was no missionary.

VII

He was only a dreamy, lone-wolf, indefatigable prober of the rheumatic mystery. All of it. He was quickly bored with the half-measures (such as sulfanilamide and salicylates) that he'd found to combat it. In his dreaming he forgot his obligation to the rank-and-file doctors. If the doctors had only got that three-phase business through their heads, they could sulfanilamide all highly susceptible rheumatic youngsters during the sore-throat season, get parents of known rheumatic children to report the mildest sore throat to their physicians, and load those kids with salicylates every day for a week or two beyond the two weeks of silent Phase Two—they'd prevent a vast amount of heart damage by recurring attacks of rheumatic fever. Oh, well.

Coburn forgot the doctors in his slit-eyed dreaming over the fact that so far, in fourteen years, he had not got at the root of the rheumatic mystery. He reminded me of Sherlock Holmes sucking at his pipe or fooling with his fiddle, when Doctor Watson thought he should be taking action.

This is Al Coburn, dreaming questions. What makes a child rheumatic? Heredity, partly? Dr. M. G. Wilson believes she has proved that it runs in families, is transmitted by the genes as a Mendelian recessive, so that in a mixed city population about five per cent of children are susceptible. This was a defect you could do nothing about, eugenically. Maybe the totalitarian Nazis and Commies could make rheumatic parents not marry; they might even bump them off to purify their national germ plasm. But not in America.

Then anyway—by Godfrey! (this was as much profanity as Coburn permitted himself)—heredity was only part of the mystery. The rich have heredity as well as the poor but it's overwhelmingly the poor and rarely the rich kids who have rheumatic fever.

Yes—by George!—it's poverty that puts the deadly finger on those kids born susceptible. But what's poverty? It's a hundred factors. Overcrowding in slums? Yes, that predisposes to hemolytic streptococcus sore throat. Yet the rich child gets sore throat too but almost always escapes rheumatic fever.

Brooding artist that he was, woolgathering through the slums on his rheumatic detective hunt Coburn was brought up sharp by a contrast. Here were the horrible warrens that went for homes on New York's East Side, lousy with rheumatic fever. Here right bang in the middle of this rheumatic desolation was a rich private school for young girls, five hundred of them. Not a case of rheumatic fever in five years!

With a cagey, slow, doubting deduction that almost made him seem stupid, Coburn sidled mentally toward his solution. Poverty has a least-common-denominator—diet. It is good diet for the rich children. It is deficient diet for the poor.

Coburn was a wanderer, a man with an itching heel, and he went to England where rheumatic fever really murders the children and young people. Here in England the top men in medicine were excited by his three-phase picture of rheumatic murder. In jam sessions with English rheumatologists Coburn ran onto a clue. The children of rural Holland were rarely killed by the rheumatic terror, though they had plenty of streptococcus sore throat. The children of urban England were killed in many thousands yearly—though they lived under the same climate of the same age and economic level and were of the same stock as the Dutch.

The difference? Diet and only diet.

He drifted back to America. Yes, diet. On the farms and in cities, hemolytic streptococcus sore throat. In the cities, rheumatic fever; on the farms close by—not much of it.

In the late 1930's Coburn again went into action. He took a leaf out of the book of the great Dr. Joseph Goldberger who many years before had been confronted by precisely the same enigma, hunting pellagra. Now, like Goldberger—nutritional survey.

Coburn and his nurses sat down at mealtime with the lucky little girls of the rich private school and the miserable waifs of the tenements all around it, watching exactly what they all ate and how much and making elaborate records and comparing their diets in regard to calories, proteins, vitamins and minerals with the supposed standards for good diets compiled by the world's most learned nutritionists.

The results gave him a grimly simple chiaroscuro. The lucky little rich girls who had no rheumatic fever in the private school were getting an excess of everything—except carbohydrates—so that they wouldn't be too rotund as debutantes. Then Coburn and his physicians and nurses picked a group of known rheumatics from the stinking tenements close by, fifty youngsters whose repeated rheumatic fever had more or less wrecked their hearts.

All were deficient in proteins, vitamin A, iron and calcium. But what special deficiency meant rheumatic susceptibility? Coburn hadn't the faintest notion.

Then an accident helped him. "The rarity of rheumatic fever in children receiving the advantages of the upper stratum of life is well recognized," said Coburn. "Yet occasionally the wealthy child contracts rheumatic fever after streptococcus sore throat."

To eke out his income Coburn was allowed to see a few private patients, and among these, fourteen unselected rich children came to him to Presbyterian Hospital, rheumatic. Their diets? All had dietary peculiarities, excepting one, the son of a doctor who ate the menu common to wealthy families. All the rest were low in proteins and ten of them—for this allergic or merely finicky reason or that—*did not eat eggs.*

Coburn was forced to a conclusion. The rheumatic kids might not eat enough meat, or butter, or milk. But, rich or poor, "One of the foods usually omitted by susceptible rheumatic children, either because of cost or taste, was eggs," said Coburn.

The thrust of Al Coburn's experimenting was now as always, broad, bold and simple. So it might be eggs? He began his test at the Pelham Home for rheumatic children, where for years he had tried to guard a selected group of kids dreadfully threatened by repeated rheumatic heartwreck after every epidemic of sore throat. Till now he had thought they were getting pretty good diets, "well-balanced"—oranges, fresh vegetables, cod liver oil included. Yet, what the Pelham Home allowed per day for food could be only thirty cents. Eggs? It was lucky that most of the rheumatic kids didn't like eggs—not having been used to them in the poor homes they had come from.

Eggs? It would be simple to test it. At Pelham Home, Coburn and his physicians and nurses had the rheumatic youngsters under strict observation and control like so many little human guinea-pigs. Except during that experiment when they'd been given daily sulfanilamide, the majority of these kids had got hemolytic streptococcus sore throat every year, followed in at least fifty per cent of them by rheumatic attacks.

Now from 1939 to 1941 under the direction of his devoted co-worker, Dr. Lucile Moore, the hitherto supposedly adequate diet of a group of these dangerously rheumatic children was reinforced with two boiled eggs and two frozen egg yolks, daily.

There were seventeen of these youngsters on the egg diet the first year and twenty-six the second. At first they kicked bitterly, complaining they'd never had eggs at home and didn't like them but by cajolery—this might help their hearts!—the eggs were got down them.

During these two years, despite the fact that there was high incidence of streptococcus sore throat, despite the fact that they were all exquisitely rheumatically susceptible, not one case of rheumatic fever occurred among these egg-eating children.

Then Coburn and Dr. Moore—it might be not only eggs—varied their experiment among children of New York's East Side, selected into groups of thirty. Youngsters living on their customary deficient diets—controls these were, scientifically—had a thirty-eight per cent incidence of rheumatic fever. Precisely parallel children, to whose deficient diet a daily serving of meat, butter, extra vitamin A and D, and two eggs were added, showed rheumatic fever in a percentage of only six point seven. Eggs only? Rheumatic kids to whose deficient diets the experimenters simply added "large amounts of powdered egg yolk" had least rheumatic fever of all—percentage was five.

Then, just as Coburn got ready to go off to the war, with the help of Dr. Moore he put the new egg hope to the severest test of all. The correction of any dietary deficiency with mere foods, with anything but pure vitamins that you can give in enormous doses, is slow. Now Coburn and Lucile Moore picked out twenty of their most highly susceptible, heart-endangered rheumatics. They waited till each one of them came down with unquestioned hemolytic streptococcus sore throat. Up to the moment of the sore throat all these twenty had been living on their miserably deficient diets.

But now eggs. Forced-feeding of the equivalent of eight egg yolks in the form of powdered egg yolk, every day for three weeks through silent Phase Two and beyond it.

All of the twenty children on this diet super-charged with eggs escaped rheumatic fever, with just one exception.

That one fought eating egg yolk, ducked it, skipped it entirely during four days of Phase Two. Even then the rheumatic attack was mild. The other nineteen escaped, completely. That season among a large number of precisely parallel, highly susceptible rheumatic children—egg-less—rheumatic fever hit thirty-five per cent after their hemolytic streptococcus sore throats.

It was Dr. Lucile Moore who saw this historic experiment through to its conclusion, with Al Coburn off to the war, but these were surely the peak days of Coburn's researching life.

Of course the chemical enemy of a child's inborn rheumatic susceptibility might well be in other foods besides eggs. From Christ's Hospital in England came news that fresh milk and butter cut down rheumatic fever and from the University of Kansas medical school came a report from Dr. Don Carlos Peete that, when people who were not poor came down with rheumatic fever, their diets were invariably low in meat, eggs, butter, milk and fresh fruits.

But eggs had the real power. They had an "x," a vitamin that could correct the allergic defect of children born rheumatically susceptible. Now bring on the most powerful of all modern magicians, the organic chemists, to track down the precise anti-rheumatic quintessence hiding in the egg.

VIII

As 1941 drew to its close I thought that nothing could stop Al Coburn now. In his fight against rheumatic fever he was certainly at the same point as Joseph Goldberger when he found that he could prevent pellagra with meat, milk, and eggs. Coburn also reminded me of George Minot at the moment when he found he could build new blood in pernicious anemia victims by feeding them liver. To the authorities of the W. K. Kellogg Foundation, Coburn made a report that should surely have made them proud of having supported him in a death fight now so near victory. "The care of rheumatic children under Dr. Moore's supervision has been so improved that at last we have passed through an academic year without a single death from rheumatic fever," wrote Coburn.

Surely now was the hour to begin field trials in the homes of rheumatic children, in heart clinics and hospitals—tests that would

confirm or refute this high hope of eggs against the rheumatic terror. This surely was the time of the pay-off of his seventeen years of
dreaming, groping, of bold and simple experimenting. Then on a
bleak snowy day in November, 1941, Al Coburn, very low, came to
see us at Wake Robin.

The officials of the W. K. Kellogg Foundation had decided to
terminate their support of his researches in rheumatic fever.

Desperately Coburn scurried around for new financial support.
To one of the very greatest and highly respected of our foundations Coburn wrote, in his application for a research grant (euphe-
mism for begging) as follows:

"The evidence we have accumulated in field studies and at Pelham Home indicates to us that the poor First Avenue child can be
as free of rheumatic fever as the Park Avenue child if he receives
an adequate amount of some dietary factor."

Isolating that factor would mean scores of thousands of children
no longer screaming with pain over their shattered hearts, no longer
blue-lipped, gasping for air, on the way to death. It would mean
that ultimately the present toll of forty thousand annually dying
from rheumatic heartbreak would be cut down to negligible.

This great foundation could not see its way clear to support Al
Coburn's project. While he was forlornly looking around for some
other financial angel, Pearl Harbor exploded. What price now the
lives of the civilian hundreds of thousands threatened with rheumatic death? There seemed a last chance, the U. S. Public Health
Service.

Ten days after Pearl Harbor, Surgeon General Thomas Parran
joined us at luncheon in Washington. That day Coburn was not
dreamy but fiery, telling Dr. Parran the adventures that had at
last brought him so near to foiling this most widespread of the
murders perpetrated by the hemolytic streptococcus.

I have never seen kindly and quiet Tom Parran more moved and
scientifically interested but, alas, financially he was unable to take
the project into the U. S. Public Health Service which was where
Al Coburn was ready to go.

In a dark small room in the Hotel Carlton we sat together the rest

of the afternoon. This was ebb-tide; Coburn would have gone anywhere, that day. He would have cut all academic connections; he
would have joined up with a commercial chemical company, like
American Cyanamid, to work with their magnificent group of organic chemists in a hunt for the "X" in the egg, if only Cyanamid
would put its financial and technical power behind a hunt that
seemed so near to trapping its life-saving, heart-guarding chemical
quarry.

About the defeat of his hopes Coburn talked in an *adagio lamen-
toso* and bitterly. You could get money for a contagious disease,
like TB; for a disease of the aged, like cancer; for a disease causing
obvious deformities, like polio; for diseases associated with promiscuous living, like syphilis. Yes, by Godfrey, for those there was
research money. But not for rheumatic fever.

Al terminated his lament, like Isaiah, and I made him repeat it
slowly so I could take it down. "Man may neglect this problem;
yet nature continues to point out its importance with high mortality of the young, tremendous morbidity, and an incalculable
amount of degenerative vascular disease following in the wake of
young rheumatic subjects, just beginning a life of service."

IX

Tom Parran had held out the hope of keeping Al's work alive
by getting him some modest grants from certain of the great foundations on which Parran served as trustee. He got them and they
played their part in helping Dr. Lucile Moore finish that last lovely
work of guarding those nineteen children with the big doses of
egg yolk after their hemolytic streptococcus sore throats.

Then Coburn was called into the Navy and the hope in the egg
faded into limbo where it remains to this day. In the Navy during
the years of the war the hemolytic streptococcus really had a field
day, causing at least a million cases of streptococcus respiratory
tract disease, fifty thousand cases of scarlet fever, and over forty
thousand cases of rheumatic fever, rheumatic heart disease, and
acute arthritis, and a staggering loss of man days.

In the Navy, to the everlasting credit of its high medical brass, Coburn was recognized as the top fighter of the rheumatic terror that he truly was; and why, during those war years he retreated from his deepest penetration into the rheumatic mystery, why he didn't push through that hope in the yolk of the egg, I do not know. In the Navy Al Coburn backed off from that, to his earliest work with sodium salicylate.

He remembered that one little fourteen-year-old Negro boy who had probably skipped his salicylate during Phase Two had come down with his rheumatic explosion, which had then been quickly snuffed out with big doses of salicylate. In the Navy you had perfect control of your human experimental animals, you could begin treating them *the day they came down with rheumatic fever.*

This Al Coburn now proceeded to do with sodium salicylate. He invented an accurate chemical test for determining the exact level of salicylate in the blood. He found you could build up that level fast by shooting big doses of salicylate into the veins. In what was the first formal attack on the Phase Three rheumatic explosion itself, Coburn discovered that these high blood levels of sodium salicylate quickly slowed blood sedimentation rates back to normal— *if you started the salicylate during the first days of the rheumatic explosion.** Then the pains in the hot swollen joints of the sick sailors rapidly faded and it was remarkable how few of them showed any damage to their hearts.

To prevent heart damage, to return the maximum number of them back to active duty, that was what Coburn must do for all sailors coming down with rheumatic fever. Especially during war, nothing is too good for our sailors. At the instant of their rheumatic explosions they were put to bed rest, dosed with salicylate, and when convalescent were transferred by air ambulance to a hospital in sunny Southern California, exposed to increasing amounts of sunlight, given the most scientific care possible.

* A physician at the Johns Hopkins reports failure to confirm this work of Coburn's but his experiment was not comparable since he gave salicylate to rheumatic fever victims in all stages, even late stages of the rheumatic explosion, when hearts were already damaged.

The results were heartening. Out of 5,600 victims of rheumatic fever between March and December, 1944, 81.9 per cent were returned to active duty. Only 2.54 per cent came back with a recurrence of rheumatic fever. Out of all of the 5,600 only five died.

Nothing was too good for our sailors and surely the Navy could have commandeered any amount of powdered egg yolk to feed to rheumatic susceptibles the moment they came down with hemolytic streptococcus sore throat. But possibly there were technical difficulties in the way of such an experiment; I don't know. Who is this writer, that he should question Coburn?

In the Navy during the war Coburn went still further back into his old research victories against rheumatic fever. He went back to his old sulfanilamide prevention of Phase One hemolytic streptococcus sore throat. This time with the safer and more powerful drug, sulfa-diazine, the Navy made an enormous experiment in the mass prevention of hemolytic streptococcus sore throat among sailors and at first it seemed a stunning success.

Feeding a moderate amount of sulfa-diazine every day the year round, in 1943 and 1944 the drug was 85 per cent effective in preventing streptococcus sore throat and—here a brilliant proof of Coburn's original science—as sore throats declined, so did rheumatic fever. In fact it could be said now from tests on a vast scale—no hemolytic streptococcus sore throat, no rheumatic fever, no rheumatic heart disease.

Alas, the hemolytic streptococcus is tricky, resourceful, treacherous, and presently new strains of this rattlesnake among microbes arose, that were resistant to sulfa-diazine, and these spread to many Navy recruit camps, the country over.

X

Al Coburn is now the Director of the new Institute for Rheumatic Fever Research at Northwestern University Medical School in Chicago and is beginning to collect substantial sums of research money. It is to the credit of the leadership of organized medicine that he personally sponsored a large contribution. Coburn is mobilizing a staff of brilliant scientists, a team including a bacteriologist, immunologist, physiologist, pathologist, biophysicist, organic chemist, and a biochemist who together with a clinician—all under Al's direction—will make an eight-front attack on the rheumatic mystery.

In his curiosity to establish the precise immunological, biochemical, biophysical machinery of rheumatic susceptibilty and to uncover the chemical enigma of what makes some hemolytic streptococci highly communicable to human beings and some not, and some hemolytic streptococci highly "rheumatogenic" and some not, Al Coburn will have to fight to keep his old hatred of the death of rheumatic children and young people with rheumatic heartbreak.

Surely he will not let that simple egg yolk prevention get lost in the new complicated scientific shuffle. Adge Coburn, Al's wife and team-mate, assures me that he is not losing it. He has worked hard for nearly ten years to develop the assistance of a trained nutritionist to work in the field, and now he has got such a person. He has now taken up where he left off before the war. He personally plans the menus and does the marketing for the new Institute so that this nutritionist may now devote her entire time to Al's interest in the power of nutrition against the rheumatic enigma.

At the beginning of the war Coburn had to leave that hope in the egg because death then had priority and all available powdered egg yolks were being shipped abroad to countries hungrier than we were. But there's plenty of egg yolk now.

Boring down deep as Coburn is now doing he will surely not bore past what lies so hopeful so close to the surface. The necessity for his new Institute has been dictated to him by what has gone before in all his more than 20 years of fighting the rheumatic mystery. He hates to leave the bedsides of rheumatic children— I've seen the prospect of it torture him—but he is convinced his fight against that riddle is the establishing and organizing of his experimental team.

That team is unique. Such teamwork has never been tried before, against any disease, from cancer to syphilis. And if he wins on this one, as he is sure he will, who knows what doors shut against the conquest of what other deaths may open when such teams begin battering at them? Knowing that the key to the rheumatic lock is in the laboratory, Al has hung up his doctor's coat for the present till his team has learned how to open that lock.

We'll leave Al Coburn in his laboratory, while he and his new scientific team are bringing up the precise and simple chemical answer so that (as Al dreams) without their being aware of it, expectant mothers, their babies, and their children can be taking tiny bits of the anti-rheumatic in their food—just as mothers and babies can now take Harry Steenbock's sunshine vitamin D to prevent dangerous rickets. And while that teamwork goes forward for its two or five or ten years in Al's laboratory, there's already more than one makeshift preventive that doctors can use against the rheumatic terror.

They can already routinely use preventive, daily doses of sulfadiazine alone or with penicillin or penicillin alone, to prevent the streptococcus sore throat so dangerous to rheumatically susceptible children.

They can build up high salicylate blood levels in rheumatic children immediately after hemolytic streptococcus sore throat attacks—with a chance of preventing the subsequent rheumatic attacks, so deadly in their cumulative succession to rheumatically susceptible hearts.

They can take up Al's discovery of the virtue of the egg even though they don't yet know its precise chemical nature. Mercifully, rheumatic fever damages only a small proportion of hearts at its first explosion. So there's time for physicians to take action to prevent subsequent more dangerous attacks by diets rich in egg yolk. And if mothers complain that it's hard to get a child to eat a lot of egg yolk every day—which it is—some wizard like Mr. Henry Blackman Sell might rise to make egg yolks into something that children will cry for.

In view of these weapons—however crude they may be—that Al Coburn has sharpened against rheumatic fever, it's marvelous to ponder his self-discipline in going back to his laboratory.

As this book goes to press, Doctors Philip S. Hench, Edward C.

Kendall and their co-workers at the Mayo Clinic, and Dr. Karl Folkers and his associates of Merck & Company, have isolated an anti-rheumatic hormone, specifically active against rheumatoid arthritis and rheumatic fever. It is a steroid chemical, called "Compound E." Its large scale synthesis may take years. Its use is not devoid of dangers. It may be identical with Coburn's "X" in the egg-yolk. Egg yolks are rich in steroid substances. Maybe Coburn and his men may find a short-cut to Compound E or an even more effective and less dangerous substance. Anyway, here's hope for our rheumatically threatened. And may the best team win.

Here was what looked like a cure, at last, for the most incurable and most highly fatal of all microbic maladies. It was reported from a hospital definitely not within the scientific orbit of the Harvard-Yale-Columbia-Cornell-Johns Hopkins medical axis.

This made the good news still more exciting.

It seemed that some obscure Brooklyn boys had solved this deadliest of all microbic mysteries and had succeeded where medical powers of the National Research Council had failed. It seemed that these Brooklyn boys were now cut off from materials they needed to go on with their cures because of opposition by the government's National Research Council that regimented American science during the war.

The possibilities were hilarious—and tragic. What about doomed people's folks who would hear of the cure only to find that the government wouldn't let their dying dear ones have it?

Mind you, nobody would want that to happen just for a good story.

CHAPTER IX

Leo the Bold

≫≫ ≪≪

A WRITER'S best reward is watching his work strike fire, and what got me down, towards the end of 1943, was the lack of excitement at the news of the possible hope in the yolk of the egg for the many hundreds of thousands threatened with recurrences of rheumatic fever and its accumulating mutilation of hearts.

In the autumn of 1943 *The Reader's Digest* carried the story. Ordinarily the public responds heavily to medical good news in this magazine. Thousands of physicians are then likely to be badgered by patients or relatives of patients, crowding and asking: "Doctor, we've just read . . . How about it?" No wonder the good doctors are annoyed. In these mobs there are many hypochondriacs who imagine they have the sickness simply from reading its description—lay people assuming they're diagnosticians. It's deplorable. It's also occasionally embarrassing to doctors who may happen not yet to have heard of a new scientific advance. Doctors are busy men.

But this time the doctors weren't bothered much; there was next to no reaction to the news of this new hope against the rheumatic terror. It was my fault. I hadn't believed Coburn enough. I'd failed to go all-out on his news and so failed to set fire to the readers. "Every damn thing is your own fault if you're any good."

Then in the days of these dark thoughts came news of a hope not against rheumatic heart disease but against an infection that is the most awful aftermath of this rheumatic danger. The microbic malady is subacute bacterial endocarditis, a slow microbic inflammation of the valves of the heart. S.B.E. is the doctors' short-hand for their big-named sickness and in 1943 an "S.B.E." notation on a patient's chart meant as good as curtains.

For all people alive with rheumatic hearts, even though their rheumatic damage has been healed for many years, this microbic malady lies in wait. It is a life-long potential threat of death. This infection was the final exit of an estimated twenty-five per cent of all recorded as dying from rheumatic heart disease. The microbes causing this infection are peculiar in that they seldom attack healthy hearts. They may invade hearts born defective but they especially prefer hearts whose valves have been hurt and scarred by rheumatic fever.

In January, 1944, I noted a newspaper account of the saving of the lives of seven successive victims of S.B.E. By all former sta-tistics all seven should have died. When such news breaks, you're wise to look first for the name of the medical journal that has pub-lished it and then for the names of the doctors bold enough to make such a sensational claim. In this instance it was the *Journal of the American Medical Association,* the Bible of more than one hundred thousand doctors who must not be fooled by false hopes. Entirely justifiably this journal seldom breaks the first medical news of a big cure; it can't be expected to stick out the first neck of hope for the hopeless, but in the issue of January 15, 1944, here was the title, in big type: COMBINED PENICILLIN AND HEPARIN THERAPY OF SUBACUTE BACTERIAL ENDOCARDITIS. Then the sub-title made the sensation: "Report of seven consecutive successfully treated pa-tients." *Two* consecutive successful treatments would have been astounding. But seven?

The men who put their names as authors under this bold title were Leo Loewe, M.D.; Philip Rosenblatt, M.D.; Harry J. Greene, M.D., and a man with no degree, plain Mortimer Russell. They were all from Brooklyn. I had never heard of any of them; that bothered me a bit till I remembered that the somebodies you've heard of have mostly done their real work while they still were nobodies. Maybe the men didn't matter. Wasn't this new penicillin so miraculous that it wouldn't matter who used it? Yet I remem-

bered reading only a few months before—in this same journal—
that penicillin had been tried and found disappointing in the treatment of subacute bacterial endocarditis. That was the official report of the National Research Council.

So I didn't hop the first plane for New York to try to contact
the senior author, Dr. Leo Loewe. In Chicago I made discreet inquiry from a doctor close to the highest sources of the medical low-
down and what he answered did not seem too encouraging. Hadn't
I noticed they didn't use the word "cure"? Mightn't the results of
the successful treatment be temporary? And shouldn't one go slow
when the National Research Council had struck S.B.E. off the list
of maladies for which it would sanction the use of penicillin?

Penicillin, all there then was of it, was needed for our boys
wounded in the war and with infections resistant to sulfas. A little
was left over for civilians sick with maladies penicillin really could
cure and the National Research Council had gone on record that
S.B.E. was not one of them.

Where would that leave Leo Loewe?

For most of 1944 I made excuses for not looking into the story.
From fear, partly, and caginess. Going out on a limb to tell about
the one-day cure of early syphilis had got me a very nasty going-
over in the *Journal of the A.M.A.* in 1942. That work was now pan-
ning out well but wouldn't it be wise to spread out the sensations?
Yet the Brooklyn news haunted me. S.B.E.'s horror had struck home
to me in 1912 when I'd got the green streptococcus (already known
as a prime cause of it) growing in cultures from the blood of a
medical student. I could see his face, grayish-brown, and his wasted
body as he lay dying from subacute bacterial endocarditis. He had
been a brilliant student and the University of Michigan doctors
regretted that they could not save him.

From time to time I asked eastern medical friends for the latest
news from Brooklyn. What they told me got more and more exciting
and set me to studying the science of the highest authority on this
slow sure death. Dr. Emanuel Libman of New York City had become famous, not only for proving S.B.E.'s deadliness, but for showing that S.B.E.—originally thought rare—was actually a pretty com-

mon killer. Reading Libman, you had to admire him for his forti-
tude, for more than thirty years, listening, looking, testing at the
bedsides of nearly one thousand sufferers from S.B.E. with no more
hope for the last than for the first of his sad series, with nothing
but a smile of unhopeful pity for any of that nearly one thousand.

II

Libman's masterly description of subacute bacterial endocarditis
was a paean of resignation. Libman was of the great line of the
observers of inevitable death, like Dr. Thomas Addison, like Dr.
William Osler. Murmurs of the slowly mounting havoc of S.B.E.
upon the valves of human hearts came to Libman's ears through his
stethoscope. Diagnosis. Regrettable. Autopsy. Hundreds of autopsies confirmed to Libman's eyes what he had heard with his ears.
This was the triumph of the "interesting case" that makes up in
fascination (for truly scientific doctors) for what it lacks in cura-
bility. Libman's case records of diagnosis confirmed by autopsy
were a triumph of diagnostic science. The death rate of S.B.E.?
Out of every one hundred attacked by it, no more than three survived. These recovered not because of Libman but by some caprice
of nature; what that was, it seemed not for men to know.

Though men of medical science rarely agree precisely on even
the simplest fact, on this one they were unanimous: S.B.E. was the
most surely mortal of all microbic diseases.

Its fatality was the more mysterious because of the usual gentleness of the germs that most frequently caused it. While various species of microbes may give rise to S.B.E., by far the commonest culprit is the green streptococcus, growing in colonies with a greenish
tinge on the surfaces of Petri dishes containing nutrient agar jelly
fortified with blood. This green microbe is really harmless ordinarily. It exists in the mouths of most of us, never hurting us at
all, but minding its obscure microbe business. Even when the green
streptococcus gets into the blood stream as it sometimes does after
the pulling of a healthy person's infected tooth, it vanishes leaving
no trace of evil. Yet it is the meanest criminal in the rogues' gal-

lery of the microbe hunters. Let it sneak into the blood to land on the scarred valves of a rheumatic human heart—then murder.

Of the green germ's homicides Emanuel Libman was the master detective. He incriminated unwitting human accessories before the fact of this strange microbe's crimes—such as dentists who pulled infected teeth and doctors who cut out infected tonsils, not knowing the hearts of their patients were rheumatic.

Libman's autopsies showed how the little green devils guarded themselves from all curative medicines. They burrowed down into the valves, covering themselves with cauliflower-like vegetations consisting of clots of blood. From these evil nests they brewed deadly mischief for remote corners of the victim's body.

In the course of the march of doom of S.B.E. lasting many months and sometimes more than a year, bits of clots of blood from ulcerated heart valves detached themselves. They swirled away through the blood to lodge in the little arteries of the brain, kidneys, spleen, eyes, skin, lungs, and the muscle of the heart itself. This blocking of arteries—embolism—devitalized one part of the body after another and sometimes, stormily, in a general blitz, simultaneously. At the same time there was a slow wasting of the tissues and thinning of the blood, a poisoning that showed itself in deepening weakness.

No sickness was more insidious. In the early stages the victims might simply feel tired, more and more tired and groggy. They might feel grippy. Their fevers were not very high. Doctors not on their diagnostic toes might think it was early TB, or walking typhoid, or even malaria. For sharp-eyed well-read doctors there was a curious red flag warning of S.B.E.—little hemorrhages, looking like red splinters, under the nails of the fingers and toes. Many victims might not know they were facing death for many months till they began fighting for breath, in congestive heart failure. Many died suddenly when blood clots blocked the arteries of their brains.

Emanuel Libman was a remarkable man. Who would want to be a doctor having to deceive his patients?

It was doom. "Once a positive blood culture is established and the microbe identified as the green streptococcus," said Dr. Harold T. Hyman of New York City, "the physician is faced with the problem of stating to the patient that the malignancy of the disease makes his situation virtually hopeless."

How would you like to be in the place of such a physician? Or such a patient?

Dr. Hyman is here quoted because without his encouragement Loewe might not have had confidence to give his stunning news to the medical world. Hyman had gone over to the Brooklyn Jewish Hospital, had seen the miracle of seven cured incurable people, had put his beady, aciduously critical eyes to Loewe's protocols, had seen that Loewe was stalling, not knowing what he really had, hedging, not daring to publish those seven cases because they were, even to Loewe himself, a bit incredible. Hyman took fire. He insisted that Loewe immediately write up his experience, for publication; insisted to Dr. Leo Davidoff, great power in the hospital, that these cases must be published immediately; called up the editor of the *Journal of the American Medical Association,* in Chicago, asking early publication of Leo Loewe's first seven consecutive successfully treated cases of S.B.E. If Leo Loewe was the discoverer, Harold Hyman was certainly the godfather of this miracle. And finally, it was a portentous telegram from Dr. Hyman—almost a year later—that made me hurry to New York to meet Dr. Leo Loewe. Hyman had decided it was time that not only the doctors but people generally should know it was no longer necessary to die from subacute bacterial endocarditis.

III

Leo Loewe was a big dark energetic man. Like a Newfoundland dog he wanted you to like him. He had none of the peculiar suavity that so often marks a big shot city doctor. He did not play his cards close to his chest. His appearance, while memorable, was not so much handsome as baroque. He was eager and his easy smile was kindly. His dark eyes looked straight at you, and his face had a custard-pie candor.

For a man who was supposed to be the conqueror of S.B.E., there was a mysterious apology in his manner. He kept saying with great emphasis, "Be*lieve* me!" He kept reaching into his bulging brief-case, fishing out reprints, letters, and telegrams to document his statements. There must have been times in his life when he was not believed and life must have done some bad things to him. His ges-tures had great energy but there were circles of a long strain and tiredness under his eyes.

That afternoon, with Loewe and Hyman in Hyman's Park Ave-nue office, Loewe brought out the manuscript of a still unpublished scientific report that he had read as the Louis Gross Memorial Lec-ture in Montreal. His series of cases of S.B.E. had now grown from the original historic seven to over sixty—three out of every four cured, instead of practically four out of every four who used to have to die.

Did I want to come over to the Jewish Hospital in Brooklyn to meet twenty-five of these people who had no right to be living? They were coming in for their follow-up check-ups, tomorrow. Loewe offered it, anxiously, as if promising me I could touch them and see for myself that he wasn't kidding about their being actually alive. His eagerness to present this human documentation was touching.

That morning through a medical friend I had heard from a professor in one of the biggest medical schools who offered to ex-plain—*confidentially*—why I should go slow in writing about Leo Loewe. Now it began to dawn on me why Loewe kept saying, "Be*lieve* me." He was a man who was being disbelieved by experts.

That afternoon Loewe kept turning to Dr. Harold Hyman for confirmation of almost everything he told me. Loewe had been a big, awkward intern at Mt. Sinai Hospital when Hyman was a brilliant house officer there; and it was now clear that through all the years Loewe had kept a humble disciple's reverence for Hyman who was much more learned, sardonic, and skeptical. Loewe gave the impression that medically he amounted to dirt compared to Hyman. As for Hyman it was plain that, in his bitter manner, he was proud of his protégé Loewe and a little surprised about him too—who was Loewe, to have made such a terrific discovery? It was also evident, watching the two of them, that Hyman was making it his duty to see to it that no scientific pickpockets would steal this discovery from Leo. Finally, Hyman was hot for all S.B.E. victims in America having the chance that Leo Loewe could now give them—to live.

The best memory of this afternoon in December, 1944, was the comradeship between these two men of a profession where envy is rampant. Life among the doctors had forced me to the conclusion that the last men to love a doctor for saving human lives are usually other doctors.

I V

They sent me out of Hyman's office to dig through the sad scientific literature of attempted cures that had failed to knock down the 97 per cent death rate of S.B.E. For thirty years doughty doctors had thrown everything in the scientific books at the treacherous sickness. And in vain. They'd tried super-doses of serums; dangerous doses of arsenicals; massive blood transfusions, overloading their patients' already failing hearts; artificial fevers on top of the defensive fire of the patients' fevers—all in vain. In the late 1930's came the new sulfas. To S.B.E. victims these were given in enormous doses justified only because these victims were so sure to die anyway.

In 1940 Leo Loewe invaded this field of death. He began with rabbits, and what he tried was not original. Doing what microbe-hunter Ward MacNeal of New York City had done before him, only more so, Leo Loewe repeatedly and persistently shot cultures of the green streptococcus into the veins of a rabbit, into hundreds of rabbits, till he reproduced subacute bacterial endocarditis on the valves of a rabbit's heart. Again Loewe showed no particular originality trying to cure these bunnies of S.B.E. He simply followed the ancient and widely-held theory that all S.B.E. cures had failed because the green streptococcus buried itself in those blood clot vegetations on the heart valves. So, before getting a cure you'd have to find a way to de-clot them. This, too, had been tried by others, who had failed, and now Loewe's troubles began.

With his co-workers, Rosenblatt and Lederer, he began his adventure with a dangerous chemical, heparin, so named from its having been first found in the liver. It was generally agreed the heparin slowed up the clotting time of shed blood, and that, if you got just the right doses of heparin into people, you could keep clots from forming in damaged blood vessels. There was scientific disagreement over whether, once a blood clot had formed, any amount of heparin would dissolve it or chew it away.

Being an optimist, Loewe took the stand that heparin would; and in every hour he could steal from his practice he began shooting heparin and sulfas into rabbits doomed with his experimental S.B.E. It could not be said that his combination was much of a cure; but this encouraged him—when he autopsied the rabbits, there seemed to be less of those sinister vegetations on the valves of their hearts.

It was heparin that should have discouraged Leo Loewe. It was extracted in finicky small yields out of vast amounts of animal tissues, which made it fantastically expensive. It was a two-edged sword: a certain dose slowed down the clotting of blood; just a bit more caused fatal hemorrhages. It seemed utterly out of the question to keep a just-right, safe level of heparin in the blood of animals or men. Heparin treatment teemed with so many technical bugs that hopes to use it to de-clot the valves of hearts in human subacute bacterial endocarditis seemed silly. It was one of heparin's minor yet exasperating evil traits that brought Loewe his first gleam of hope. What annoyed him was that he had to keep injecting it again and again to keep effective levels of it in the blood of rabbits so that Loewe and his colleagues had to keep going back to the laboratory all hours of the night. Loewe's hope was Dr. Ralph D. Shaner.

This tall swarthy Hoosier of Spanish descent was the medical director of the pharmaceutical firm of Roche-Organon, Nutley, New Jersey. Wasn't there some way to prolong heparin's action so that you wouldn't have to make so many injections, particularly in the middle of the night, Loewe asked Shaner. This medical director had eyes so dark and piercing they looked right through you. Shaner looked very hard at Loewe and pulled a scientific rabbit out of the hat: Certainly there is a way to prolong heparin action, answered Shaner—Pitkin's Menstruum.

It was plain that this was Greek to Loewe. That delighted Shaner. Behind a façade of twisted modesty this sardonic Indianan hid an immense and precise knowledge of the pharmacology and good or bad effects of organic chemicals, including hormones and vitamins. But his real hobby was poking about in unlikely hospitals and laboratories for cantankerous medical inventors and geniuses who were generally unsung. Shaner's warped pride was to be a catalyst (and catalysts are anonymous) to bring eccentric inventors (like Pitkin) and ambitious death-fighters (like Loewe) together, to see what in the way of fantastic discovery might transpire.

So now Shaner told Loewe about the strange Dr. George Philo Pitkin, who was a surgeon, a millionaire of Bergenfield, New Jersey, and (to the public and even the medical profession) an obscure authority on spinal anesthesia. He would be tough to work with, explained Shaner. Pitkin was a bit incredible. Besides his surgical practice and anesthetic science, he was a kitchen sink chemical inventor and had still had time to make millions as a lone wolf Wall Street speculator. Though fifty-six, he looked like an old man. In a conference if he answered at all it was in an almost completely unintelligible mumble. After many hours of this, it appeared that Pitkin agreed with Shaner that Roche-Organon might produce his Menstruum—patents applied for—and made up of gelatin, glacial acetic acid, glucose, and water according to the formula of Pitkin's cook-stove science.

Shaner had stood Pitkin's eccentricity because tests made it apparent that Pitkin's Menstruum greatly prolonged the pain-killing action of morphine. Pitkin alleged (though without proof) that his Menstruum would retard the absorption and prolong the action of *any* water-soluble drug when you injected the mixture under the skin of a human being. Now Shaner beamed at Loewe.

Heparin was water-soluble!

"Loewe and I were elated," said Shaner, recounting their first conference. Their joy certainly might have been premature, based as it was on Loewe's general optimism and Shaner's belief in old

Pitkin. Nobody had tried to put heparin into Pitkin's Menstruum.
So now these two optimists tried it and it worked beautifully and
just one shot of the new heparin/Pitkin was enough to build up
levels safe and effective in the blood of a rabbit for as long as two or
even three days. So that Leo Loewe and his assistants no longer had
to go back to their laboratory to inject their rabbits in the small
hours of the morning.

Yet Loewe hadn't much of a cure for S.B.E. in rabbits when he
tried heparin/Pitkin in combination with sulfas. And yet, in rabbits that died, when he autopsied them, the blood clot vegetations
did seem much less on their heart valves.

v

On this wisp of hope, Leo Loewe began trying heparin/Pitkin
plus sulfas on human beings doomed with S.B.E. Ralph Shaner
excited old Dr. Pitkin out of his trances. He argued Roche-Organon
technical men out of their skepticism. He got large batches of the
new heparin/Pitkin (fabulously expensive) for free for Loewe. In
the early summer of 1943, Loewe reckoned up the effect of heparin-
sulfa on his first seventeen cases.

Just two of these people remained alive.

Had he cured them? Loewe had to bow to the immense experience of Emanuel Libman which told him no. On any of fifty kinds
of treatment or on no treatment at all Libman had recorded three
out of every hundred surviving. Isolated "cures"—such as these two
of Loewe's—might be nothing but spontaneous recoveries. Who was
Leo Loewe to contest Libman whose renown was based on thirty
years of his experience of S.B.E.'s incurability? Loewe was nobody.
Loewe was sanguine, temperamentally. He turned to autopsies of
patients his heparin-sulfa treatment had failed to save. On autopsies Libman had built up his authoritative science of S.B.E. despair.
From autopsies Loewe now tried to ravel out a thread of a feeble
hope. He squinted at the mutilated valves of the slit-open hearts of
patients he had failed to save. The blood clot vegetations that
guarded the green streptococcus in its murder? They were still

there. Heparin had not abolished those vegetations. Loewe had to admit it. And sulfas in enormous doses conjointly with heparin/ Pitkin had not wiped out the green streptococcus. To this the victims who were dead gave testimony. Yet Loewe took heart from what he saw inside these dead hearts. He reported: "Autopsies show a diminution of vegetations, which are smaller than might have been anticipated."

But could you call that scientific? Loewe had no way in the world to measure the vegetations on the heart valves as they had been while these people were still alive. Then how did he dare to *anticipate* that those vegetations should have been larger when measured in victims who now were dead? It seemed wishful thinking, or so all cold, objective scientists would agree. It was definitely encouraging to Leo Loewe who was imbued with an unscientific fourth dimension of science—call it faith, or hope. Loewe kept himself from going to pieces from despair by looking for a bright side, however dim. Wasn't the heparin/Pitkin wonderful? One shot of it under a patient's skin slowed up blood-clotting time—safely—for as long as three days. Too bad the patients had to die.

"If we only had a better curative agent than the sulfonamides," said Leo Loewe, always hoping.

VI

To his help in the steamy Brooklyn summer of 1943 came another collaborator, as unlikely a candidate for any medical hall of fame as were Ralph Shaner and George Philo Pitkin. Loewe's third helper bore the highly anonymous name of John L. Smith. He was at this time executive vice president of the Charles Pfizer Company in Brooklyn, and together with his technical men—engineers, fermentation chemists, mycologists, bacteriologists—Jack Smith was trying to industrialize the till recently useless existence of a common mold, *Penicillium notatum*. Jack Smith and his men were groping to cajole this fungus into pouring out a golden flood of life-saving penicillin on a large scale. Their prospects did not seem bright. Along with competing chemical companies they were dreaming up deep fermentation of penicillin in huge, fifteen-thousand-gallon vats, and this showed up their biological naiveness because the mold definitely preferred to make penicillin on the surface, not in the depths of the soups that nourished it. Large-scale deep fermentation? Moonshine. The slightest invasion of air-borne microbes, contaminants (and it would take super-human bacteriologists to keep contaminants out of those big vats) stymied the timid mold's penicillin production.

Now in June, 1943, Leo Loewe went to Jack Smith and begged that smallish, gray-eyed, gray-haired, pleasantly poker-faced Pfizer executive for penicillin to save the life of a doctor's little daughter who was dying from subacute bacterial endocarditis. As usual, Loewe's treatment with heparin/Pitkin plus enormous doses of sulfa-diazine, had failed. At this time Pfizer was turning out pitiful smidgins of penicillin by surface fermentation in pilot plant vats. Loewe could hardly have come to Jack Smith at a worse moment.

At this time it would be fair to call penicillin the most cruel of life-saving weapons ever found by men. It was by far the most potent enemy of man-murdering spherical microbes that go by the name of coccus. Penicillin could wipe out pneumococcus pneumonia; it was death to blood-poisoning, including childbed fever, caused by the hemolytic streptococcus; it promised cure of the often deadly staphylococcus osteomyelitis that gnaws at the marrow of the bones; one shot of it cured gonorrhea; tried out in test-tubes against the green streptococcus of S.B.E. (and this particularly excited Leo Loewe) penicillin was powerful. Penicillin was epochal. It was the opening gun of the greatest of all medical revolutions. It was the first of the new antibiotics, products of one microbe fatal to others. Penicillin and its sure-to-be-discovered antibiotic brothers promised life to millions who used to have to die, hinted rescue for more doomed people than have been saved in all previous medical history. Penicillin was at this moment desperately needed for hundreds of thousands of war-wounded and for millions of civilians beyond help from sulfas, to keep them from dying.

But penicillin (and this was its cruelty) could only be made by American pharmaceutical manufacturers in pitiful dribs and drabs, in ounces where pounds would not be enough, and in the rest of the world it could practically not be produced at all.

VII

The doctor's little daughter was going to die. Leo Loewe pled with Jack Smith for penicillin. Jack Smith seemed a business tycoon with a rigid exacting exterior—so Loewe then described him. Jack Smith had to tell Loewe that medical authorities, working under directives from the National Research Council, were right then getting ready to report that penicillin, for all its magic, was disappointing when tried out against subacute bacterial endocarditis. There wasn't an extra unit available for a project deemed hopeless by the highest authority.

Jack Smith's discouraging news did not impress Leo Loewe. Look, this little girl was going to die, didn't Mr. Smith understand?

Loewe argued. The National Research Council's physicians, when they made those disappointing trials, did not know about the heparin/Pitkin that might check the accumulation of blood clot vegetations and might even chew them away to let penicillin really get at the microbes mutilating the heart valves in S.B.E.

What Loewe asked of Smith was very soon going to be against government regulations. "I'll come and see the patient," said Jack Smith, finally. What Jack Smith saw in the face of that dying girl is not what usually influences tycoons in their plans of support of research.

Now Jack Smith (as a young chemist he had worked with famous microbe-hunters Theobald Smith and Marion Dorset) yielded to Leo Loewe's plan of attack. Maybe he was moved by Loewe's dogged effort to save this one little girl. Maybe it made Jack Smith remember his own child who had long ago died for lack of life-saving science. For whatever reason, it seemed that there was sentiment beneath his rigid, exacting exterior of a business tycoon. He relented and allocated penicillin to Loewe and this was June 19, 1943.

By the 23rd of July, all traces of the little girl's subacute bacterial endocarditis had vanished. Her chart at Brooklyn Jewish Hospital was marked: "Discharged for further observation at home."

From here on Jack Smith was Leo Loewe's collaborator. During the excitement of the fading away of her fatal infection, as the golden mercy of penicillin dripped, twenty-four hours of every day, from a big reservoir down through a tube to a needle into a vein in the little girl's wrist for three days—and then as the little girl got better and very cantankerous they couldn't go on with the continuous intravenous drip and had to inject the penicillin into her muscles—during that time Jack Smith made visit after visit to her bedside, like a doctor. He watched this child become the first of all human beings to be brought back from death by Loewe's double-barreled weapon, heparin/Pitkin plus penicillin. By Pfizer Company's penicillin.

One swallow does not make a summer, and this cure was only an isolated event, laughingly described as a "series of one case" by scientific physicians who insist that discoveries must be statistical, and to them this would mean nothing, really. It was not even the green streptococcus that had threatened the little girl's life. It was merely a pneumococcus that, lucky for her and for Loewe, had happened to be extremely sensitive to penicillin. Within a week after that little girl had gone home, Loewe stood at the bedside of a woman for whose life he had been fighting since May with heparin/Pitkin, plus fifteen courses of giant (in themselves dangerous) doses of sulfa-diazine, plus urea, plus vitamin C. There had been, Loewe told Jack Smith, "a complete lack of response," which portended the inevitable. No wonder, for this time it was the real murderer, the invincible assassin, the green microbe that gnawed at her heart and swarmed in her blood.

All right, he could have it, Jack Smith told Loewe who now proceeded to take that first step off the reservation, that first departure from the orthodox and the official, that is the beginning of discovery. The failures of the National Research Council's doctors against S.B.E. had been made on a dosage schedule of forty thousand units of penicillin daily, no more. Loewe looked at the grayish-brown face of the sick woman and asked himself: "Why only forty thousand units of penicillin?" It sounded big. It was really next to nothing. Hadn't the National Research Council's doctors been fooled by this big figure, 40,000, that meant only a wee bit of penicillin—actually? Of actual penicillin there was, in these doses, only twenty-four milligrams, hardly a thousandth of an ounce; compared to the ten grams of sulfa-diazine he had been giving her, in vain, that amount of penicillin was infinitesimal. Loewe looked at this heavily poisoned, hopeless wan-faced woman and asked himself a common sense question that was ridiculously simple: "What's unique about this new penicillin?" Anyone could have given the right answer:

Penicillin is as good to human beings as it is bad for the bugs that kill them.

Then why only forty thousand units daily? So Loewe took a first cautious step beyond the dose declared a failure by the National Research Council and into the woman's wrist veins he dripped from sixty to a hundred thousand units of penicillin a day while heparin/Pitkin went under her skin. Within a few days the green microbes disappeared from her blood, blood culture after blood culture in the middle of August turned out negative for green streptococcus, and it seemed that the green devils were really gone, and she felt marvelously better and knew herself that she was on the way back to life.

On August 28th the *Journal of the American Medical Association* was going to publish the National Research Council's report on what penicillin would and would not do to save human life, including the fact that penicillin was disappointing against S.B.E. Though Jack Smith knew this, it was in that very week that he let Leo Loewe run wild with his new big doses of penicillin against S.B.E., starting treatment of two more dying S.B.E. victims on August 26th and another on August 27th. That day, the 27th, his triumph over the death of that woman brought Loewe back to the bedside of a thirty-four-year-old man for whose life for six months Loewe and his assistants had fought a losing battle against the green streptococcus. Loewe had given the man the works: massive doses of sulfas which themselves might have killed him, plus heparin/

Pitkin, plus artificial fever, and yes, even plus penicillin in those originally standard, government, forty-thousand-unit, futile doses and despite all this the green microbes had only laughed and proceeded with their slow murder. Loewe and his men hated to make rounds to this man's bedside because he was so obviously going to die.

If penicillin is not only harmless in one hundred thousand unit daily doses (as it had shown itself to be for that woman) and since this man was now downhill on the road to death, why not two hundred thousand units—daily? The difference between this man's living and dying might be just that simple; and that day, August 27th, the man began again to live. The next day, August 28th, should remain humorous in medical annals, for this day the *Journal of the A.M.A.* gave out the gloomy news, by the National Research Council—official!—that, of seventeen cases of subacute bacterial endocarditis treated with standard government doses of penicillin, four were dead, ten had shown no appreciable improvement, and of three who had seemed to get a bit better, two relapsed soon after treatment was discontinued. In view of these disappointing results, the National Research Council, *now rigidly controlling the use of all penicillin,* announced that it had decided to break off this particular death fight for the time being.

In effect, that day, August 28th, subacute bacterial endocarditis was declared out of bounds for treatment with penicillin.

On the day of the publication of the National Research Council's official thumbs-down on penicillin for S.B.E., a fifty-two-year-old woman was carried into Brooklyn Hospital, dying. She was in coma. She had been given the last rites at another hospital, and discharged so her death wouldn't count in that hospital's mortality statistics. She was paralyzed from blood clots detaching from her heart valves and swirling through her blood stream to block the blood vessels in her brain. She was blinded by blood clot embolisms in her eyes. The admitting physician marked her as moribund. Leo Loewe looked at her. He was not of the breed of searchers who make their statistics look better by ruling out the ones too far gone to save. This day of the government edict against it, Leo

Loewe and his men began giving the woman massive penicillin treatment plus heparin/Pitkin.

She came out of her coma into a delirium. Jack Smith came to visit her. "Get away from my bed," she screamed at him.

The next day the woman was sitting up in bed, clear-headed. She talked rationally with Jack Smith, thanking him for the penicillin. Smith smiled and said to Loewe: "I'm no doctor but you don't have to be a doctor to see she's better." Within two weeks blood cultures showed her completely clear of her infection. In a few weeks she had completely recovered her sight and the use of her muscles. A little later she was back at her secretary job, thanking them all at her office for helping her after her insurance had run out. Still later, back at the Jewish Hospital for a checkup, and feeling grand and proud as one of the exhibits to try to convince high government authority that Loewe was now curing S.B.E., she heard this very important governmental person say that, while penicillin might be a remarkable drug, it couldn't raise people from the dead.

"But I was," said the gray-haired lady. "I sat up in my coffin. I was resurrected."

By now seven successive victims of S.B.E. seemed, even to the most skeptical, to be going to live though they'd had no right to. Now—I will never quite understand why—Jack Smith was informed by the National Research Council that he was to allot no more penicillin to Loewe. At the same time, a couple of these seven people who had seemed cured, began feeling a bit seedy again, a bit feverish, seemed threatened with relapse. Loewe worried. If only they could have another two, or four, or if necessary six more weeks of two hundred thousand units of penicillin a day! Maybe they could be—salvaged, that was the word Loewe used, begging more penicillin from Jack Smith.

It had become illegal. Jack Smith was a law-abiding citizen. But wait. The National Research Council had permitted him to retain, monthly, eight million units of penicillin for the Pfizer Company's own use. For research. To try to unravel the still mysterious chemical structure of the great antibiotic. Jack Smith did not want to go against the government. But he had made rounds, many times, to the bedsides of these first seven people with Leo Loewe. These seven alive again. These seven walking out the door of Brooklyn Jewish Hospital. In his mild manner of speaking, Jack Smith gave out that it was his *conviction* that Pfizer's penicillin had had something to do with these seven being still alive. And now some were sick again?

Jack Smith told Loewe that despite the government edict he'd have more penicillin—but only for cases that had already been under treatment.

In a rough way it was legal, since Jack Smith was giving Loewe Pfizer's own eight million units. On the other hand it was like bootlegging because those units were supposed to be used for chemical research. But wasn't it truly research of the very highest order, though not in the narrowly chemical sense, to find out, whether or no, plenty of penicillin used long enough would cure these seven people permanently?

During this early autumn of 1943 it seemed as if not only the government but fate itself was against these people having any chance to live. Ralph Shaner broke the news to Loewe that there'd be no more heparin/Pitkin. Because a big batch of Pitkin Menstruum (for army medical use with morphine) had gone sour in production, Dr. George Philo Pitkin had erupted out of one of his mumbling trances into a tantrum and terminated his agreement on Pitkin Menstruum preparation by Roche-Organon.

Shaner looked at Leo Loewe, aghast, distraught, almost in tears. Loewe was dead sure heparin/Pitkin was mightily helping penicillin's curative action. Shaner was sardonic in his opinion of humanity in general. "People are no damn good" is the caption under a cartoon of an ape-like misanthrope that's the sole wall decoration in his office. Now Shaner brought Loewe, eager, dog-like, and imploring, to Pitkin, telling him how his Menstruum was helping to save these lives. Pitkin relented seven days before he died from an appendectomy. Roche technicians were sour on Pitkin Menstruum which was very difficult to manufacture. Shaner brought Loewe, eager and imploring, to the famous pharmaceutical industrialist,

Elmer H. Bobst, Roche president, telling genial and kindly Elmer Bobst how Roche's heparin/Pitkin was helping penicillin to save those lives. To Pitkin, Shaner suggested that this might strengthen his patent application for Pitkin's Menstruum. To Bobst, Shaner suggested that heparin/Pitkin might have quite a commercial future. Elmer Bobst went into action.

Leo Loewe again had heparin/Pitkin. And so, because Jack Smith and Ralph Shaner and Elmer Bobst absolutely believed in him, Loewe kept his seven successive doomed victims of S.B.E. alive.

VIII

In late October, 1943, Loewe had the great honor of a visit from the National Research Council's arbiter of who got penicillin and who did not. This B.C.M. (Big Committee Man) came to Brooklyn Jewish Hospital to inspect the ex-dead victims of S.B.E. It was open-minded of him to come to Loewe's humble clinic. It would have been a bit difficult for him not to come because, ever since the grapevine had it that S.B.E. was being cured at Brooklyn Jewish Hospital, the National Research Council was being bombarded for release of penicillin to cure this incurable sickness. The important visitor looked over Loewe's records. He examined the ex-victims, including the lady who said she had sat up in her coffin. The B.C.M. made his inspection, maintaining more than his customary reserve.

Though America is a comparatively free country, yet it is not wise to be brash with government authority. So Leo Loewe and Jack Smith were now conciliatory. They were almost apologetic about having saved these lives, irregularly. They told the big National Research Council arbiter that they would suspend further investigations pending re-study of the S.B.E. problem by his committee. However, they did ask him would there be positive action by his committee, and if so, when.

The big National Research Council man was deadpan. He admonished Loewe and Smith, saying their position would be much better if they had got their penicillin from the National Research Council instead of obtaining it by the back door from Pfizer. Leo

Loewe and Jack Smith kept straight faces at this admonition, not reminding him that when Loewe started saving these people, the National Research Council had stopped releasing penicillin for S.B.E. You say Jack Smith and Leo Loewe were subservient? Yes, maybe. But you have to be tactful when dealing with government authority.

Loewe now turned in a report on his cases treated, lodging a specific request for penicillin to continue his project. Then Loewe sat back and waited. And he waited. For lack of penicillin he terminated treatment of Case 8—please remember this one—who was better but not yet cured. Loewe waited and waited, and it became more and more irksome because relatives of other doomed S.B.E.'s were clamoring, and it was hard to explain to them that the wheels of big government committees grind exceedingly slow.

In December, the desperate husband of a forty-three-year-old woman, fatally sick with S.B.E., broke Loewe down. At another hospital, this lovely woman had been treated for eight months, intermittently, with penicillin alone, not combined with heparin/Pitkin. The penicillin had been shot into her muscles, not dripped continuously into her veins, and it had been officially furnished by the National Research Council. This poor woman had slipped down-hill and down, and was now listed, officially, as one of those temporarily improved. She was, statistically in the National Research Council records, a treatment failure.

Luckily for this woman her husband loved her so much that he broke Loewe down to the degree that he once more appealed to Jack Smith. Hadn't Jack stipulated that he'd release penicillin for patients still under treatment? Yes, but this woman had not been under treatment by Leo Loewe. Yes, but, by God, she'd been under treatment by pencillin, and she'd almost got better, time and again, her blood had been temporarily sterilized of green streptococcus, time and again.

"Okay, Leo, you can have it," said Jack Smith.

In the strictest sense, Jack Smith and Leo Loewe now broke their promise to the National Research Council man.

"It was inconceivable that this patient should be permitted to die, so she was accepted for treatment"—that was the way Leo Loewe tried to justify their going against government regulations.

When it came to a matter of life-or-death, Jack Smith was not only sentimental but a rationalizer. It was Jack Smith's, it was Pfizer's penicillin that had kept this woman alive eight months in 1943, even though another doctor, not Loewe, had given it. But now, weren't Loewe and Jack Smith really one and the same man, at least a death-fighting team, and wasn't it the same as if Loewe had actually given the woman the treatment? Since Jack Smith had gone on record that he would not abandon any patient, when the government edict was issued (though it might be stretching a point morally) this put the woman in the bracket of those Jack Smith could not turn down.

It was by some such sophistry that this dying woman began getting penicillin, massive doses by continuous drip into the veins of her wrists and heparin/Pitkin under her skin. In three or four days to Leo Loewe making rounds at her bedside she said: "My appetite's back. For the first time in a year. I'm eating like two horses."

After twenty-one days of continuous treatment, her blood was clear of the green streptococcus and she went home, cured.

Her case was historic. She was the first who would surely have died with penicillin alone, but was cured by penicillin in massive doses plus heparin/Pitkin. She worshiped Loewe and Jack Smith. About the big National Research Council penicillin man, she was cheerfully sardonic. "Look at me, am I alive?" she asked, her dark eyes sparking. She looked wonderful. "Well, take a look at me," she repeated. "To those government doctors I'm statistically dead."

It seemed as if Jack Smith was going to be in hot water with the government for releasing the penicillin that had saved this woman's life. About her, the big National Research Council penicillin man had made inquiry, from the doctor who had originally treated her and failed to cure her. She had died, hadn't she? She had relapsed again and again. She'd been officially listed among the treatment failures. No, said the doctor. He understood that Leo Loewe, after the supposed treatment failure, had given her massive penicillin and heparin/Pitkin treatment at Brooklyn Jewish Hospital and that she had responded successfully. It seems she was cured.

For the big National Research Council penicillin committee man, this insubordination of Jack Smith's was too much. He called a special meeting of his committee, to discuss bringing Mr. John L. Smith, executive vice president of the Charles Pfizer Company, up on charges. It is reported that this committee meeting was a stormy one. Naturally. Jack Smith's conduct in allocating penicillin against government regulations, for the treatment of a disease for which penicillin had officially been declared disappointing, was reprehensible. On the other hand, Jack Smith's helping to save a human life by breaking government regulations—that conduct, when aired, would mean banner headlines on the front pages of newspapers. And then would the faces of the government committee men be red?

After all, in our country, even in wartime, it was not likely that a life-saving disregard of government regulations would put the offender in a concentration camp or get him shot in the back of the head. After all, the National Research Council shouldn't get the name of being a scientific Kremlin. Wasn't our science getting a bit too totalitarian? So Jack Smith was not brought up on charges. But he'd better step carefully. After the meeting, one of Jack Smith's friends on the committee phoned him that beginning on a definite date he'd have to refrain from giving Leo Loewe any more penicillin.

Very well, Jack Smith promised.

That night he phoned Loewe. How many S.B.E. patients did he have under treatment? For these, what would be his presumptive penicillin requirements for the next three weeks? Would he come over to Pfizer and pick up that much penicillin, personally, before Jack Smith's promise to the committee became finally effective? It was life-saving boot-legging. It had a smack of the black market without profits, excepting life. It was like Loewe sneaking round to the back door of the Pfizer fermentation plant in the old brewery to draw off an illicit canful of penicillin in the dark of the moon.

These events of the summer, autumn, and winter of 1943 were

epochal in the history of penicillin. In all his spare moments and on Sundays Jack Smith made rounds with Leo Loewe at the bedsides of these eight who were being rescued. As one after another came back from what before had been a one-way trip across the River Styx, Jack Smith went back with the news to the penicillin plant at Pfizer.

"You've saved another life," he'd tell the engineers, fermentation men, mycologists, bacteriologists, organic chemists, mechanics and floor-sweepers at Pfizer. This made them feel as if they were more than human. Deep fifteen-thousand-gallon vat fermentation impracticable, impossible? Nuts. They teamed up to make a miracle of super-sterile Paul Bunyan bacteriology on a fifteen-thousand-gallon scale. They learned how to keep those huge vats free of the faintest trace of contamination. Penicillin production zoomed from milligrams to ounces to pounds of the golden mercy.

"All my life, before this," said Jack Smith, reminiscing, "we'd been earning our living and making money fermenting stuff like citric acid and so on. Now we were fermenting—for human life. Nothing could stop us."

"Why not?" I asked the straight man's question.

"Because isn't human life a sacred thing?" asked Jack Smith. "All our Pfizer people felt that. Every time I'd come back from the bedside of one of these poor devils who was coming back to life, I'd make the rounds at the brewery. Then you should have seen them turn out penicillin."

It was a production line with life at the end of it. In the brewery, in the packing room, in the laboratories the Pfizer staff tacked up admonitions. "EXERCISE SCRUPULOUS CARE . . . CONTAMINATION OF PENICILLIN MAY CAUSE DEATH . . . PENICILLIN MUST BE ABSOLUTELY CLEAN AND STERILE—ARE YOU DOING YOUR BEST TO INSURE THIS? PATIENTS DEPEND ON YOUR CARE AND WATCHFULNESS TO PROTECT THEM."

Every unit of penicillin was given to Leo Loewe for his S.B.E. patients, free. When Jack Smith, the business tycoon with the rigid, exacting exterior, this gentle, gray-eyed man, came to their bedsides, the patients felt that here was somebody not quite of this world.

Jack Smith deprecated their worship. It was Dr. Loewe and his associates who had saved them. It was the workers at Pfizer.

Next to his share in saving these lives (which he held to be modest) Jack Smith prized his independence. While other pharmaceutical and chemical houses had availed themselves of government grants for penicillin plant expansion, Pfizer had gone ahead on its own funds, so the government didn't have the economic pistol at Jack Smith's back. But now he could be his own man more than ever. He knew how Loewe's saving of these S.B.E. victims had fired the Pfizer men to turn tricks that revolutionized penicillin production and that this deep fermentation know-how had been passed on to all other producers. Now there was promise that penicillin would soon be pouring out of the giant fermentation vats in a golden torrent.

Jack Smith, a really gloomy, doubting man, was almost happy. Soon Leo Loewe wouldn't have to go on his knees for penicillin to try to save a life. Early in 1944, having officially re-studied Loewe's first eight cured cases, the National Research Council re-opened the project of penicillin treatment of subacute bacterial endocarditis—this time with Loewe's recommended doses.

When Leo Loewe brought up the fate of a twenty-one-year-old man, Case Eight, Jack Smith urged Loewe to take a broad view of their governmental troubles. Case Eight has been sick for more than a year with S.B.E. In the early autumn of 1943, Loewe had almost cured him with massive doses of penicillin plus heparin/Pitkin. Then in late October, the government had cut Loewe off from further supplies. The man relapsed. He lingered on, infected. Then when the National Research Council re-opened its project, Loewe started treating Case Eight again, giving him super-doses of penicillin totaling forty-eight million units. He died. Laboratory tests showed his green streptococcus had gained in resistance to penicillin by forty fold during the months the National Research Council committee had forbidden its use in S.B.E. Loewe was chagrined. Jack Smith was a great one for asking questions. Could Leo prove that it was the interruption of the treatment that had raised the microbe's penicillin resistance? Not for sure. But Jack couldn't prove it hadn't.

But didn't the tragedy have its bright side? Hadn't this death taught them they must blitz the nasty sickness, they must sock the sickness with enormous doses of penicillin from the first and go on uninterruptedly with huge doses till cure?

Jack was certainly philosophical. He tried to comfort Leo, at the same time handing it to the government committee. "The committee should be given credit for its negative results," said Jack. "Those people who died after the committee's little, inadequate doses— those negative results were really a challenge to the bold investigator." Events now following made it fair to call him Leo the bold.

IX

For now to Loewe at the Brooklyn Jewish Hospital came a parade, in clanging ambulances and on stretchers, of many forlorn who were heartwrecked by S.B.E. Now Loewe faced another hurdle —the prospect of deaths ruining his first perfect statistics. Of the cases that now came Loewe said: "Many were in pitiful condition when we started treatment. Many were in congestive heart failure so that it was hazardous to further burden their circulation with the massive dose intravenous drip. Others were far gone with ulcerative endocarditis, throwing off emboli, blood clots lodging in their brains."

Loewe refused none of these. "Despite these risks, we had no choice but to start therapy," said Loewe, "since refusal meant the imposition of a death sentence."

As always in any death fight with a beginning no matter how brilliant, Loewe began running into statistics. Patients began to die, spoiling his record. "I didn't care about the damn statistics, I just wanted to save a life," said Loewe.

In 1944 he began a scientific slugging match to keep all possible doomed alive. At the end of 1944 out of fifty-four cases of subacute bacterial endocarditis, sixteen were dead, some with hearts that were too far gone, heart valves chewed away, heart muscle devitalized, some with brain embolisms, others actually cured of their green microbe infection but dying from heart failure. And yet others—and this seemed most ominous—failed to respond to more and more massive penicillin doses because they had the ill fortune to be infected with a special, a new green bug, *Streptococcus sanguis,* identified for Loewe by Professor J. M. Sherman of Cornell University of Ithaca, New York. This sanguis varmint seemed to have resistance beyond the most massive possible doses of penicillin.

Loewe would not give up. He consoled himself by comparing his records with those reported by the National Research Council, fifty-five cases of S.B.E. treated with penicillin at other medical centers, fifty-five cases and only three of these remaining alive after one year of study. Of Loewe's first fifty-four, thirty-eight were now well and strong.

From every death Loewe learned, developing what he called the orchestration of treatment of subacute bacterial endocarditis. From the complexity and intensity of the scientific effort to save the poorest, the most no-account of these forlorn, you'd think they all had the importance of the President or of old Mr. John D. Rockefeller, Sr. Subtle laboratory tests determined the precise resistance of the microbes isolated from the blood of every patient, week after week. When that resistance seemed to be as good as limitless, Loewe increased his doses of penicillin to as high as ten million units daily. When a given microbe seemed reasonably sensitive to penicillin as determined in the test-tube, then, to make sure, Loewe still poured five and ten times what should have seemed an adequate amount of penicillin into patients infected with these not so resistant germs. To follow the progress of their improvement, Loewe and his laboratory workers made test after test of the blood sedimentation rate of all patients. To be sure that heparin doses were adequate, test after test was performed on the coagulation time of every patient's blood. Loewe and his associates, along with dental surgeon M. D. Levin, found the secret of why certain patients kept relapsing despite more and more massive treatment. They discovered that teeth, infected at the roots with the green streptococcus, kept feeding the microbes through the blood onto

the valves of the heart. So now they began detecting all such infected teeth by X-ray, pulled them and immediately applied penicillin locally while they kept dripping it into the victim's veins.
The relapse rate dwindled. They zoomed the gradually returning
strength of their patients who were recovering under massive penicillin doses by high protein, high vitamin feeding. Originally, when
they had cleared the green microbe murderers out of a victim's
blood by continuous penicillin drip treatment for two weeks, they
had thought this was long enough, only to be confronted by relapses of the treacherous sickness. Then, in those cases where their
laboratory tests revealed microbes tough to penicillin, they stretched
the continuous drip to five weeks and even four times five weeks,
to keep a patient from dying, to wipe out all green streptococcus
infection. Leo Loewe and his death-fighters used Jack Smith's
penicillin like drunken sailors. It took many thousands of dollars
and grinding toil to save a single one of these most endangered
lives. Not one of those imperiled was turned away for lack of
money.

By January, 1945, Loewe could report: "If the patient is in good
condition, the duration of the disease less than three months and
the causative organism sensitive to penicillin, a satisfactory result
can be anticipated, barring accidents, in virtually every case of
subacute bacterial endocarditis."

This was already the hope for victims who two years before had
only three chances out of one hundred to remain alive. Now Loewe
began groping for the salvage of the last forlorn, to rescue them
no matter how tough their infecting microbes might be toward
penicillin, no matter how deplorable their condition, no matter
how long they had been infected.

It is often remarked about doctors that they use powerful new
remedies uncritically, for everything from flu to housemaid's knee.
In this life among the doctors I've often seen the opposite—a
curious reluctance to use a new scientific weapon full power or to
try to pass beyond its first apparent limitations. In their hesitance
to probe the power of a new cure up to and beyond its limit (and
this seems more frequent the more highly scientific the physician)

it is not that the doctors are nonchalant about whether a given patient lives or dies. Is it maybe that they are deterred from an all-out fight to wipe out every possible death (and even those impossible!) by a superstition that each new weapon is too good to be true? It could be, when we remember how recent is medicine's power to save any lives at all.

Of such superstition Leo Loewe seemed devoid, absolutely.

X

Loewe seemed reckless to try to save those most surely doomed and, aside from his belief in penicillin's still untested powers, another circumstance bolstered his doggedness in the face of death. Physicians are held back from all-out use of new science by the costliness of new scientific magic. Here Loewe had luck. At the bottom of his scientific reports you're likely to find this acknowledgment:

"We are extremely indebted to Mr. John L. Smith of the Charles Pfizer Company for his keen interest, valuable suggestions, and constant co-operation. Through him we were able to obtain the lavish supplies of penicillin utilized in all our experimental studies."

All the growing army of Loewe's S.B.E. patients were experimental. In the early penicillin days with production still feeble, when Loewe was confronted by two S.B.E. victims at once, the one well-off the other poor, the poor patient got priority. When penicillin was still, most of it, going to the government at twenty dollars per hundred thousand units, Jack Smith was diverting millions of units of the anti-biotic to the S.B.E. victims at Brooklyn Jewish Hospital—all of it free. Here in the face of the sternest issue of live-or-die, was a premonition of a far-off future day when whether or not you live will not be a matter of whether or not you have money.

This was Jack Smith's religion, and that gave Loewe his chance to test penicillin's power utterly without limit against what he called bizarre bugs—such as the rare murderer, *Veillonella gazogenes.*

A thirty-five-year-old man entered Brooklyn Jewish Hospital in

April, 1944, his blood obstinately infected and his heart valves imperiled with this curious coccus that by laboratory tests showed resistance to penicillin seeming far beyond the levels of the anti-biotic that Loewe could hope to build up in the man's living body. For fifteen months he slugged at this ghastly gazogenes microbe with mounting daily doses of penicillin and heparin/Pitkin, start-ing with two hundred thousand daily, failing, going up to five hundred thousand, failing, then a million daily, failing, going up to two and then five million and finally ten million units of penicillin daily by drip into his veins, day and night, continuous, for weeks on end, till the man had to be sent home so that his veins, mutilated by a year of incessant injection, could recover and so that he could get back his morale.

Again and again the gazogenes bugs had vanished from this man's blood under Loewe's heavier and heavier treatment, only to re-turn again, Loewe failing and failing to cure the poor devil but returning to the assault over and over, till after fourteen months he had used up 460,670,000 units of penicillin, still failing. Loewe was stubborn to the point of what many a scientist would call stupidity. It was illogical to try to cure such a highly penicillin-resistant microbe with penicillin. Then Loewe heard of a chemical, sodium para-amino hippurate. It was said to slow up the elimina-tion of penicillin by the kidneys, so that the anti-biotic, leaking out of the body more slowly, would accumulate in far higher levels in the blood. Dangerous, maybe, this blocking of the kidneys? Maybe. But the man was going to die anyway. With super-levels of penicil-lin, mightn't you overwhelm those ghastly gazogenes? Maybe.

In six weeks the man walked out of the hospital, feeling fine, the gazogenes microbes blitzed out of his blood and he has re-mained in excellent health now for more than four years.

XI

In December, 1944, Rhea and I were working with Leo Loewe and Jack Smith, getting ready to write how they had rescued many people of whom it could be said they had had both feet in the

grave. We were recording the obscure medical victory of this salvage of fifty or more forlorn during those somber days of mass
murder of scores of thousands in the Battle of the Bulge. Wasn't
science wonderful, and who would win, the curers or the killers?
So long as there were such bold, gentle, brainy, straight-shooting
men as Leo Loewe, Jack Smith, and Ralph Shaner, there was hope.
Leo the bold, Jack the gentle, and Ralph the sardonic Spanish
Hoosier, the three of them had this in common: for them human
life was sacred. They worked as if there was no bulge battle, they
did not mention it.

Just before I sat down to begin to write their hopeful story, a
letter arrived from a member of the faculty of the medical school
of a great university. The letter warned me about Leo Loewe.
Among other remarks that were querulous about Leo's work, the
writer stated that one of his colleagues considered Leo to be "at
least potentially dishonest." The letter was designed to stop me
from telling Leo's victory to the world. Was the letter writer speaking for others as well as himself? For certain members of the
National Research Council committee that had muffed the peni-
cillin-S.B.E. discovery? I don't know. Character assassins in the
highest scientific circles cover their tracks with admirable skill.
Here's what infuriated me, here's what this letter boiled down to:
it didn't really matter if millions of people (among whom were
thousands of future victims of S.B.E.) didn't know about this hope
for their lives.

That night I read this letter to Jack Smith and Leo Loewe. I'll
not forget Loewe's look as he heard himself described as potentially dishonest. His face was the color of ashes as he heard himself defamed for saving human life. Jack Smith's face set into hard
lines. Loewe reached into his brief case and produced a letter.
"This man's colleague calls me potentially dishonest?" asked Leo.
"Here's what that same colleague wrote me not long ago.

"Dear Dr. Loewe: No doubt I am only one among many who
have already congratulated you on what appears to be the first
really authentic report of chemotherapeutic success in subacute

bacterial endocarditis. I believe your work has marked another milestone in medical progress."

As this sank in, we all sat quiet. Then I began laughing and laughed and laughed. But *some*body was actually, not potentially, dishonest, and we'd smoked it out. Somebody was lying, and it wasn't our Leo. Had the sender of the letter put that smear on Leo into his colleague's mouth? Or did the colleague talk out of both sides of his mouth, defaming Leo to others and congratulating him directly?

"Here's the famous letter, Leo," I said. "Do anything you want with it."

"But aren't slanderous letters considered confidential by the slanderers who write them?" asked Jack Smith, mildly.

"Use the letter, Leo," I urged him, laughing.

"I'm hurt," said Leo.

"Nice guys, these scientific colleagues of yours, Leo," I teased him. Leo's eyes told me I shouldn't rib him. I laughed at what was going to happen to the sender of the letter and to his colleague and sat down and wrote an acknowledgment to the member of the faculty of the medical school of the great university, the fastest I ever wrote anything, without hesitation or a blot or a correction, about fifty words to the effect that his letter to me had been turned over promptly to Dr. Leo Loewe so that he might defend himself against its charges of potential dishonesty, et cetera, though in the opinion of the undersigned, Dr. Loewe was a great man who needed no defense.

This was and still remains the best moment of my writing life.

Leo looked at my little note, then at me, and I'll swear he didn't believe I'd send it. Uncle Jack (that was what we were all calling Jack Smith by now) looked at my note and laughed and looked at Leo.

"We're tough competitors in the chemical business," said Uncle Jack. "But my competitors are all fine fellows. Not back-stabbers. They're straight-shooters. Leo, what the hell's wrong with your doctors?"

Then all four of us had a last one, for the road—Rhea, Uncle

Jack and I drinking to Leo. Rhea special-delivery-stamped my little note, and the four of us, arms linked, went down to the lobby, dropping the note in the mail box with great ceremony. We said good-night, this time all laughing, and it was the best night of our writing life.

The special delivery note brought a telephonic apology to Leo the following afternoon. The letter of defamation had a wonderful effect on Leo. It infuriated him not at his defamers but at the green microbes of subacute bacterial endocarditis. In his first fifty-odd cases he had reversed the old ninety-seven per cent death rate to a cure rate of three out of every four; he kept zooming his doses of penicillin; and in his first one hundred and twenty-four cases his cure rate crept up to 82 per cent, four out of every five. With a new chemical, caronamide, he blocked his patient's kidneys against leaking out of penicillin and reached levels of penicillin, in their blood, seven times higher than any ever before known. On a series of the very rag-tag-and-bob-tail rearguard of thirty-three S.B.E. doomed who had been given up for dead at other treatment centers, Leo made ultimate miracles, giving them as high as 40,000,000 units of penicillin a day, giving some of them 4,000,000,-000 units continuously in epic eight weeks without stopping, raising their penicillin blood levels with caronamide till you'd swear their arteries held nothing but the golden magic and no more blood at all, badgering and belting the most virulent and evil of the green streptococcus sanguis into unconditional surrender. So that of those thirty-three people given up for gone, eighty-one per cent lived and were cured. In his total series, now nearing two hundred (of whom formerly ninety-seven out of a hundred would have died), better than four out of five lived and walked out the front door of the Brooklyn Jewish Hospital, cured. He was nearing a total reversal of this ages-old march of death. In the summer of 1948 I asked Leo Loewe if he could start a new series, from scratch, with all he knew now about super-massive penicillin dosage, caronamide, and heparin, what would be his cure rate?

"If I lost any case of subacute bacterial endocarditis now," Leo Loewe answered, "I'd be *distraught!*"

"You ought to come to one of our follow-up sessions, Paul, with all Leo's cured patients at the hospital," said Uncle Jack. "You'd see scores of living people who were dead. It's like a convention, the strangest convention in the world."

For those who had once tried to hinder this most brilliant reversal of the march of death, Uncle Jack held no rancor. "Why don't you sum it all up this way?" asked Uncle Jack, groping for just the right words, trying to be just and fair as he knows best how to be, of all the men I've ever known.

"We had a tough fight and a conviction it could be done, and with the National Research Council's committee's co-operation—when they were convinced—then, when evidence was presented that penicillin was effective in the treatment of subacute bacterial endocarditis, they acknowledged the fact and recognized its merit."

In this summary Uncle Jack was more than generous. The National Research Council committee did recommend daily doses of 500,000 units of penicillin. But on this dosage (as against Loewe's 40,000,000 units in the most desperate cases) there still were many treatment failures, and the cure rate is still not much over seventy out of every hundred. As if Leo Loewe must not be deemed too much of an innovator, there are those who say that heparin is not necessary, does no good, and may even be harmful.

Loewe is waiting for the evidence. "The moment any group," he says, "presents a series without heparin with a cure rate as good or better than ours, I'll stop using heparin."

Leo Loewe's boldness and Uncle Jack's generosity are bringing a pay-off far beyond the lives saved from S.B.E. Uncle Jack's men at Pfizer, by dreaming up production techniques that have spread through the pharmaceutical industry, are primarily responsible for turning loose an avalanche of penicillin so that it no longer has to be used stingily. Loewe's daring has fired physicians to new boldness and shrewd uses of penicillin on other death-fighting fronts. They have reversed staphylococcus blood poisoning from eighty-five per cent fatal to close to that per cent curable. They have devised new treatment dodges like penicillin aerosol to be inhaled to cure deadly lung abscesses incurable by penicillin injections.

When it could be used at last in bold and generous doses, so awe-some was penicillin's power over strepto-, pneumo-, staphylococcus and many another dirty germ that it is now listed as effective against eighty-nine and effective or helpful in sixteen other disease con-ditions. Yet penicillin is no cure-all; at least sixty-three maladies remain against which it is powerless. Here again the deep fermen-tation production techniques, born of Loewe's desperate demand for unlimited penicillin, are now being turned to the manufacture of other anti-biotics, streptomycin, chloromycetin, and aureomycin. It's fair now to hope for an anti-biotic against every microbe that ever killed a human being, to save millions of human beings who used to have to die. Used at their full strength these weapons will justify Pasteur who prophesied that it will be within man's power to wipe microbic maladies from the face of the earth.

We had been looking forward to one of our old-time roaring jam-sessions with the ace venereal disease man, just home from four years in the Caribbean. He'd knocked VD out of our armed forces in those lovely, be-pocked islands. The British high brass of the Caribbean wanted him to direct the public health program for those islands. Surely the U. S. Public Health Service would promote him and roll out the red carpet in his honor.

But our ace came in, subdued, telling us he had retired from the Public Health Service, quitting three years before normal retirement age. "You can't do that," said Bundesen. "What're you going to do?" "Going back to Hot Springs to catch up on my fishing," said the ace. His smile was bitter.

Here was the world's best VD field man saying good-bye to VD forever. It took us three years to pry out of him how a government can kick a faithful servant in the groin. This day he sketched a few of the highlights. Then he made us laugh, explaining he couldn't sing the Calypso songs Trinidadians had composed in his honor. They were too dirty.

Finally he hinted that, when he'd caught up on his fishing, he was going after arthritis, now neglected, just as he'd started after VD, neglected in 1912. He was going to begin life over. His optimism stirred us, though it was more than a little pathetic.

CHAPTER X

The Ace of Hearts

⋙ ⋘

IT made Leo Loewe and Jack Smith proud to have honorable mention in an anti-biotic story in *The Reader's Digest,* telling of millions who used to have to die but now could live. "But can they?" asked Uncle Jack who was quizzical, always the doubter, the needler, never complacent. "You say all may now live who could possibly be saved? Not by a damn sight," he said, with emotion.

We broke off the argument, celebrating the completion of my yarn about anti-biotics. Then, with ceremony, Jack invited us downtown to Sammy's on the Bowery. That is a saloon where a boisterous and pathetic troop of down-and-outers, male and female, ex-actors, prostitutes emeritus, dilapidated gamblers, almost-geniuses, all of them panhandlers, all lost ones of the lower five—put on a show that (very sadly) tries to revive the tenderloin life of the gay nineties. Here Uncle Jack lost his moroseness about medical failure to use penicillin to its full potential. Here at Sammy's, in an atmosphere reminiscent of "The Iceman Cometh," Uncle Jack was *intime,* as the French put it. Old bums crowded round us. They equipped us with low, lavender-colored derby hats; they adorned us with enormous mustaches, black and bushy. Jack's smile was now without its mirror image of melancholy. He introduced us very formally to Lucile and Mabel and the round little fat Professor with the sideburns and the silk tile hat. We bought everybody unlimited gins and bourbons. This evening they did not have to suffer the indignity of cadging for the alcohol to anesthetize them against the pain of failure that the lives of all of them had been. To this sad-gay company Uncle Jack was Santa Claus come true.

I watched this multi-millionaire prince of penicillin producers, wondering. The bums knew he felt they were brother and sister human beings, and that he was saying to himself, "But for the grace of God. . . ." We closed the joint at last, and taxied Leo home to Brooklyn. Then, as dawn copper-burnished the northeastern sky over Manhattan, Uncle Jack and I taxied through the Park and philosophized with a fourth-dimensional sentiment peculiar to the fag-end of such a night. Jack took it upon himself to advise me.

"Why don't you stop writing about the doctors?" he asked.

"But what do you want me to write about?"

"Here's what I'd like to see you do," said Jack. "Put on your old blue-checked shirt and blue denim slacks. Don't have a dime in your pocket. Go down and panhandle your living, on the Bowery. Get to know those people at Sammy's. Then write for us about them."

Uncle Jack regarded them as a least common denominator of what's in all of us, stripped as they were of the respectability, the pomp and circumstance in which we, because we've been lucky, pass our so-called successful lives.

"You mean you want me to try to make like Gorky?" I asked. "I'm no Gorky."

"Go on down and find out if they're human," he urged. "Find out if they have the right to penicillin."

There was a kind of socialism close under his rigid exacting exterior of the business tycoon. Or maybe it was plain good Samaritan, since Jack was devoid of Marxian ideology.

"How're you going to get penicillin to everybody?" I asked.

"By making so much of it that it'll be cheap like pepper and salt."

"How?" I asked.

"By turning on full production," he answered.

"What's stopping you?" I asked.

"Government rules and regulations governing its distribution. It's only sold on doctor's prescription."

"Does that make it more expensive?"

"By prescription it costs five bucks for a shot of 100,000 units," said Jack.

"But what does the penicillin itself cost?" I asked.

"We sell 100,000 units in bulk for 10¢," said Uncle Jack.

I remembered a letter from a man who'd had to stop treatment for subacute bacterial endocarditis because he'd run out of penicillin money. From another man who'd been cured—by *eight thousand dollars'* worth of penicillin.

"We could make it cheap as pepper and salt if—" And then Uncle Jack slumped down, tired and looking way past his age.

He came back to the attack. His quiet talk took on a bitter, a savage bite. Did we need prescriptions for aspirin? Whose life does aspirin save? Isn't penicillin as harmless as aspirin? Isn't it the greatest life-saver in history? If it got to be as dirt cheap as he, Jack, knew how to make it, people could swallow it in tablets, plenty, to build up high blood levels. Then couldn't they abort their own bronchitis, pneumonia? And what about VD? If a man wanted to step out, romantically, why shouldn't he first swallow a few cents' worth of penicillin? No syphilis. No gonorrhea. You could *wipe out* syphilis and gonorrhea. Uncle Jack saw visions. If folks had plenty of penicillin in their medicine closets, what couldn't they do to wipe out the secondary infections after colds, those colds, hanging on, that cost more than a billion dollars in lost wages, every year. And look at all the trouble Leo had to go to to cure subacute bacterial endocarditis. What about preventing streptococcus sore throats, by daily tablets of penicillin, for hundreds of thousands known susceptible to attacks of rheumatic fever, and candidates for S.B.E.?

Penicillin by prescription for this purpose would come to four dollars a day—ridiculous.

Uncle Jack had a little hope. "The Federal Food and Drug Administration people are uncertain as to which course to follow—as to whether or not they should limit penicillin to sale by prescription," said Jack.

"What would it take to make penicillin cheap like pepper and salt?" I asked.

"Doubling all present production. That'd take about $20,000,-000."

"And a knock-down battle with the doctors," I said.

"You mean certain doctors," said Uncle Jack, laughing.

He looked at me deep out of his tired gray eyes. Now we were back in front of the Hotel Gotham, our New York home; it was broad daylight and garbage cans were slamming and banging. I was tired, let down, and wondering whether I'd ever be not tired enough to dare to tell people what Uncle Jack could do for them. A lot of good doctors would be on his side. A lot of good doctors still wouldn't appreciate penicillin's weird combination of deadliness to microbes and gentleness to men and they'd fight its general distribution. A small vanguard of doctors (who actually welcome co-working with "the laity" as fuddy-duddy doctors call us ordinary people) would actually help promote Jack's campaign. If only Jack had a pioneering doctor like O. C. Wenger to organize putting penicillin in the hands of young people to prevent syphilis and gonorrhea.

Wenger has co-worked with parsons, pimps, professors, prostitutes, with all who hate disease most intensely because they themselves are suffering. Wenger is a realist. He'll use fair means and foul to beat down human misery. His weakness is that his spectacular and often buffoonish epidemiologic stunts affront government bureaucrats so they won't back him. That was his downfall finally and now he was no longer available in the VD fight.

How he and Uncle Jack would have hit it off, both of them so raw-nerved to human pain and both so un-Pecksniffish!

11

In 1936 and 1937, Rhea and I had worked with Wenger closely and I had written about him in *The Fight for Life*. At the end of the chapter on "Wenger against syphilis," I had all but buried him. In September, 1937, he'd got orders from the U. S. Public Health Service, telling him that his venereal disease control work—then at its peak—was over in Chicago. The ostensible reason for the orders was that the obliterative arterial disease of his feet (I never saw a man who could walk farther or faster despite obvious pain) would be intensified by Chicago's climate. I suspect the deeper reason for his transfer to the south was that his VD methods and publicity were a bit too rough, that they would sully the dignity of the Public Health Service when splashed all over a big city like Chicago. (Though what city is as rough as Chicago?) Bundesen and I were bitter about Wenger's leaving. But, alas, Wenger had a crudity frequent in pioneers; and officers of the Public Health Service should be gentlemen.

Wenger had a coronary attack the day he got orders to go. I can see him now, slumped in a chair. His ruddiness was gone. "What the hell," he growled, "why don't they let me bump off with my boots on?" His face was gray. It was the first time in history that any large city had been subjected to a syphilis blood test dragnet of hundreds of thousands of its citizens. A giant blood-testing seine was sweeping through the community. It turned up tens of thousands of cases of the sinister sickness still unknown. It got tens of thousands under treatment that might prevent many thousands from going mad, or dying of heart disease, or passing the curse to their children.

At the height of all this, Wenger was shipped down the river.

I thought he would surely die, but this burial was premature. In 1948, the night I told Uncle Jack about him, Wenger was in Hot Springs, Arkansas, getting ready to tackle arthritis. Just as he had started against syphilis in the same city twenty years before, now again he had no money, not even the official backing of the U. S. Public Health Service; American arthritis big shots were laughing at him, he had only a prayer, only his silly optimism, his insight into human sorrow, his magnanimity.

Why hadn't his coronary attacks killed him? "Oh, I keep having twinges. To hell with 'em. Let's get after arthritis."

But much water had gone over the dam for him between his leaving Chicago in 1937 and his new arthritis fight in 1948. What was it that made Wenger tick, kept him alive, kept him fighting?

III

How can you fight any plague if you don't know where it is, if you don't know how many have it and don't have them tagged and don't know where they are? That's what his blood test dragnets had accomplished before Chicago, among the Negroes in the south, showing them infected as high as thirty in every one hundred, shocking the whole nation, shocking Congress into giving the Public Health Service a real VD division, giving the country its great VD fighter—Dr. Thomas Parran. Behind all this was one man, O. C. Wenger; and now on a shoestring he was going to try to start a dragnet to uncover the far greater misery of arthritis, past sixty, one whole life behind him, starting all over.

From his days as a cub doctor he had been unrespectable, radical, and drastic. He was a bad organization man. He was purely a guerilla fighter. He had felt he had the answer to the way to wipe out venereal disease as long ago as 1912. Wenger was then a tough young medical officer in the Philippines constabulary, disgusted to find his command rotten with syphilis.

Treatment in those days (salvarsan was not then in general use) was feeble and largely ineffective. "And I wasn't a YMCA boy or a boy scout," said Wenger. "I knew I couldn't prevent syphilis by telling those goo-goos to be good and not fornicate."

A constabulary troop would come into a Leyte village in the evening; after chow the men would scatter; the tropic night would come alive with amorous sighs and giggles from huts and bushes. "I set a deadline for their reporting back," said Wenger, "lined 'em up, gave every one of 'em the works, argyrol and calomel ointment, whether they needed it or not, and I was sure they all needed it."

His experiment was a stunning though obscure success. Syphilis vanished from constabulary commands. He repeated this victory on a big scale in the U. S. Army in France in 1917-18. "We didn't get our low VD rate by shutting down the French houses," said Wenger, "nor by getting the doughboys to associate only with nice girls—who weren't all of them so nice, either." No, they simply socked the soldiers with calomel ointment and argyrol.

Then Wenger joined the U. S. Public Health Service and became its one-man VD division. His enthusiastic plan to use his experience to generalize prophylaxis, to spread knowledge of prevention among playboys and flappers of the sinful 1920's—that got the official cold shoulder. The VD policy of the Public Health Service was dominated by a curious activity, not science, not medicine, you cannot call it religious—it is a form of do-gooding parading under the name of social hygiene. To his disgust Wenger found himself detailed to try to suppress prostitution. "You don't suppress whores, you just drive them under cover." He was supposed to conduct lectures on the perils of lechery. "All the social hygiene lectures ever given haven't kept a handful of men from exposing themselves," said Wenger.

Wenger believed that this was a free country where sexual conduct was every man's and woman's private business. Wenger was a seamy-sided yet strangely clean man who had known the seamy side of life from his hobo days onward. Imagine him telling young people that ping-pong and square dances are as much fun and safer than what goes on in roadsters and the bushes at night! Now Wenger forgot his social hygiene. He set himself up as a VD clinic in Hot Springs, Arkansas, the thermal waters of which were supposed to have magic against the sickness of the sinister name. He had no equipment, no money, no nothing. He began by bumming a syringe, some salvarsan and mercury off kind-hearted old Doc Deaderick. He treated an infected derelict he found hanging round the Government Free Bath House. He also treated an infected forlorn woman. These two people married and became his aides in what gradually grew to be the model VD clinic of the U. S. A.— treating six thousand victims yearly.

"Those first two patients are still as happily married a couple as I've ever known," said Wenger. So began his great art of rehabilitation, effective because he did not mix syphilis up with sin.

In that great Hot Springs clinic that he built in the Govern-

ment Free Bath House it was hard to tell Wenger from his patients
—except that he was more raffish-talking and a more picturesque
cusser than any bum or public woman among his thousands of
sick and dilapidated charges. "What the hell was I going to do?"
he asked. "Respectable doctors weren't interested in syphilis—
especially among poor people."

He had eyes that seemed sometimes gray, sometimes china blue,
and stubbly crew-cut hair and the build and temperament of prize-
fighter Ace Hudkins, the Nebraska Wildcat, with Hudkins's sub-
lime don't-give-a-damness and Hudkins's willingness to take six
punches in order to give just one. As Hemingway puts it, venereal
sickness is the occupational disease of those who live regardless of
consequences and of all men Wenger understood this best because
that was exactly the way he had always lived. "I never had syphilis,"
he'd tell his patients, "but only because I've been lucky."

Like Ace Hudkins, too, Wenger never knew when he was licked,
and he was licked time and again, because he was so sanguine and
would try every imaginable VD-fighting treatment, good or bad.
His patients and everybody who met him loved him—except Public
Health Service bureaucrats whom he annoyed with his crazy
schemes and impolite proposals. "Syphilis a sickness of the underworld?" he would snort. "You'd be surprised where I find it." He
was a shameless panhandler for money, not for himself but for his
army of the alleged sinful. Lacking federal funds, he begged hundreds of thousands of doses of expensive salvarsan from old Colonel
Metz, the head of a great pharmaceutical company.

By no means all of his patients were hobos and to save time for
them, to rehabilitate them rapidly, to get them back to work
quickly, he telescoped the standard treatment of eighteen months
or more into three months—saturating his patients with enormous
doses of salvarsan, mercury, and bismuth. He got away with this
because he treated the victims not like outcasts but as valuable
human beings. To bums and down-and-out women who came sick
and starved (attracted by a nationwide underworld grapevine about
this Doc Wenger) he fed hearty meals cooked by Mrs. Wenger in
her own kitchen. God knows where he found the money. In the

cold of the winters of the deep depression, many of his patients had no shelter, and he talked the government into building Camp Garraday, lovely amid the pines outside Hot Springs, where they could boondoggle in return for good housing and three square meals a day. Here into thousands of them he fed the strength for them to stand his ferocious, intensive VD treatment. "God, Doc Wenger's got a heart," his patients told each other.

"The poor devils, what else could we do?" asked Wenger.

That clinic had a gay atmosphere. Here we saw more than three hundred women, young and middle-aged, shuffling in a strange production line, Wenger like a German *feldwebel*, hustling them along, herding them ahead, urging them to make it snappy as one after another lifted her skirt to get the lightning quick jab of bismuth into her behind, in this process hardly stopping walking. "It won't hurt much, honey," Wenger would re-assure a scared newcomer. "Step along now, sugar," he'd urge another.

"Doc is sure a regular guy," the patients said. He partook of their disreputability. On his left upper arm he sported a macabre tattoo—skull-and-crossbones. How had he come by it? In the Orient, trying to get a couple of drunken officers back to their ship before it sailed for home. "Found 'em in a water-front cat-house getting those tattoos and they wouldn't come along till I had one too," explained Wenger. His candor leant charm to his vulgarity. "Every time I look at that damn tattoo it reminds me I've been a damn fool, I'm human," he explained.

Wenger was impatient at the lack of progress in venereal disease eradication. In his years at Hot Springs he had done more of that than any doctor in America. But treatment should be the duty of all doctors. Yet, if they didn't look for this so largely hidden sickness, how could they treat it? And medical practitioners weren't looking for it because it is not for doctors to look for any sickness; the sickness must come to them. Wenger's blood test dragnet had found scores of thousands of cases of the hidden sickness as he had among southern Negroes and all over Chicago. Getting at early cases and scotching their infectiousness would break the contagious chain. But Wenger said that was only pouring water on thousands of individual little fires. It was piecemeal; it was too slow. Why not give everybody their own fire extinguisher and teach them to use it? Why not *prevent* syphilis?

"Look," Wenger said, "I knew how easy it was to prevent it in 1912. But here's the Public Health Service, cold about it in 1937."

In his last days in Chicago, Wenger went off the reservation. In the fight to wipe out other infectious diseases he had powerful precedent for urging prevention. Smallpox had been brought to the brink of eradication by mass vaccination of whole populations; ditto diphtheria, by mass toxoid inoculations. Hadn't typhoid fever been reduced to next to nothing by mass sanitation of water and milk? Not by finding cases and treating them, but by blocking the entry of typhoid microbes into the human mass. In short, you prevent communicable disease in two ways: you vaccinate to make the population proof against the microbe; or you hit the germ before it attacks its human prey. By any known science you cannot immunize human beings against syphilis and gonorrhea. Yet both these plagues have an Achilles heel, because you know precisely the route by which their microbes sneak from sick to healthy. Both are transmitted by sexual contact. And this chain can be broken.

This became O. C. Wenger's obsession. He'd helped break it among soldiers under army discipline. It was another matter to spread prophylaxis among the civilian male population. Men simply wouldn't go for prevention that was so technically ponderous and unpleasant. So, each year, America suffered hundreds of thousands of new cases of syphilis and millions of cases of gonorrhea.

Toward the end of his Chicago duty, Wenger heard of what sounded like a wonderful new chemical prophylactic. Women would love it. Not only murderous, supposedly, to microbes of syphilis and gonorrhea, it was said to be death to spermatozoa. In short, it was a contraceptive. In short, it was the simplest kind of birth control. Wenger was agog. Women who did not want babies (and what promiscuous, VD-carrying woman did?) would go for this progonasyl as its inventor, kitchen chemist Frank Bickenheuser of Tulsa, Oklahoma, called it. The preventive was a colloid mixture of triethanolamine, mineral oil, oleic acid, vegetable oil, and organic iodine. Wenger called it "wildcat jelly" for short. Squeezed by the woman herself out of a little tube into her genital opening just before sexual contact, this remarkable jelly spread rapidly and completely over the internal mucous membranes of the genital passage. Here it was supposed to ensnare spirochetes, gonococci, and sperm. Its effect lasted many hours. In Chicago, Wenger began a wildcat jelly prevention experiment with his inimitable whoop-de-doo.

Shortly thereafter, he was ordered from Chicago.

IV

Obscurely he started all over, going back to what he had proved to the hilt in the 1920's. He began a blood test dragnet for syphilis and a treatment program among the heavily infected black inhabitants of Glynn County and its adjacent counties in southwestern Georgia. From Chicago VD control this was a terrible demotion, yet it did not kill his enthusiasm. Here among the live oaks with their lovely decadent streamers of Spanish moss and among the pitiful Negro huts, churches, and jungle dance-halls, Wenger began testing a new VD-fighting toy, a beautiful mobile VD clinic compactly housed in a big trailer. It was his new bad-blood wagon. Midwinter in January, 1938, Rhea and I went down to see our ace VD man, and we will always be nostalgic for those warm Glynn County days and for those mysterious and hilarious nights.

On a Sunday evening under an enormous live oak in Darien, Georgia, Wenger's bad-blood wagon is parked before a beautiful old Negro church. Wenger is shouting, like a circus barker: "Free pink lemonade and hot dogs for all who'll take a blood test!" The congregation, fathers and mothers and their children, young and adolescent, swains and dusky damsels, fascinated by this funny government doctor, pass into the trailer, shed their blood for the Kahn test, then pass out for their reward. Now comes the Negro parson (some buck, Wenger said in awe), an enormous man in a handsome overcoat though the night was balmy. According to Wenger, he deserved special consideration.

"Ask the Reverend if he'd relish a slug of your White Horse Scotch, Windy," Wenger whispered to Dr. M. E. Winchester, Glynn County's superbly able health commissioner. The Negro minister tosses down an eight-ounce cup of straight Scotch without blinking an eye and disappears into the church to edify his flock.

"The sermon will be really something," says Wenger, half closing his eyes, throwing back his head and laughing.

Then we all set out for a jungle Negro juke-box dance hall, somewhat sinister and many miles away. Here Dr. Wenger becomes a demoniac master of ceremonies, soliciting nickels from us to keep the juke box blaring its aphrodisiac music, clapping his hands, stamping his feet, urging the dancers on as they become more wild and wanton. In a back room the blood of all of them is skillfully drawn by Negro Public Health Nurse Beatrice Johnson, whose assistant records their addresses and names. Between dances couples vanish into the sub-tropic night. It might seem that Wenger was only engendering more venereal disease with his whooping up of the hot music. What he did was to gain the confidence and devotion of the dusky celebrants. They understood that he did not disapprove of their revelry; what other outlet did our Jim Crow civilization give them? They knew Wenger was out to guard them from the venereal consequences of their poverty-stricken bacchanalia.

In Glynn County that year Wenger and Winchester drove the syphilis rate downward toward an all-time low.

At the Cloisters, on Sea Island, Wenger gave me an assignment. It was unorthodox and dangerous. For a new magazine, *Ken,* first issue, I must write the inside story of the new prophylactic, pro-gonasyl, Wenger's wildcat jelly. Title: *Enlisting Women Against Shame.* We should try to break the story during the Senate hearings which, it was hoped, were going to bring millions of dollars of VD-fighting money to the U. S. Public Health Service.

I protested. The service did not (at least officially) encourage venereal prophylaxis. It encouraged discovery of early cases of syphilis and their treatment, in order to break the chain of VD contagion. Would Dr. Parran approve of such a story? No. "You can't mention me," said Wenger. "You'll have to take the rap your-self, Paul."

I pondered, then remembered Surgeon General Thomas Parran's admonition to me in 1936 when he asked me to help him publicize his VD fight. "Go to Chicago, get hold of O. C. Wenger," Parran had said. "Attach yourself to Wenger, and hang on. Do everything he tells you to. Wenger taught me almost everything I know about VD," said Parran. "He's done more than anybody to bring us to where we are now."

Wenger's devotion to the VD fight, his utter lack of ambition to be a Public Health Service VD bureaucrat, his disdain for bureaucratic power, his sympathy for all VD afflicted, his immense knowledge gained not alone from books but in "the field" (in dens of iniquity, by association with low characters, from organization of the world's model VD-treatment clinic), his personal poverty and asceticism, his forgiving every kind of sinful folly in other people, his hatred of venereal misery and his understanding the animal instinct that caused that suffering—these traits of O. C. Wenger demanded that I do his bidding.

"But where's the published scientific evidence of the effectiveness of your wildcat jelly?" I asked him.

It wasn't published yet, he said. But he showed us a microphoto-graphic movie film of the action of the wildcat jelly on spermatozoa. They were immediately made motionless; it was as if they were strangled when this mysterious jelly touched them. This wildcat jelly was harmless to the delicate membranes of the genital passage of women, Wenger assured us.

"If we can only get the women to use it," Wenger said, excited, "all women who don't want babies, the men will get their venereal prophylaxis at the same time, whether they want it or not."

"But where's the proof that it works, not under the microscope but—"

Wenger interrupted me. He recounted a curious human experi-ment that had been made by two physicians in Tulsa, Oklahoma.

Four women, volunteers, were examined clinically and by labora-tory tests and found to be free of gonorrhea. The women were then kept in two locked rooms under constant observation by one or another of the investigators. Two men were brought to them. Both were suffering from acute gonorrhea. The wildcat jelly was injected into the genital passages of the women. They then mated, successively, with the infected men. Unprotected by the jelly, the chances were overwhelming that the women would catch the contagion. For ten days thereafter the women were kept under day and night observation to take care that they used no other method (than that of the previously injected wildcat jelly) to guard themselves. All four remained free from gonorrhea.*

The story of this sinful (from the social hygiene viewpoint) experiment, published in *Ken,* caused "excitement and indignation," according to the newspapers, among health experts gathered in Washington for Congressional hearings on syphilis control.

This excitement and indignation was precisely what Wenger wanted. "Doesn't Herman Bundesen tell us that to irritate is to stimulate?" asked Wenger.

The officials of the Public Health Service were irritated, no question. "I do not approve of using human beings, instead of animals, for such tests," declared a Public Health Service brass-hat (though passage of venereal disease from animal to animal by sexual intercourse is unknown and experimentally not feasible).

"I doubt if it is as perfect as the testers hope," he continued. "Even if it were, it would not solve the venereal problem. Prophylaxis has not proved to be the answer among the civilian population."

This new type of prophylaxis had never been tried among the civilian population.

The General Manager of the American Social Hygiene Association declared himself to be "surprised and disturbed" over the matter. The General Manager scored a direct hit against me, properly insisting that publicity regarding any such medical meas-

---

* Subsequent parallel control experiments proved that women similarly exposed but without the wildcat jelly's protection, came down with gonorrhea. All these experiments were published by Drs. H. H. Porter, Robert B. Witcher and Mr. Cecil Knoblock in the *Journal of the Oklahoma State Medical Association,* February, 1939.

ure be preceded by frank and full reporting to competent medical associations. (Alas, such reporting came a year later.)

What really alarmed the health officials and social hygienists was that the wildcat jelly would prevent both venereal disease and unwanted babies. This was most embarrassing, since this was sure (according to the health officials and social hygienists) to cause dispute, and protest from Catholics. What dismayed me was Dr. Parran's perturbation. I was the last to want him to lose his VD money which had seemed to be in the bag. By telephone Tom Parran scolded me, and the gentleness of his indignation only made it bite the deeper. It all proved to be a ripple in a tea-pot. The Public Health Service got its multi-million-dollar VD-fighting funds with no fuss whatever about Wenger's wildcat jelly.

"But didn't Tom Parran tell me to follow your directives," I asked Wenger, *"completely?"* Wenger threw back his head, half closed his eyes and roared with laughter. "He didn't mean so damn completely, Paul," said Wenger.

Wenger had got what he wanted: prophylaxis, smoked out into the open. Yet this so far is one of our many failures. Public Health Service scientists tested the killing power of the wildcat jelly (not in human sexual contact experiments) but against syphilis spirochetes, in the laboratory. Not publishing their results, they reported, confidentially, that it was no good. Frank Bickenheuser, the jelly's inventor, in a VD clinic approved by the City of San Antonio, Texas, armed some hundreds of women with tubes of wildcat jelly. He left a parallel number without the new preventive. All plied their trade, and the two groups were observed clinically and by laboratory examination, for months. It seemed as if the prophylactic bore out the promise of the famous experiment in Tulsa, the jelly giving remarkable protection while the unguarded women came down with syphilis and gonorrhea at expected rates of infection.

Then a social hygiene official arrived on the scene. Bickenheuser's clinic was not only condoning but encouraging prostitution. The naughty ladies and their workshops were suppressed by San Antonio authorities. The wicked women scattered, went underground, no longer reported to Bickenheuser, and his experiment was ruined. So ended Wenger's adventure with the wildcat jelly; and our ace was definitely in the dog-house with his Public Health Service.

Maybe some day some bold health commissioner, brave like Herman Bundesen, will revive Bickenheuser's and Wenger's experiment with progonasyl, which is still manufactured and sold for other therapeutic purposes.

At the beginning of the 1940's Wenger, accompanied as he had been for years by his dynamic, devoted wisp of a woman assistant, Miss Charlotte Reamey (famous as "Miss Charlotte" to all VD-fighters) cruised from one military camp to another along our southwestern border. His assignment was venereal disease epidemiology. He was supposed to track down the bad women who were heavily infecting our newly mobilized army.

"Here's what you bump into when you try that," he said of his frustration at Fort Huachuca in Arizona, where he encountered a regiment with what was probably the highest VD rate in the U. S. Army. "On every leave, the GI's waltz across the border into Old Mexico, where the prostitutes are practically one hundred per cent infected." Wenger quizzed the boys as to exactly where they got their infection.

"I don't know," they would answer.

"Was it on the line?"

"I think so."

"Do you know the girl's name?"

"No."

"What did you call her?"

"Toots."

"Do you know where she lives?"

"No. It was dark. The street didn't have house numbers."

"What did the girl look like?"

"She had black hair and dark eyes and smoked cigarettes."

After a baffling conduct of hundreds of such inquiries, Wenger rendered an official report on his failure at finding sources of VD infection, to the VD Division of the Public Health Service in Washington. For a long time Wenger had received only the most formal

acknowledgment of his reports and wondered if anybody so much
as glanced at them. Now he tried tactics uniquely Wengerian. In
epidemiologic terms—deadpan—he recommended that our country
enter diplomatically into a convention with the Mexican government. All public women round our military installations to be
tattooed with a number and this to be done with illuminated paint
so that the men could read the number in the dark and be ordered
to memorize it. In Washington at the VD Division there was up-
roar. The news of Wenger's plan spread like wildfire among state
and U. S. Army VD Control men, who greeted Wenger and Miss
Charlotte with hilarious approval.

"After that," said Wenger, "the whole Bureau waited for our reports like political candidates for election returns. They read 'em
from cover to cover—not only the high brass but the stenographers
and the file clerks."

v

The highest complacence, the most holier-than-thou social hygiene do-gooders, could not keep Wenger down; he was so gay, so
cleanly obscene, so honest. Also he was indispensable.

In 1941, with Miss Charlotte, he was ordered to Puerto Rico as
adviser in VD control. In this lovely, poverty-stricken jewel of the
Caribbean, VD was heavy among the twenty-odd thousand prostitutes of the sad island. Here prostitution was not only sanctioned
by custom, it was legal. Why not? In what other way, especially
since American wage laws had ruined the needlework industry,
could these poor women earn their livings? How otherwise (Wenger
was raw-nerved to social injustice) could they support their children, or little brothers and sisters, or fathers and mothers? At the
air bases of the Caribbean Defense Command syphilis and gonorrhea flared among the ground crews so that pilots (worried about
the sickness of their mechanics) became low in morale. Wenger
understood that his orders implied he was to take all measures to
put down venereal menace.

His attack was original and totally terrific. The VD-fighting ace
assembled prostitutes by thousands. It was no trouble to find them,

their profession was respectable. He lectured them, not at all on changing their morals but pointed to their duty to protect American soldiers and sailors. He registered them. Not by his hilariously proposed tattoo but by discs, cards, photographs—so that they could be spotted and kept under observation as possible sources of venereal infection. He began putting them under continuous anti-syphilitic treatment, one shot a week, whether they needed it or not—and this was unheard of, bold, uniquely Wengerian, and a bit dangerous. "What are a few reactions, or even a death or two—balanced against the death and insanity they are spreading?" asked Wenger.

His nurses taught the at first reluctant daughters of joy the mystery of borax douches and the machinery of venereal prophylaxis, male as well as female. Wenger equipped some two thousand prostitutes with handsome tapestry bags (ordinarily used for carrying knitting) each containing a bulb syringe, a pound of borax for antiseptic solution, condoms of assorted sizes; calomel ointment and argyrol which they were to insist all of their temporary sweethearts must use, post-romance.

"We turned those dames into walking prophylactic stations," said Wenger, beaming.

In the streets of San Juan you might see Wenger, arm in arm with one of the leading madames, going toward one of his lectures at the treatment clinic; as Wenger and the madame marched they accumulated a growing regiment of prostitutes, all respectful, each equipped with her tapestry bag that was the prettiest of her accessories, all imbued with patriotic pride stoked up by Wenger's fiery but completely amoral admonitions. The tapestry bags had before this been employed by ladies of spotless reputation. Wenger was sorry when now the impeccable lady secretary of the insular health officer carried one, only to be asked: "How is business?"

Wenger and Miss Charlotte organized every conceivable kind of blockade against the attack of the spirochete and gonococcus. Not only were the Puerto Rican girls under constant, powerful anti-syphilitic treatment, not only did their madames see to it that they performed their rite of personal prophylaxis, but in the "hotel" rooms used for their assignations Wenger turned the medicine cabinets over the wash stands into prophylactic cases. The girl could not collect her fee from the madame till she had douched herself, and her temporary boy friend had taken his prophylactic in her presence and, usually, that of the madame.

"This," said Wenger proudly, "is the nut of the whole preventive idea." He displayed the gleaming apparatus. "Look," said our ace VD fighter, "the man rolls off the woman, his feet hit the floor, and he's facing the open prophylactic unit. A *minu*te between exposure and prophylaxis may make a tremendous difference in the venereal disease rate!"

In this Wenger was scientifically sound, for the great German microbe hunter, Wilhelm Kolle, had proved that the evil spirochete of syphilis may drill its way through and under mucous membranes and into the blood and lymph of a new human victim within minutes after contact with syphilitic infection.

Then, to make doubly sure, the soldiers were subjected to a second prophylactic treatment on their return to barracks. The results were fantastic. The venereal disease rates in the various commands dropped almost vertically. The U. S. Army medical and line officers were delighted. At Losey Field—a venereal plague spot—new cases of syphilis and gonorrhea dropped toward zero and now for two months not a single new infection was reported. So it was in Puerto Rico.

In Washington, among the high brass of the Federal Security Agency, the results were astounding too, but there were no huzzas for poor old O. C. Wenger. There was a roar of indignation. Medical officers of the Army and Navy in a meeting of the Interdepartmental Committee shouted that *treating* women—when Wenger didn't even know they were infected—was malpractice! (They couldn't deny it was an excellent way to keep possibly infected women from endangering our men.) Civilian, social-hygienically inclined heads of the Office of Health Defense and Welfare Services shuddered. They blushed. This Colonel Wenger was encouraging promiscuity and prostitution. Officers of the Public Health Service—his own beloved service—denounced Wenger's methods as "unfortunate and inefficient."

While the Caribbean military high command beamed at their men's new freedom from venereal disease, in Washington social hygienists went after the scalp of O. C. Wenger. "Any system other than one of rigid repression of prostitution," so came a cold reprimand from his Bureau to Wenger, "is absolutely contrary to the policy of the Public Health Service."

At high tide of his VD victory, Wenger was recalled from Puerto Rico. "The trouble was I hadn't asked them how to control VD; I just did it," said Wenger, laughing.

Inside him he wasn't laughing. He was lonely. He was a guerilla fighter, a simple partisan against sickness and suffering. He thought nothing of promotion which was just as well, because he wouldn't get it despite his victory. He wanted no power. He knew that it was not by remote control from the center of the power that you really fought venereal disease.

In Washington bureaus Colonel Wenger's name was a by-word. All over the Caribbean—among generals and admirals worried over VD sapping their commands and complements—Colonel Wenger's Puerto Rican fame was spreading. On the Isthmus of Panama now invaded by thousands of lusty, husky young American anti-aircraft crews, airforce men and sailors, VD rates were soaring alarmingly. Paging Colonel Wenger! Dr. Joseph Earl Moore, immensely famous syphilographer, inspected Panama. He recommended to the Public Health Service—specifically—that Colonel O. C. Wenger be sent to clean up the deplorable VD situation. Where was Colonel Wenger? In the dog-house. Hard-bitten and able General M. C. Stayer, Health Officer of the Canal Zone, asked immediate help. Paging Colonel Wenger. Send us this fellow, Wenger.

In Washington, frightfully embarrassed though they were about Wenger, they had no trouble-shooter to compare with him. So Wenger—as always with little Miss Charlotte, his alter ego—reported to General Stayer in Panama. "Let's clean it up," said General Stayer, who was a practical and hardly a social-hygienic man. The VD rates among American Army, Navy, and Airforce personnel in some commands were touching 265 per thousand men per annum. It was an appalling situation.

In Panama, Colonel Wenger went to see El Presidente of the Panamanian Republic. "Just what do you intend to do here?" asked El Presidente. "I intend to protect not only American soldiers but your people from venereal disease," said Wenger, amiably.

El Presidente directed Colonel Wenger to go to the city square, to read what, on a great bronze plaque, had been promised to the Republic of Panama by the late President Theodore Roosevelt: WE, THE PEOPLE OF THE UNITED STATES, WILL DO NOTHING TO INTERFERE WITH THE INTERNAL AFFAIRS OF THE REPUBLIC OF PANAMA.

The Panamanian Minister of Education came to Wenger, proposing that all houses of prostitution—excepting those in which he and his friends were financially interested!—be placed out of bounds for men of our armed forces. Wenger pointed to Theodore Roosevelt's promise on the plaque in the public square.

One of the principal industries of the Republic of Panama was now prostitution. With the arrival of our young American heroes, flush with money and full of beans, professional romance had now expanded to a five-million-dollar yearly business. Wenger wrote his prostitution-suppressing superiors in Washington, quoting Theodore Roosevelt's sacred promise engraved in the public square. "I can't tell Panamanians to close their whore-houses," wrote Wenger. "You'll have to tell Congress to tell Panama to put those houses out of bounds for the men of our armed forces."

While he needled his Bureau that way, with General Stayer, Wenger whirled into direct attack on the root of the evil, à la Puerto Rico. Public Health Service brass had declared that proprietors of night spots could never be depended upon to co-operate with VD control forces. To rebut them, Wenger told how he was invited to one of Panama's swankier brothels. "The young madame was beautiful," he said. "When I came for the inspection she all but threw her arms around my neck." She showed him proudly over every corner of her establishment. "I've done everything you've recommended, Colonel," she told him. "Look at our plumbing (proudly). There's not a case of VD among our girls. And they're under treatment practically all the time!"

Not only in venereal but in social and economic fields, Wenger was a bit of a Sherlock Holmes. With Miss Charlotte he became an authority on Panama's graft-ridden, vice-riddled history. He discovered that in Colon the legal red-light district was located on property owned by the Panama Railroad Company. The Panama Railroad was owned by the U. S. Government. Its president *ex officio* was a U. S. Army General who was also Governor of the Panama Canal Zone. It was therefore under the authority of the Secretary of War. The Secretary of War had been persuaded by social hygiene groups to repress prostitution wherever it might endanger our armed forces. The Government was in the position of receiving income from the railroad which rented its property to the houses of prostitution! Mr. Franklin D. Roosevelt now desired the return of this property to Panama in exchange for land for air bases and army posts.

Colonel Wenger was happy. He himself was all for repressing prostitution, if feasible. Here was a golden opportunity. Colonel Wenger wrote, detailing this embarrassing situation, to the Public Health Service. "Now if the Service can see its way clear," wrote Wenger, "to present the facts to the Secretary of War in person and of course in confidence . . . and have a clause inserted in the transfer of this property (back to Panama) *prohibiting its use for immoral purposes,* we would be doing something progressive."

Wenger chuckled. Would they dare tell the Secretary of War?

Wenger, General Stayer, and Miss Charlotte made allies out of Panama's wicked ladies and its forces of evil. On the re-check of rates, conducted a year after they'd begun their battle, the VD rates in our armed forces in the region of the Canal Zone had tumbled to 14 per 1,000 per annum. This was far under the rates in the continental United States where prostitution was suppressed around military installations.

In Panama there was no suppression of prostitution. Just venereal prophylaxis.

Why were the social hygienists who dominated our national VD fight so irritated by Wenger? The answer is simple. The social hygienists believed that the prohibition of illicit sexual intercourse would do away with venereal disease. Precisely, says Wenger, as the prohibition of motor-cars would do away with automobile accidents. Wenger, on the other hand, had some fundamental knowledge of human nature. Years before the Kinsey report solemnly disclosed that fornication is nearly universal among American males, Wenger realized this. On this rudimentary knowledge he took direct action.

VI

Where is Colonel Wenger? Paging O. C. Wenger. President Roosevelt has stopped at Trinidad, returning from the conference at Casablanca. The President tells the brass of the Caribbean Defense Command that there's so much venereal disease in the British 8th Army in Africa that the medicos aren't even trying to control it. The President hopes the same is not true of our American forces in Trinidad. Alas, in Trinidad the VD rate among our forces is touching 300 per 1,000 men per annum. The President is horrified. He passes The Word through the Secretary of War via the Federal Security Agency to the Public Health Service. No time to suppress prostitution and so stop our boys' romancing. The President has passed The Word. Where is Colonel Wenger? Paging Wenger. Immediate, triple-A priority plane passage for Wenger and Miss Charlotte.

"How is it you never have to wait for air transportation and never get bumped?" "Because Army and Navy line officers hate VD and know I can knock the hell out of it," says Wenger.

Here in one regiment in Trinidad is the hottest VD plague spot in the whole U. S. Army—99th Coast Artillery Regiment (anti-aircraft). VD rate: 465 per 1,000 men per annum. Appalling.

"Remember," said Wenger, "we didn't do it. What we did there was only as consultants. The work was done by the Regiment. Not only by medical officers. By the Regiment's colonel and all the way down to the humblest Negro GI."

Wenger's angle was simple. He simply got them all to hating syphilis and gonorrhea. The regiment was Negro. "Cotton patch Negroes. Amoral. Most of them illiterate," said Wenger. "We got them to read enough to be ashamed of the big letters, VD, in red, stitched on the back of their uniforms when they came down with syphilis or gon," said Wenger. The GI's, going off post on leave, were taught the sacred meaning of the oath they all were required to take, that they would take prophylaxis, instantly after exposure. And if recalcitrants didn't get an oath's sacred significance? "Then," laughed Wenger, "their squad companions taught them. If they came down with VD, their pals would beat them up." Men down with VD were made to eat, standing up, in a corner in the mess-hall while the regiment jeered at them. One GI sergeant made a sinister-looking noose out of the kind of rope that hangmen use and the rope was labeled: A GIFT TO THE NEXT VENEREAL FROM BAT-TERY B. Each man, as he left on pass, was required to touch that noose. Nothing else. "It was effective," laughed Wenger.

Nobody lectured the men about their sins, not even their colored chaplain, explained Wenger. The chaplain gave the GI's this classic advice. "If you have to live like a dog and act like a dog, then for God's sake be a *clean* dog!"

If a single GI broke the rules and became infected, the colonel refused passes to all the regiment for a period. "Of course you know what the boys did to guys like that who made the whole regiment the loser," said Wenger. There were rewards, too. Non-coms who had no VD in their outfits for six months got leaves to go to their homes in the U. S. A. via government transportation and $50 in spending money. Huge thermometers were erected in the regiment's camp indicating the course of the VD battle. "B Battery. 113 Days. No venereals," ran one proud legend. Military inspectors of the regiment reported their amazement that this outfit, it seemed from the colonel down to the lowest black GI, were all more interested in their VD eradication than their anti-aircraft shooting, which at the same time became more accurate as the men became more healthy. The men became missionaries, zealots in this cause that grew to be more than a bit religious. Wenger relates that he saw one member of the 99th drag a companion out of a rum shop yell-ing: "Come out here, you son of a bitch, or I'll report you to the Sergeant who'll beat hell out of you."

Within six months in 1943 the VD rate of the 99th tumbled from its shameful 465 per 1,000 men per annum down to under 50. When Wenger and Miss Charlotte left Trinidad in 1945, the regiment's rate was 18, far under that of supposedly more intelligent and moral white troops of the area, far under rates in the continental U. S. A.

Wenger spread his battle against the spirochete and gonococcus throughout the towns, encampments and steamy jungles of Trinidad and in that island he became legendary. He helped to instigate the organization of a Negro U.S.O. to give entertainment to compensate for the only entertainment the GI's had had, namely, the satisfaction of their reproductive instinct. Neither Wenger nor any line or medical officers taught the men that sexual activity was sin. Yet, with a grin, Wenger noted a curious fact: that, as VD rates went down, so did the rate of sexual exposures. "Those black boys were wonderful co-operators," said Wenger. "They enjoyed being healthy. It was a form of kindness to which they hadn't been accustomed."

The Bishops of Trinidad, both Anglican and Catholic, commended Wenger. "We, of course, cannot endorse what you are doing," they said, "but we'll do nothing to prevent it."

In the tropic nights in Trinidad, Wenger was stirred, hearing his name sung in Calypso songs. "They sure praised me," he said. "I'd sing them for you, only they were so dirty they made me blush and forget them."

Between 1943 and 1945 Wenger and Miss Charlotte expanded their campaign far beyond that against VD. "Tracking down VD in that population," said Wenger, "you found it shot to pieces with tuberculosis, leprosy, hookworm, yaws, malaria, sprue—everything." He flew to Washington. From public-health-conscious, shrewd and gracious Mrs. Florence Kerr (very high inside the New Deal) Wenger wangled vast hospital, laboratory, and medical equipment, took a boatload of it back to Trinidad and organized the famous Caribbean Medical Center to attack not only VD but the general physical deterioration of the poor folks of the island.

In the summer of 1945, Wenger requested orders for Washington.

Three years before retirement age he resigned from his beloved Public Health Service.

Among the big British brass in the Caribbean there was disappointment. "We still need an Adviser to direct the overall program for the West Indies and it is a great disappointment that you cannot return to plan and guide the extension of the campaign. Is your decision irrevocable?" wrote Sir Rupert Briercliffe, chief medical officer.

Yes, he was quitting, answered Wenger.

"Your strenuous work and your capacity for producing results have been a source of admiration to all of us," wrote Sir John Macpherson, co-chairman of the Anglo-American Caribbean Commission.

Sir Bede Clifford, the Governor of Trinidad, stated that the Colony owed Colonel Wenger a lasting debt.

Co-chairman Charles W. Taussig, of the Anglo-American Caribbean Commission, wrote praising Wenger to Surgeon General Parran of the U. S. Public Health Service.

"Dear Tom," he wrote, "there is no praise too high for Dr. Wenger's distinguished work in the establishment and successful operation of the Caribbean Medical Center. The Commission is proud to have been associated with the achievements of Dr. Wenger."

VII

If there is any record of what the Public Health Service thought of the Caribbean work of its VD-fighting stormy petrel when he resigned in 1945, I haven't seen it. Wenger gave out that he had retired for reasons of health. It's true his coronary arteries were bad. The arteries of his feet and legs were not good. Thus arterially partially obliterated, he could still outwork most men half his age. Disillusion was, I believe, his real reason for retiring. That, and lack of spiritual wages from a service he'd slaved for now for over 26 years. He had thought of his report on the Puerto Rico campaign as his masterpiece. That report had ended with a special section detailing Wenger's original, amusing, and disreputable (to pious moralists) methods of knocking VD out of our armed forces. The Public Health Service ruined it. The Service would not even accept his complete report for its confidential files. Wenger was told he'd have to delete that special section or the Service would destroy the whole report. So the special section was cut out, and the report went through, thus bowdlerized and entirely ineffectual.

"Here I'd been a VD field man since 1919," said Wenger after his retirement, summer of 1945. "I wasn't against the Service's policy of finding early cases and treating them to non-infectiousness."

Indeed Wenger had developed that very policy, himself.

"But I'd gone beyond that," he went on. "I knew now that prevention, prophylaxis, was the way to strike at the roots of VD. And, by God, the Service couldn't advocate prophylaxis."

It seemed that over the Public Health Service there was a mortmain, a social-hygienic dead hand that made prophylaxis an almost forbidden word. Wenger made no public fuss about this at all, though he was a bit bitter. He loved the Service. He was a simple, honest, straight-shooting unhypocritical partisan who was groggy trying to understand the contradictory strategy and tactics handed down from Washington. Wenger laughed and said: "Here was the Secretary of War demanding repression of prostitution with the objective of controlling venereal diseases." By prostitution Wenger meant all sexual intercourse, casual or commercial, outside the marriage bond. Repress sexual intercourse? It was to laugh.

"At the same time, here was the Chief of Staff of the Army, ordering the establishment of prophylactic stations, all over, to serve the soldiers whose illicit sexual intercourse was to be suppressed." It was to laugh again.

Then Wenger said: "And here was the Army Quartermaster bidding for 67,000,000 condoms and prophylactic packages—so where the hell are we?" Then we all laughed. What a Wenger!

"They wanted us VD men to fight sin and syphilis at the same time. If you start fighting sin, you stop swatting spirochetes. These sin-chasers think it's sin, not the spirochete, that causes syphilis."

Wenger told us that in 1943, when he was in the middle of his Trinidad battle, the Assistant Director of our wartime Defense

Health and Welfare Services had tried to get him to go back to Puerto Rico to help American police repress prostitution, arrest the girls, jail them, in a land where prostitution had been legal since Columbus.

"All they'd do is drive the gals under cover. They wouldn't repress them, they'd *diffuse* them. They'd wreck any health officer's program. Just when he'd found the infected women, was keeping tab on them, keeping them under treatment."

Now Wenger revealed his heart. "What I wanted to know from that sin-chaser," he said, "was what provision had been made, after those gals got out of jail, to equip them to earn a legitimate livelihood? To give them decent work at a decent wage?"

No provision whatever. If there was one thing Wenger hated worse than spirochetes, it was the sadism, the inhumanity of social hygiene. "I call that double-crossing," said Wenger. His gray eyes glittered. His face grew dark with anger. "Our boy scouts would make those poor women even more anti-social. They'd make them enemies of society who'd try to infect every man they could!"

In short, the would-be repressers of prostitution (butter wouldn't melt in their mouths) had forgotten a man they professed to worship, the Man of Galilee who had been gentle to Mary Magdalene. Profane, formally irreligious, he was a disciple of that gentle man, two thousand years removed.

So now our ace had bid his VD field-life good-bye. He had no money; he would have to live on a miserable pittance of his retirement pay, having never been promoted beyond the rank of a Lieut. Colonel in the Public Health Service. "What the hell, what do I want with money?" asked Wenger. He was ascetic. He didn't drink or smoke. His necessities were meat and potatoes, and his one luxury was mince pie.

Back at Hot Springs, Arkansas, he very soon caught up on his fishing and then went to see what he could do for his old-time great and good friend, Regina Kaplan, R.N., superintendent of the Leo M. Levi Memorial Hospital. Kappy (so Wenger always called her) was trying to organize a National Arthritis Research Foundation. It was absolutely ridiculous. She had no money, no experience in the big-time begging racketeering fundamental to creating foundations. It was a project surely more hopeless than the national VD fight when Wenger had started his one-man war in Hot Springs in 1919.

When Wenger came to Hot Springs, Kappy was treating thousands of down-and-outers, with every imaginable ailment and deterioration, in her poor little hospital. "She was treating poor devils with clap and syphilis, in a VD clinic she'd converted from a potato bin," said Wenger. "The potassium permanganate was spattered from floor to ceiling. I asked her, 'My God, Kappy, do you call this a *clinic?*'"

Kappy and Wenger owed each other a great deal. Wenger at his clinic took the venereals off her hands and, in return, Kappy made room in her little hospital—it was all for free—for all the complicating diseases suffered by Wenger's VD patients—everything, from TB to cancer, and arthritis.

"You take care of this nasty syphilis," said Kappy, "I'll take the rest of their troubles."

Wenger and Kappy were like identical twins in that they lived outside themselves in the sorrows of everybody, absolutely. "Some gal, that Kappy," said Wenger, describing this small, fiery, white-haired, black-eyed Jewish lady. "She'd murder her own mother, if she thought it would help the Levi Hospital," said Wenger, in Kappy's presence. "Oh, Dr. Wenger," Kappy protested, laughing.

Kappy and Wenger also had this in common that, for many years, each one of them had slogged at the heart-breaking job of rehabilitating physical wrecks who had come to the end of their hope, at Hot Springs.

Kappy had all kinds of sick folks at the Levi, but mainly the arthritics, thousands of arthritics, more than 20,000 in 20 years, most of whom had exhausted their own and their family's money, stocks, bonds, and every other resource, having dragged from the big clinics in the east, from the midwest University Hospitals, from the Mayo Clinic till at last they converged into a grim medieval parade of hobbling, bedridden forlorn who were the more pitiful because they came stretching out their gnarled twisted hands toward the supposedly magic thermal waters of Hot Springs.

Many years before Wenger's return to Hot Springs in 1945, Dr. Mark J. White, of the Public Health Service, had wanted him to establish an Association for the Study and Prevention of Venereal Disease. "It should be at Hot Springs," said kindly Dr. White. "It would be a cry coming from the final accounting in VD; it is a cry coming from the end of the road."

Now in 1945, Wenger's incomparably sharp observer's eyes, sizing up what went on along the main stem in Hot Springs, and in its bath houses, dives and cheap hashhouses, saw a most curious change from the 1919 days when, single-handed, he had started jabbing his syringe needles into the veins and behinds of thousands of venereals. Where were the venereals? Where were the tabetics, walking on their heels and slapping down their feet in their tell-tale ataxic gait? Where were the ghastly gummatous wrecks devoid of noses? Where were the blue-lipped invalids heart-wrecked with syphilitic aortitis? Where were the wild paretics, then incurable and dangerous in their agitated manic moods? Where were the sweet young things, sweet till you disclosed the red spots on their bellies and the red rash on their arms?

It was amazing. It was true. This venereal army had vanished from Hot Springs. The town was no longer the end of the road for syphilis. Wenger knew that this did not mean that the disease was conquered. He did know that this meant that there was now opportunity for its victims to get treatment in clinics, in hospitals, in doctors' offices all over America. It meant the disease had been smoked out into the open. It meant that it had become medically respectable. It meant that Surgeon General Thomas Parran's bold call to arms, Parran's brilliant conquest of its unmentionability, was getting hundreds of thousands, nationwide, under active, effective treatment. So that fewer and fewer pain-racked, pavement-slapping derelicts disgraced our cities; so that asylums were being emptied of their burden of manic and demented doomed paretics; so that the toll of syphilitic heart-break was lessening.

"In several months in 1945," said Wenger, "I only found two

syphilitics in the whole town." Wenger was a modest man, but he permitted himself a smile when I looked him in the eye and asked him who had put the fire into Tom Parran's guts to start this battle that was nationwide now, and with hope of complete victory. Wenger's round, blue-gray German eyes narrowed and gleamed.

About arthritis Wenger was savage. "You take this arthritis," he said. "Look at these poor devils. It isn't a disease they've got, it's a calamity."

The practicing doctors? They hated to see arthritics come dragging into their offices. They had no cure to offer, as there was now, for syphilis. The complicated management of the wreck-jointed sickness was beyond the skill of the vast majority of doctors, working individually. Arthritis in its pain-racked course demanded as much care and skill as did the treatment of TB. For TB in our country there were more than a hundred thousand hospital beds. For an estimated 3,000,000 arthritics there were not more than 200 free beds in all the land.

"Nobody but a millionaire can afford to have arthritis," said Wenger, "and damn few millionaires get it." It is a poor man's sickness, but even well-heeled victims become pauperized in their pilgrimages in search of relief of pain. And these pilgrimages, in scores of thousands, ended at Hot Springs. "You know what these poor devils are? They represent the greatest failure of American medicine," said Wenger.

Now Kappy, in her fond and foolish hope to convert her Levi Hospital into an arthritis research center, had set Wenger and Miss Charlotte (on no remuneration) at the job of answering letters from arthritics (from California to Maine) who'd read items announcing Nurse Kaplan's campaign for a National Arthritis Research Foundation.

"Here's a poor guy writes me," said Wenger. "His wife's had rheumatoid arthritis for 16 years. Her hip joints are shot. Her fingers are permanent claws. She's totally bedridden. They've been to Harvard, Johns Hopkins, Mayos. After selling and spending practically everything, they're down to 3,000 bucks. Should they come to Levi?"

"You know what I want to write him?" asked Wenger. "I want to tell him the best thing for him to do is to buy a handful of rat poison for his wife and himself."

"What did you answer?" I asked.

"I told him we'd put his wife on the waiting list at the Levi," said Wenger. He had an irrational faith in Nurse Regina Kaplan with whom he'd worked now, off and on, for almost 25 years. Then he told me what Kappy had made, out of next to nothing, of the Levi Hospital.

VIII

When Kappy had begun her fight, the general lack of knowledge of how to combat arthritis was only one of her headaches. That was 30 years ago. Though thousands of arthritics hobbled round Hot Springs in hopes that its hot baths would help them, they wanted no part of the hospital she had just been asked to manage. Though sponsored by the order of B'nai B'rith, and offering free care, non-sectarian, the hospital had only nine patients despite its then 40-bed capacity. Kappy found its patients on diets of badly boiled potatoes, skimpy, badly cooked cheap meat, and prunes for dessert. They were tended by three "practical" nurses who could barely read or write.

Kappy started a one-woman revolution. She demanded a free hand from the hospital board and got it. Deliciously cooked meals, high in meat protein, replaced the food that had been hardly fit for dogs. She organized a school of nurses recruited from good-looking high-school graduates. She changed the drab interior of the building into the hominess of a poor man's club. The swarm of sick people soon clamoring to get into the Levi Hospital made an out-patient clinic mandatory, so that she could give this sad human overflow some sort of medical care.

For such a clinic Kappy hadn't a cent of money. She cleaned out the old potato cellar to house the clinic. She had no equipment. Then a local mechanic came in with a smashed hand and she personally gave him care that was as skilled as it was kindly. The man's boss phoned for the bill. Kappy's eyes sparkled. "The Levi Hospital doesn't send bills," she answered. "But come and see what we've got when you have time." The employer donated the clinic's plumbing and added $50 for extra equipment.

Kappy's hospital had no doctors. Local physicians opposed her outpatient department thinking it would take pay patients away from them. "Come and see the kind of patients I'm treating," she urged them. Presently, leading Hot Springs doctors were devoting their lunch hours to treating her penniless forlorn.

It is interesting how, early in her work with arthritics, Nurse Kaplan had stumbled upon a weapon that even today is not really thoroughly used against rheumatoid arthritis. Her remedy was super-nutrition. Rheumatoid arthritis is notoriously a sickness of those in the lower income brackets, though occasional well-to-do people may suffer its torture. For many years treatises on the management of this mysterious and horrible sickness have advocated a "well-balanced and nutritious diet." But that's all, just that vaguely.

In those early days, Kappy was witness to a miracle. A 19-year-old girl, Esther, came to the Levi. She was anemic, undernourished, and helpless. Her fingers were spindle-shaped. Her joints were hot and swollen. When an orderly accidentally jarred her bed, she screamed with pain. One of the Levi staff physicians diagnosed rheumatoid arthritis, acute and early. Now Kappy became Esther's unethical, you might almost say black market, "doctor." (We will put "doctor" in quotes so as not to offend physicians who feel that all healing is the prerogative of the bearers of the mystic letters M and D.) Kappy had been a nurse in a hospital in Denver. Now for Esther, her reasoning was of the crudest. If super-diets were good for TB, why not for this disease which, like TB, strikes mainly at the under-privileged? Now Kappy did what no doctor (excepting men like Goldberger, Tom Spies, or Al Coburn) would have had the time to do. At every mealtime Kappy was beside the pain-racked girl's bed, gruffly kidding her into larger and larger meals of beef, liver, milk, eggs, fresh vegetables, and beef, and liver, and beef, and more of it. It was a reversal of the march of doom.

After five months Esther went home, transformed, and she maintained her recovery. The idea of that super-diet was not new: what was important and unique was that Kappy made Esther eat it.

What would the highly scientific physicians of the American Rheumatism Association say to this? Many, if not most of them, would say pseudo-science. Many, if not most, would smile, saying here was another one of these "series of one case." They would justly point out that many cases of rheumatoid arthritis get better by themselves. They would say this was a flagrant case of *"post hoc ergo propter hoc."* This is the Latin denunciation of all healers who do not use parallel, untreated, control cases and who do not know the chi-square formula for statistical significance. They are correct. Yet maybe they are a bit too scientific. If you carry a bed-ridden child out of a burning house, they would dispute your claim to have saved the child's life. The child might have got out anyway. To be sure, what you should have is 100 burning houses with similarly helpless children in each one, and carry 50 out and leave 50 lying, and then estimate how many in each group burned to death. One admires their cold science, but one would like to remind them that all new discovery begins as a series of one case, or at most a few cases. Poor Kappy. She had no time for science.

Yet other recoveries like Esther's taught her (or let us be semantic and say con*vinced* her) that, in the early months of rheumatoid arthritis, super-high protein, high vitamin, high caloric diet may start some sufferers back toward health. Unhappy Kappy. Most of her patients came in a joint-locked, chronic condition, far beyond such victories. The doctors on her Levi Hospital staff taught her that in rheumatoid arthritis there are no quick miracles. One of her doctor friends could cite the case of the lady school principal; her joint torture had been triggered by her school worries plus artificial menopause after an operation. She had been on the brink of permanent invalidism; her recovery was remarkable; but what had this doctor had to do?

Something, alas, that was out of reach at the Levi Hospital. Four months of rest in bed; chemical correction of the lack of hydrochloric acid in her stomach so that she could utilize her food;

three square meals of high protein food daily; baths, physical therapy; estrogens to relieve her female hormone deficiency; orthopedic
correction of her shoes; finally, three months in desert sunshine.
All this brought her back to a full-time job, uncrippled. Hot Springs
arthritis experts taught Nurse Kaplan that ideal treatment of
rheumatoid arthritis should be sanatorial, exactly as TB is sanatorial, with the patient under full-time control of physicians; and
then to get a good recovery, you had to spot the treacherous sickness
early.

Unfortunate Kappy. For most of her patients the Levi was the
end of the road; and her hospital board had ruled that she could
keep her patients not many months, or until they were rehabilitated, but hardly more than 60 days. Who was this optimistic small
fighter, Kappy, to dream that at this poverty-stricken, inadequate
Levi Hospital she could battle the long-drawn-out torture of rheumatoid arthritis?

She turned herself into a finagler. She bothered the big shots of
the B'nai B'rith with her unreasonable begging for money, more
and more money. What did this Kaplan think they were made of?
She hounded Jewish Welfare agencies. She raided the local community chest. She turned politico and, by treating county patients,
got county funds.

She took lessons from Wenger in the art of cajoling, of panhandling, of all but stealing some of the monies that now began
flowing out of Washington in the splendid spending of the 1930's.
She expanded her hospital, its bed capacity going up from 40 to
125; its budget rising from $50,000 to $125,000. For the hospital's
pathologist, she wangled money from God knows where for a laboratory where technicians could do blood sedimentation tests to
reveal the waning of the activity of rheumatoid arthritis under her
super-nutrition, chemical tests indicating the thickening of their
thin blood, chemical tests tracing the correction of their almost invariable starvation for protein. Yet it was mockery. Yet she had to
keep sending the great majority of her arthritics home less than
half mended. She was foolishly optimistic. Chemistry would find

something to speed up their recovery, never doubt it. Kappy's hope
was as invincible as it seemed silly.

She was a demon, a vixen with flashing black eyes fighting for
her patients with the important Hebrews of the hospital board.
She raged when they were proud to show a high annual turnover
of patients. Turnover! Turning them out rather, one-tenth, one-
fifth, one-half cured! She pep-talked herself with home-made
aphorisms. "These big shots, trying to hinder me, don't need this
help themselves. Don't let them interfere with these people in
pain." So she won some wretches a few more weeks in hospital.
She was a combination of beggar and sob-sister stretching out hospital stay for her patients.

From Wenger she learned a slick technique of prying government appropriations out of New Deal and Army brass for purposes they had not intended. That way she finagled her famous
therapeutic pool. Kappy had a quick eye for the least improvement
in a wrecked joint and a sharp ear for the slightest easing of pain
reported by her suffering ones. As the years went by, she saw, more
and more clearly, how they could move their bodies, no matter how
crippled, more easily in tubs of warm water. Hot Springs thermal
water? She couldn't say. Maybe just warm water. But if she could
only have a pool like that of the President at Warm Springs,
Georgia.

"For 12 years Kappy yelled pool, pool, pool to her hospital board
and they turned her down," said Wenger. Then when the war
began, Hot Springs became a defense area. Army surveyors called
for more hospital beds. Keppy talked the surveying brass into
adding two additional wards to the Levi.

"Then," said Wenger, "how she finagled it, I don't know; it
didn't have a damn thing to do with ordinary hospital needs, but
she got the money not only for the wards but for a pool to be
built on top of them."

The Army brass got her top priorities for her pool and helped
her fight through Washington red tape; and with ample Lanham
Act funds, she built one of the most beautiful and scientific thera-

peutic pools in the world, right in the middle of the war when nobody from the President on down was giving a damn about arthritics.

IX

For the rehabilitation of her crippled patients, Kappy was a ball of fire. In their treatment she was unscientific in the sense that she tried to get the doctors to throw the whole therapeutic book at them, not knowing exactly what it was in the book that might help them. The most notable of all Kappy's experiments was that with Georgia Hauke, who had come from Milwaukee with far-advanced, progressive rheumatoid arthritis. She was so little capable of movement, so bedridden, so deteriorated that there was not much more time for her to live.

Georgia Hauke was admitted to the Levi, on a stretcher, in May, 1946. The combined arthritis experts of the nation would have said that in Georgia's case, Nurse Kaplan was hardly justified in offering any hope at all. When rheumatoid arthritis had hit Georgia in 1938, she was a 17-year-old high school girl, husky, vivid, and lovely. Now as she came into the Levi it was tough for Kappy, hardened though she was to tragedy, to look at what was left of Georgia. "She looked moth-eaten," said Kappy. "She weighed only 90 pounds. She couldn't feed herself. She was totally helpless." Georgia was by far the worst of the derelict thousands Kappy had seen in 30 years.

Kappy looked down at Georgia. "Hello there, gal, kind of messed up, aren't you? Well, you're not going to stay that way long."

How dared Nurse Kaplan hold out any hope? Only because she had caught a gleam in the sick girl's eyes. It was what Kappy called "the will to get well." Kappy and Wenger held this belief in common: that the will to get well is the most potent medicine of all. "The patients have got to do 98 per cent and the doctors only 2 per cent of the fighting against arthritis," said Wenger. Yet, in this case of Georgia, wasn't Kappy being a bit of a charlatan? She should have faced it that this human vestige was beyond the power of science. Except for a few short intervals of painful hobbling and shuffling a few steps, for almost eight years Georgia had been bed-fast. She was a postgraduate authority on rheumatoid arthritis. She was an alumna of years in a voluntary hospital—a very good one; many months in a county hospital—where she had been a human guinea-pig, experimented upon by medical school professors, in-terns, and medical students; months in a chiropractic spa where treatment had made her condition more desperate; and finally she had been an inmate of three nursing homes. It had made her feel as if she was in a nest of moles to see so many old hopeless people huddled in these horrible institutions. She had been afraid she would dry up and become old, too, if she stayed in these places.

Again and again, between 1938 and 1944, Georgia had got to her feet for a few pain-racked, stiff-jointed steps, only to be knocked flat—by an infection of her spleen, then of her kidney, then by two successive sieges of pleurisy, then by a bout of flu. And worst of all, came the flare-up of her arthritis when her mother died, of cancer. When she came to the Levi her arms were pinned to her sides, her fingers were like claws, her hips were locked, her knees stiff as if set in concrete. When asked if this or that attention hurt her, Georgia smiled at the Levi's nurses.

"Never mind," she said. "Go ahead. Pain is part of me."

Through all these years (as Georgia told me later) a strange medi-cine had kept her alive, and fighting. It is a remedy I do not myself understand at all. Here was Georgia's own self-prescription, not dispensed in any hospital or by any doctor. "As I grew worse," said Georgia, "God became a definitely personal friend. I turned to Him at any time for help . . . for the ability to hang on to faith in Him when everything about *me* seemed to contradict His being."

This friend of Georgia's was strongest whenever her doctors failed her. "Every time they'd try some new treatment—I always felt sure that this time it would do the trick—then I'd go down in despair when it failed—then I'd pray for faith and hope. And it would come," said Georgia. "There's no living with this disease on your own. You could never stand it."

Such was Georgia's own explanation of what Wenger and Kappy called her will to get well. Georgia is the first of all I've met, to make me wish I were not agnostic. Georgia is the first to make me wish that I, too, could get strength from prayer.

It was in January, 1947, that I first saw Georgia Hauke. Wenger had got us to come down to Hot Springs and we were to try to do a story for *The Reader's Digest* that might tell the world about the arthritis research foundation that Kappy and Wenger were struggling to organize. In my bones I felt it was an ill-starred project but Rhea and I would do anything we could to help along any dream of Wenger's. We'd no sooner got to the Levi than Wenger took us to meet Georgia Hauke who had been there for seven months—five months beyond the time allotted to the over-crowded Levi Hospital's patients. From the deteriorated, emaciated, almost motionless residue of half-alive humanity that she had been when she came to the Levi, Georgia was now transfigured. There she walked, shuffling slow and clumsy, but there she actually walked down the ramp of Kappy's pool, down into the sparkling, clear, mysteriously greenish Hot Springs water. Georgia's face was rosy. She was lovely. She had gained 31 pounds. In the water of the pool she now walked confidently. Then she went up and down the pool, swimming a fast backstroke that a healthy man would envy. She rested, hanging onto the pool's ladder. She looked up at me and said: "This pool's my life," and her dark eyes were like stars.

Georgia has this in common with Kappy and Wenger: she is a fighter. Out of the water, she could only walk aided by two canes in a grotesque, hip-locked shuffle. Georgia laughed, telling how she'd been beaten by a beetle crawling in a race down the hospital's sidewalk. But she could now stand on her feet an hour-and-a-half at a time.

"Every day I feel myself getting stronger," said Georgia. "The doctors had said my hip and knee joints were clean gone. They're beginning to work again—even if it's only a little."

"What's given you your new lease on life?" I asked her.

Well, her doctor was wonderful. She'd had the book, thera-peutically. Liver shots. Big doses of therapeutic multiple vitamins. Daily prostigmin to fight her muscle spasms. Gold injections. Many hours in the sun. Manipulation by a wonderful physical therapist, under water. Then there was the wonderful food Kappy served them. Then the pool was most important of all. But Georgia said that, at the Levi, there was another medicine. It wasn't to be measured in ounces of protein or in milligrams of multiple vitamins. It was that here at the Levi she wasn't a mere number, or even a patient, but a human being. Look at the hospital's restaurant where Kappy made you feel you were a guest at a good hotel. Look at the swell parties they had, on every patient's birthday.

"We forget we're cripples. We're just less and less incapacitated," said Georgia. They all competed for recovery, a gang of fighters against a cruelty that Kappy made them believe they could conquer.

Miss Kaplan? "She's our dynamo," said Georgia, who had now become Kappy and Wenger's boldest experiment. Together they had arranged that Georgia's stay at the Levi was to be unlimited. When she came there, she was a zero risk, medically. Now they were going to try every possible weapon of science to bring her back to what Georgia herself calls "maximum possible function." Georgia, Kappy, and Wenger were going to show the world how far you can come back from nowhere.

I shan't forget the day we left Georgia, that January in 1947. She sat, her knees still stiff and her legs straight out, wrapped in a bathrobe, just out of the pool, her face glowing. She knew there was a rough road ahead for her. Electric muscle stimulation, massage, manipulations, heavy painful exercises.

"What's your blood sedimentation rate?" I asked her.

"My sed rate has been going down and down, ever since I've been here," said Georgia. "It's close to normal now. When it gets down to normal, and stays there, it'll mean my disease has burned itself out."

"Then what?" I asked.

"Then the surgeons can give me new joints," said Georgia.

"They're going to have to hurt you plenty," I said, "before you throw away your canes."

"Okay," she answered, smiling. "But if I get maximum possible function, won't that give hope to a lot of people who were as far gone as I was?"

It was time to go. I told her I'd try to write the story of Georgia,
Kappy, and Wenger. "Maybe you'll be the poster girl for a national arthritis campaign," I said.

Georgia looked up at me with a little smile that was skeptical,
sad, yet gallant. "Maximum possible function," she said in hardly
more than a whisper. "Ceiling unlimited," she said. Then her eyes
filled with tears and so did mine as we shook hands good-bye.

                                    X

I wrote the story, but the doctors to whom it was submitted for
criticism turned it down, unanimously. Wenger tried to console me.
"Just as you depend on Rhea for a woman's reaction," he wrote,
"so I depend on Miss Charlotte. She points out that you have hit
the docs in their most vulnerable spot. . . . You have given Kappy,
a nurse, a mere nurse, with just an R.N. after her name, credit for
restoring a patient to health when the medical profession had
failed.

"Charlotte says can you expect the profession, who refused to
acknowledge Pasteur, to admit that a mere nurse had succeeded
where they failed? To make matters worse, you give the *patient*
credit for knowing something about arthritis. You say Georgia
talked like the real arthritis specialist she is. All this is the rankest
kind of medical heresy."

Wenger chided me, gently. "But you do not stop there—the
whole idea (for a National Arthritis Research Foundation) stems
from a Jewish source (he meant Kappy) in Hot Springs, Arkansas,
the graveyard of arthritics, where the failures of the experts come
as a last resort. That, I think, is what really killed your story."

Of the failures I've made trying to write about life among the
doctors, this was the most shameful, most stupid. We all failed, for
that matter, Wenger, Miss Charlotte, Rhea, Kappy, and Georgia.
Georgia put herself at occupational rehabilitation therapy in 1947,
writing a book, the history of her arthritis, picturing herself as a
girl trying to climb a glass mountain. It is the first intelligible, vivid,

and accurate account of rheumatoid arthritis I've ever read. Georgia failed. Two of the greatest publishers in the U. S. A. read her manuscript, rejecting it because her stark story of pain would make people not want to read it. But Georgia has not really failed. In 1947, Georgia, still aided by two canes, walked ten blocks to Mass and ten blocks back up the steep hill to the Levi Hospital. On New Year's Eve she danced, for the first time in more than ten years. Her blood sedimentation rate is normal now. Her active disease seems burned out. Now, gallant as always, she is going through new months of pain; she is getting her new hip joints at Permanente Hospital, in Oakland, California.

Yes, we all failed, except Georgia. Kappy and Wenger didn't get their arthritis research foundation. In New York, a spectacular dinner, given by one of our greatest movie magnates for the purpose of raising a hoped-for $500,000 starting fund, turned out an absolute bust. Bob Hope gave his time free and was most funny, but nobody gave much money. The kindly magnate was set back many thousands of dollars.

Nationwide publicity about the new Foundation brought Kappy and Wenger thousands of letters, but not with the anticipated enclosures. Rheumatoid arthritis is not usually found on Park Avenue or the Gold Coast; rich people rarely have it in their families; and it's when a disease is in a rich person's family (like polio or cancer) that the person is most likely to be generous. Among the thousands of letters flooding in and answered faithfully by Wenger and Miss Charlotte, some enclosed dirty, used, torn one-, two-, and five-dollar bills.

The majority of the letters were only wails for help from arthritics who'd spent everything without relieving their deformity or pain. Many offered their own twisted bodies—without reservation—to be experimented upon by the foundation's doctors. Others offered to sell their bodies, as hobos used to do to medical school anatomy departments, to get funds to reach the projected mercy at Hot Springs.

"I'm going north to see the National Arthritis Foundation buried," Wenger wrote me in the summer of 1947. "Then we'll plan something else, less grand, starting small, and grow.

"Don't forget," he added in his invincibly optimistic vein, "we have many advantages here in this arthritic graveyard, Hot Springs. We see the failures of the greatest arthritis experts, nationwide. They can't keep their patients from coming here. Most of them come, sooner or later. We'll get a good idea from those patients as to just how the specialists are failing." This was really looking on the bright side.

"Now I'm going fishing again, and forget all about it. I'll be thinking of a newer and smaller project. The next time you'll have a different story and one that will make the grade."

XI

To help Kappy clear up the ruins of her foundation and to eke out his miserable Public Health Service pension, Wenger started an arthritis practice in Hot Springs. "I've seen more actual and genuine misery in three years of arthritis work than I saw in 30 years of venereal disease," said Wenger, "and that's saying something." Among his hundreds of patients, Wenger noted this curious fact: the patients were optimistic, no matter how crippled, how far gone. It was their doctors who were pessimistic. And yet, as Wenger sketched his plans, with Kappy, for a modest arthritis clinical research center where they'd start small, and grow, Wenger found more than straws of hope for rheumatoid arthritis to grab at, the more so if their peril could only be discovered early.

There was the best of evidence (bright with hope if you could only get an organic chemist team to tackle it) that rheumatoid arthritis was a chemical lesion of the human body. Dr. Philip Hench, of the Mayo Clinic, reported that among 45 patients with rheumatoid arthritis, fibrositis, osteo-arthritis, and low back pain—all were relieved of their agony, partially or completely, at the moment they developed jaundice. The sudden and often complete remissions went hand in hand with the intensity and duration of the jaundice. Here was hope: that arthritis is not an inexorable, irreversible disease. The same occurs in rheumatoid arthritic women who become pregnant—their symptoms magically disappear only to return after they've had their babies.

What was the chemistry? In both jaundice and during pregnancy there's a great increase in organic chemical compounds, called lipids, among them cholesterol, in the blood. These chemicals belong to the family of the steroids. In pregnant women the estrogens (also steroids) are high in their blood. Dr. Hench has even gone so far as to put up a finger post for enterprising organic chemical researchers. He points out that all these steroids contain a common chemical grouping—the phenanthrene nucleus.

The anti-rheumatic principle of the future, guessed Dr. Hench, which would be effective in alleviating all types of arthritis, would contain this phenanthrene.*

These chemical hints excited Wenger, who was absolutely not a chemist but would have given his eye-teeth to test out the hundreds of phenanthrene derivatives chemists might offer him—if he only had a clinical arthritis research center. For years there had been a proprietary phenanthrene compound, a complex of steroids on the market, known as "Ertron," widely used (and only by doctors) for the alleviation, not the cure, of rheumatoid arthritis.

This Ertron (reportedly because of a certain flamboyancy in its early advertising claims) earned the official frowns of the American Medical Association and many of the powerful medical politicians of the American Rheumatism Association. Many favorable reports of the gradual, yet definite, power of Ertron against severe rheumatoid arthritis were published—though not, mind you, in journals controlled by the above associations. Professor Paul B. Magnuson and his associates, at Northwestern University Medical School in Chicago, reported that Ertron had arrested severe, chronic, rheumatoid arthritis in more than 60 per cent of a group of sufferers

---

* Dr. Hench and his associates at the Mayo Clinic have announced the discovery of "Compound E," specific against rheumatoid arthritis, on April 13, 1949. Compound E contains the phenanthrene chemical group.

unresponsive to all other treatment. This then made it possible to correct their crippled condition by orthopedic operations.

The Editor of the *Journal of the American Medical Association* rejected Professor Magnuson's manuscript. Meanwhile, a conservatively estimated 40,000 American physicians are treating rheumatoid arthritis with Ertron. Even a high medical politician of the American Rheumatism Association is known to employ Ertron, though he is said to dispense it, discreetly, in unlabeled bottles. It is not clear whether the good doctor's surreptitiousness is for the purpose of keeping the arthritics from knowing what they're getting, or for keeping other doctors from knowing what he is giving.

To Wenger this all seems very silly. "If we only had a clinical research center down here, we could test not only Ertron * but any new chemical, without prejudice, not politically—but scientifically," says Wenger.

Wenger sees what's lacking in the fight against rheumatoid arthritis. One or another of several treatments for this malignant ill have been tested in many clinics and hospitals. But never to the limit and for the years it may take to determine their power—because free beds and research funds have never been available.

Wenger knows that there are other weapons frequently effective against rheumatoid arthritis—if you could only catch cases of rheumatoid arthritis early, and then use all the partial weapons together, full power, and with no economic limitations. The anti-arthritic "X" (small amounts of Compound E) may be hiding in those high protein, high vitamin meals with which Kappy has returned many of her rheumatoid arthritics back to health, to freedom from pain, to working. Is there anti-arthritic virtue in the thermal waters of Hot Springs? Many patients swear that this is so. And Wenger smiles at the sneers of the high authorities of the American Rheumatism Association at the Hot Springs water.

"They've never been down here even to test it; and it's helped many patients who were those fellows' failures," he says.

---

* It is possible that Ertron—a steroid complex—contains Compound E in small amounts.

XII

In 1947 when his new arthritis fight was at its ebb tide, Wenger received the decoration of Honorary Member of the Order of the British Empire for his wartime victory, by disreputable prophylaxis, over venereal disease among American and British armed forces in the Caribbean. That gave him courage in his new fight against arthritis, because, after all, he'd begun his VD battle 35 years before he got this recognition. Meanwhile, getting his toe in the door in his plot for a clinical arthritis research center, he works—disregarding the obliterated arteries of his legs and his coronary twinges —at his funny little arthritis practice. His patients are all poor, nearly all at the end of their tether. With Miss Charlotte he helps them over housing difficulties, getting shelter over their heads; he takes them round in Miss Charlotte's car to get them comfortably located; he moves patients who are not satisfied, helps them re-pack, locates new quarters, gets them settled again; when they're in great pain, he shops their groceries; when they're sick, he gets them admitted and transports them to the Levi Hospital; he does not charge them for personal visits he makes to cheer them up—they only pay when he gives them treatment, and then he exasperates Miss Charlotte by almost invariably taking less from them than the bill she renders; he brings them soup and roasts from his own home when they are sick or down in the dumps; he takes them sight-seeing; above all, he listens to their tales of misery.

Many have said that Wenger is the only doctor they've ever had who'll let them *talk* and tell all the story of their suffering.

Now at last in 1948, Lt. Col. O. C. Wenger, U. S. Public Health Service (retired), has come full circle, back to where he started at Hot Springs in 1919. He is back in his old clinic in the Government Free Bath House. The old venereal parade (thanks largely to Wenger) no longer marches there. The need for a VD clinic (thanks largely to Wenger) has disappeared. Now, gaily, profanely, and with utter sympathy and kindness, he is medical host and father confessor to an army of twisted, pain-racked, stiff-jointed people. It is a new cry from the end of the road. Wenger is organizing his first experiment—a scientific test of the thermal waters of Hot Springs.

"The government has got to help me," says Wenger, and his laugh is gaily sinister. "This bath house is on the government reservation. Government circulars more than hint that there's antiarthritic virtue in this Hot Springs water. But is there? Those circulars bring thousands of poor devils here, and raise their hopes.

"The government's got to help me. I've got them coming and going," says Wenger, closing his round eyes, throwing back his head and now really laughing. "If the waters are inert, then the U. S. Government, by their claims, are perpetrating one of the cruelest hoaxes in history. If the waters *do* have power (and the big arthritis authorities deny it, mostly) then the government's denying a suffering public the information and the facilities such an important agent under government control should deserve."

Wenger, though famous as a VD field man, has no name as a man of science. This I now make bold to give him. "Personally," says Wenger, "I believe the waters have definite therapeutic action on arthritis. But I nor nobody else can prove it without thoroughly controlled investigation.

"What I want," he says, "is some reasonable explanation of what all us doctors down here see daily: in the hot water here one patient improves remarkably while another gets worse, both of them with the same diagnosis and nearly identical symptoms."

He is planning parallel series of treatments with Hot Springs Thermal water and city water, with identical temperatures and with the source of the water unknown to the patients. If this is not science, then the present writer is a theologian.

At the same time Wenger is sharpening up the old weapon, of his invention, that first uncovered the nation's hidden syphilis and then gave Surgeon General Thomas Parran his chance to stir us to a fight against that venereal menace. This new dragnet will uncover arthritis—especially rheumatoid. "Arthritis is not reportable," says Wenger, "so we haven't the faintest notion of how much of it there is or where it is or who's got it."

Wenger explains that often there's an insidious, pre-rheumatoid condition, a loss of weight, fatigue, profound exhaustion. But that's not measurable—it's premonitory to many other maladies. "But there's another pre-rheumatic or early rheumatic condition that we *can* really spot," he says. "In the great majority of the early ones, there's a disturbed bone physiology, a sort of rarefaction of the bones of the fingers—regional osteo-porosis—that you can spot, clearly, by X-ray."

Then his blue-gray eyes grow round and gleam and he's the Wenger of the old blood-spattered days, "the community blood-shed" he used to call it, with a laugh, the syphilis Kahn test of 700,000 citizens in Chicago. "Why not such an X-ray dragnet for early rheumatoid arthritis?" he asks. "Why not try it on 5,000,000 people in different cities all over the country? Why not?

"Goddamn it, why not?" he shouts. "Doc Diederich down here says no case of arthritis would become invalid if caught early and properly treated. Don't the big shots of the American Rheumatism Association say you can check the great majority of arthritis if you get at it early? Why not?" *

Who will stop this fighter who was once the VD ace of aces, now with a new fire, a new youth despite his sick arteries and his 64 years of all-out fighting, now in training to become the nation's ace against arthritis? Nobody will stop O. C. Wenger. Death will not stop him because he will not die while he has this new battle to live for. Is this man, not really a doctor, miscast in this book of life among the doctors? He is more than a doctor.

Last year, a man came to Wake Robin, pitifully bent almost double with progressive arthritis of the spine. He was a highly skilled draftsman. He was broke. He was at the end of his tether. Out of his eyes, seamed at their corners with years of frightful pain, gleamed determination—a last desperation. His eyes, like Georgia's, shone with a courage out of this world. "I've waited round here four days just to see you," said this derelict, Albert Hoehne.

I called Wenger in Hot Springs. "Sure we'll take care of Al," said Wenger. "Tell him we'll get him located. Tell him we'll get

---

* When it at last becomes abundant, it is to be hoped that Wenger will be given a chance to fight early rheumatoid arthritis with Compound E or a safer and more powerful steroid, which seems to be in the offing.

him the best doc too. Money? He'll get treated for free. You get him his vitamins, Paul. Get the Ford company (his employers) to get him a few months' leave with pay. Tell Al we'll do anything for him—including springing him out of jail if he gets into trouble."

Al Hoehne went to Hot Springs to Wenger and is now struggling on the way back to life.

Yes, O. C. Wenger is a bit above the rank and file of physicians. He is more than a doctor, and my best insight into his mysterious humanity came not long ago, when he told me how nearly he did not become a doctor at all, almost 40 years ago, in his last year in the study of medicine.

Within a few months of graduation, our ex-gamin of the St. Louis wharfs whose chief fun had been annoying the city's policemen, our ex-hobo who had served time for being caught by railroad dicks for sleeping with other tramps in a box car, had got into serious trouble. He had gone to the rescue of a prostitute who had had her throat cut. "In fact," said Wenger, "her head was about half severed." For his pains, he got shot in the leg.

Up to this time he had been a brilliant student, excused from final examinations. Now he was brought before the Rector of the university, an S.J., a Jesuit.

"To my dying day I'll not forget that old priest," said Wenger. "Our meeting took place in his study late one afternoon in January, 1908. The sun was coming through the stained-glass windows as I sat opposite this white-haired man of 70, awaiting my fate.

"I went into that meeting with a chip on my shoulder. I came out, understanding for the first time the meaning of charity. As I entered the room, the Rector smiled and said, 'Good evening.' Then the old man said, 'I came near calling you *Doctor* Wenger. But come, sit down.'

"He sat opposite me with the kindest smile I've ever seen. He said he wanted me to know that anything I cared to tell him would be as sacred as if given to him in confessional. He said he wanted me to know that, though I was not a Catholic."

Wenger told him the whole story, only omitting the names of the girl's would-be murderers. "I frankly admitted I knew this gal, had been a frequent visitor to the place and all that. The expression on the Rector's face remained just as serene. At last the old man told me he'd have to think it over, but for me to go back to my studies."

A week later Wenger received his sentence. His atonement was to take all senior exams, make two state boards, and make a place on the city hospital staff.

"It's curious, Paul," O. C. said, "I was never impressed by any religion whatever—but I do think, if the young man going into medicine would have the training of a priest, he would make a much better doctor."

That's why, among the hundreds of wonderful men of medicine I've known, O. C. Wenger has been my best teacher. Almost 40 years before, I had not so much as begun to realize that medicine is nothing if it is merely scientific; Wenger had the insight that medicine is one with religion. Finally there was this to remember about him: like Bundesen, Coburn, and Leo the bold, to accomplish a mission essentially religious, Wenger certainly had to be rugged.

PART FOUR

THEY FELT THE PAIN OF
OTHERS

><<< >>> <<< <<<

Here's what it might mean—countless men and women would escape from the pain-racked existence of the deformed and crippled, from a state which till now was regarded as permanent and inevitable. The catch in it was that the discoverer, a young neurologist, was poor as a church mouse, and no university or foundation, nor any of the government services believed in him at all. The young neurologist thought he had an ace-in-the-hole. It was only one case, of the getting up and walking of a woman wheel-chaired and bedfast for many years, with a disease considered, neurologically, hopeless. We were never sadder at not being able to suggest any way to spread the test of his new science.

But you never know. Within a year he had scores of victims of this terrible disease under treatment. Hundreds of victims of this crippling torture were clamoring for his new therapy. Their fierce will to walk and help themselves forced him to learn how to help them to live, though he could not cure them.

They taught us all that the doctor is the patient's servant.

>>> >>> <<< <<<

CHAPTER XI

The Patient Is the Hero

IF your life has been surprise and adventure, if you have known the salt of life, if life has made you laugh much more than cry, then it's common decency to give back the best you've got to the most you can reach, especially those who have been less lucky than you. But to do that you have to believe truly in what you've got to give, and in the 1945 autumn I was not sure what to believe, any longer. In August, 1945, the annihilating exploit of the A-bomb boys revealed the horrible perversion of which science is capable, and it made my dream seem folly.

I might easily have called off this book of life among the doctors if it hadn't been for a handful of comrades it would be shameful to let down. Of this cohort, not the least was Ralph Shaner. He was unmarried, a lone wolf, a shy, mild man with the sharpest tongue I've ever heard waggle in any human being, but a selfless man, incessantly instigating and encouraging medical research, not the ivory tower variety but always with the hope to ease pain, shorten misery, stave off dying. He had no academic position, though professors always welcomed the money he could get them in his role as medical director of one of the big pharmaceutical houses. Unlike many of my medical maverick friends, Shaner never seemed interested in his own activities but was constantly inciting me to look into the obscure adventures and incipient discoveries that he thought might be made by contemned and poverty-stricken aspirants to a doubtful medical immortality. It was notable that their names were never box-office. Shaner maintained—with a snarl—

that when a name has become medically box office, the productive life of that name's owner was almost certainly over. Shaner's overall cynicism was really something, yet he belied it by the way he gave and gave and gave. This dark-eyed, venomous, gentle, and seclusive man, forever sticking his neck out with his employers to help some futuristic forlorn project, had a don't-give-a-damn spirit that shamed me into occasionally sticking my own neck out with him.

It was part of Shaner's charm that he was a champion of the disreputable in science. Of all modern discoveries which have made our doctors blush, that of the male hormone, testosterone, is the most raffish. To many doctors it seems morally wrong that the secret of manhood should be set down in chemical symbols. Or, on the other hand, many doctors snigger at the mention of testosterone. Toward testosterone Shaner's attitude was objective. Regarding it his knowledge was immense, extending from its chemical synthesis by the Yugoslav genius, Dr. L. Ružička, all the way to the amusing and belated synthetic manhood of the celebrated gelding, Holloway. It was Shaner who guided me into and through the bibliography of the male hormone.

Shaner was a man who could pull lost causes out of fires. He made Leo Loewe's conquest of unconquerable subacute bacterial endocarditis possible, by his rescue, you may remember, of the heparin/Pitkin menstruum from the suspicious and quarrelsome Dr. George Philo Pitkin. He encouraged me to tell the shady story of the machinations of certain medical big wheels who detested Leo Loewe more than they loved to save doomed human beings. It is regrettable that Shaner's verbal taking apart of medical big wheels has been too libelous to print.

About the new medical branch of geriatrics Shaner was sardonic. The doctors, said Shaner, have suddenly discovered that there is such a thing as old age. Here he was reaching farthest into the future, as the instigator and constant encourager of the present researches of the medico-Talmudic explorer, Dr. Henry A. Rafsky, now in the process of getting himself into academic hot water by demonstrating that we are not as old as our arteries but as old as our livers.

Shaner's philosophy helped me to battle my discouragement. In Shaner, who was a Hoosier of Spanish blood, the death-loving Spaniard was in contest with his devotion to the fight for life. Shaner loved death in order to understand and combat it, though as a Spaniard he also understood (as Ernest Hemingway puts it) that death is the only security. Yet for Shaner, death was evil. The trouble with us Americans, Shaner contended, is that we think of evil as the mere absence of good. "For me," he said, "evil is a positive force, with an excellent chance of final triumph." To make his point, Shaner cited the most recent and astounding of all scientific victories, at this moment when the radioactive cloud was drifting eastward in the stratosphere from Hiroshima. "Now take these A-bomb benefactors of mankind," laughed Shaner, "do *they* represent a mere absence of good?"

"You take them, Ralph, you can have them," I said. "They're what's got me down."

"And well they may," he answered. "Have you the guts to tell their evil? And how they're whitewashing their murder with promises of future good that's hiding in their atom?"

Hadn't it been the most exquisitely interdigitated scientific collaboration ever? Talk about teamwork. Talk about discipline. Talk about discretion. It portended a new, an almost priestly scientific brotherhood. What selfless comradeship had led to the shattering blasts this August, 1945, when the cunningest and deadliest congeries of scientific brains in all human record had brought victory for the global strategy of our late great leader who, as a potential killer, made Hitler look small-time.

What depressed me more and more this autumn of 1945 was the more and more lurid light of the horrid dawn of a new human era where science for death would defeat science for life, the A-bomb boys saluting this ghastly morning by showing what science can do (in a split second and almost effortlessly) to wipe out hundreds of thousands of non-combatant men, women, and children . . . whose crime it was that they were alive and human. How prophetic our late great President had been, when with iron in his melodious voice he had warned the enemies of democracy that, since they'd asked for it, they'd get it. . . . And now they had it. The A-bomb boys had delivered more than they'd promised; they'd given their late Commander-in-Chief better than two billion dollars worth of terror. They had delivered more than mass sudden death; they'd presented him a dividend—of insidious corruption of human tissue, of slowly rotting bones, of falling hair, of sloughing skin, of cancer that might take years to kill, of mutated germ plasm that would yield amusingly horrible little human monsters in coming generations. And the bomb itself was only a beginning. Our late great leader may go down in history, too, as the President at whose instigation it was discovered how to taint the earth with radioactive gases to blight all life, ubiquitous, with no place to hide.

"Yes, Paul, that's your science," Ralph said gently. "So much for your hope and savior of mankind." Ralph's smile made wrinkles round his black, impenetrable eyes.

Bitterly I admitted that W. L. Laurence had been right about me when he told one of my friends that "de Kruif is crazy." Laurence, the prophet of the omnipotence of atomic energy, was vindicated. I had been insane to believe in science as the savior of mankind. "Why write a book about life among the doctors?" I asked Shaner. "Why go on with it?"

"Now you can really write it. With no damned *message*," he said. "Write it for fun. Write it just for the hell of it."

For me, this was a pivot moment in thirty-five years of working. Now at last for me these men of science were no longer gods, but in their destructiveness even infra-human.

"What's got into us?" I asked. "Who do these openers of Pandora's box think they are, anyway? Now they've perpetrated this horror, they're demanding a voice in administering it, for the good of mankind."

The pioneers in radiant energy hadn't planned on making these A-bomb boys their inheritors. The genial Swiss Becquerel, gentle Konrad Roentgen, forgotten Pierre Curie and his more and more famous Madame; Niels Bohr (aren't Danes peace-loving?); and Einstein (doesn't his fluff of white hair look like a halo? You'd swear he wouldn't harm a mouse)—all of them excepting that tough-looking German, Hahn—weren't all of them working for the good of mankind? Did they dream they'd hatch this A-bomb brood? They had seemed such innocent magicians. No, better yet, they were like that old medieval sorcerer who worked out the secret of creating water out of nothing. You remember how, while the old wizard was away, his apprentice found the secret formula, turned it on, and then couldn't turn it off, and, if the old sorcerer hadn't come back, he would have inundated the world?

"You've got something there," said Ralph, beaming. "It isn't the original scientists' fault. What we've got now is just scientific curiosity—perverted."

"What we've got now is irresponsibility," I said.

Shaner has always had a way of letting me get just so low. He knew how I loved contrasts. He now began telling me a most ridiculously hopeful little story of a 32-year-old neurologist in Washington who was getting next-to-nothing a year for discovering how to put broken-down cripples back on their feet. He was making them rise and walk. His yearly budget was hardly more than twelve thousand dollars, including food for himself, wife, and three children. I listened to Ralph's pathetic story. He made me see this lonely boy, Herman Kabat, the neuromuscular rehabilitator, and then I could see the solemn scientific boys at the head of the government Office of Scientific Research and Development, directing their thousands of scientific myrmidons in the most gigantic research in history, spending two billion dollars—the sky's the limit, boys.

The two contrasting pictures, the spending of two billion dollars to get human beings to rot and die as against the spending of a precarious few thousand dollars to get human beings to rise and walk—two projects going on simultaneously in Washington—their contrast was hilarious. In the face of death what is so comforting as laughter? Back to Rabelais, the guide of our youth. "To laugh is proper to the man."

"Let's hear something about your Herman Kabat," I said to Shaner.

11

Shaner said he had happened on to Herman Kabat in the early 1940's when Kabat was making some curious experiments with a synthetic drug, prostigmin,* prepared by the pharmaceutical house of which Shaner was the medical director. Kabat said that, in certain badly spasmed victims of infantile paralysis, this prostigmin could out-kenny Sister Kenny, which amazed not only Shaner but Kabat as well, since this observation of his on prostigmin was absolutely accidental.

This chemical had made its medical bow in a most humble way in Switzerland in the 1930's. It was found potent to relieve gas pains after surgical operations. This made it a minor godsend not only to patients but to surgeons fearing the intestinal paralysis that occasionally is responsible for those successful operations following which the patient dies. What is more, prostigmin proved to be a powerful antidote to the horrible poison, curare, which South American natives paint on the tips of their arrows that put victims into a completely helpless and fatal paralysis. Of course this didn't make prostigmin any great shakes as a medical discovery since few human beings are in peril from poisoned arrows.

Then in England, in 1935, this humble prostigmin worked nothing short of a miracle. That year, Dr. Mary B. Walker showed astounded physicians of the Royal Society of Medicine in England how the drug could instantly restore the muscular strength of victims of a most awful affliction. It was a mysterious, progressive and highly fatal tiredness, a disease known as *myasthenia gravis*— de-jargoned this is "grave weakness of muscles."

The eyelids of these sufferers droop and their face muscles weaken so that they have a sleepy, deadpan expression. They start to eat. Their jaws are apt to tire before they've finished a mouthful. They try talking. Before a sentence is finished their voices fade to a whisper. They try to climb a short flight of steps. Their feet feel as if they're going to drop off before reaching the top. They die, usually, when they get tired of breathing.

Into such a victim, before characteristically doubting doctors, Mary Walker sent one shot of prostigmin. Within ten minutes the patient's droopy eyes came wide open. Another few minutes and

* Authorities of organized medicine insist on calling it "neostigmine." I do not know why.

the patient raised tired arms high above his head. In danger of choking, he breathed easy again. He told of a soaring of his strength. Watching Dr. Walker's demonstration, one physician said it was restoring a patient from purgatory to paradise.

As in the case of diabetics with insulin, sufferers from myasthenia gravis have got to go on taking prostigmin for the rest of their lives, not difficult because it can be given by mouth. From a disease often fatal in a few months, this muscle weakness is now an ill in which many victims can have an almost normal expectancy of life. But this still does not take prostigmin off the back pages of newspapers. Myasthenia gravis is comparatively rare.

Yet, when Herman Kabat made his first injection of prostigmin into a polio victim in 1942, there was reason to believe the drug might be hiding an unknown but deep significance. What was the cause of this fatal weakening of muscles? Nobody knew, but it seemed certain that the disease was a breakdown in the machinery of one of the master chemicals of the human body—acetylcholine. This compound is absolutely vital to the transmission of all nerve impulses. Without it you can't so much as wink an eye, wiggle a finger, move any muscle or even have a thought. Two searchers, Otto Loewi and Henry H. Dale, have received two separate Nobel prizes for uncovering acetylcholine's vital significance, proving that all nervous activity is not purely electrical but electrochemical.

All life's activity is an alternating giving-it-the-gun and stepping-on-the-brake. Muscles contract, then relax, and so on. The off-again-on-again chemical action of acetylcholine is curious. If it's secreted at a nerve ending to make a muscle contract, for example, why doesn't that muscle go on contracting, into a spasm? An automatic opposite chemical action stops it. To terminate the action of acetylcholine there is another chemical at hand, cholinesterase, an enzyme that splits acetylcholine into choline and acetic acid.

Muscle action, gland secretion, thought, yes, life itself, is an incessant chemical sparring between these two strange compounds. And myasthenia gravis, that fatal weakness of muscles? It's maybe too little acetylcholine or too much cholinesterase. And when you inject prostigmin? It seems chemically to grab onto cholinesterase so that it can't stop the maybe enfeebled acetylcholine from its nerve impulse stimulating action. Anyway, it seemed plain that, whatever might be the precise method of its acting, prostigmin is a chemical trouble-shooter of breakdowns in the machinery of acetylcholine.

This was something more than a scientific suspicion when Dr. Herman Kabat made his first injection of prostigmin into a woman in Minnesota, severely crippled with infantile paralysis.

III

When Kabat made his first momentous prostigmin injection he was the purest of pure scientists, one of that strange breed of human beings who works just for the curiosity of it, just to know, and damn the consequences, maybe life-saving, maybe life-annihilating, who knows, and you must not care too much about the consequences because if you do, you will destroy the purity of your curiosity. When Kabat made that first prostigmin injection into a woman, not only paralyzed but badly muscle-spasmed with polio, he thought his prostigmin might actually make that spasm more violent; he was not wanting to hurt the woman, you understand— but only wanting to find out, in the interest of science, what *caused* the spasm.

At this time Kabat was still well on the sunny side of 30. He earned his Ph.D. at the incredibly early age of 22, pioneering investigation of the emotional areas of the brain, with the famous Dr. S. W. Ranson at Northwestern University. Kabat had only recently completed his M.D. at the University of Minnesota. He was now researching, obscured by the effulgence of Sister Kenny, making somewhat exasperating inquiries into how the Sister's treatment worked, exactly. Kabat didn't question it that the Sister's hot foments and exercises helped ease the muscle spasm which tortured many polio patients. But how? Sister Kenny had properly stressed the neglected fact that paralysis is only one consequence of polio and that frequent deforming, painful, crippling damage is done to victims by muscle spasm and loss of muscle co-ordination. But how?

Young Kabat was annoying to the crusading Sister who had stirred a tempest in the American scientifico-political poliomyelitis teapot by maintaining that polio was mainly a trouble of muscles, not of the nerve cells of the spinal cord. Young Kabat (and in this he was supported by his collaborator, Dr. Miland E. Knapp) was soon pretty certain that the Sister was as wrong about this theory as she was right about her treatment. You could find no polio virus in muscles. What's more, curare, the arrow poison which blocks the junctions between nerves and muscles, knocks out muscle spasm in polio. Spinal anesthetics, acting on the nerve cells, wipes out spasm, too. Kabat was up to the minute on nervous-system chemistry—what about the master nervous-system chemical, acetylcholine?

If spasm had a nervous and not a purely muscle origin, then anything that zoomed acetylcholine action *should increase the spasm*. At setting up experiments to answer fundamental questions Kabat was smart as a whip. What best zoomed acetylcholine? Prostigmin. Why not? Prostigmin was the acetylcholine trouble-shooter, par excellence. Why not inject prostigmin into an already spasmed polio victim? If the spasm's origin was nervous, that would prove it was so. A shot of prostigmin into this badly spasmed woman, and the spasm would get worse! This was not medicine. This was not the art of healing. This was pure science, cold as a banker's heart.

This 30-year-old unfortunate had been laid low by polio affecting both arms, both legs. At the same time many of her muscles had violently contracted, shortening, hardening, causing terrific pain—spasm. In polio, muscle spasm may be a major disaster portending permanent deformity. The woman was flat on her back in bed. Despite intensive treatment with Kenny foments, she still could not sit up after three-and-a-half months though the Kenny therapy was begun right after the onset. Both her feet were pulled down by muscle spasm, foot drop. Her back was stiffened and knifed through with pain. She was helpless.

Kabat injected his test dose of prostigmin. Her muscle spasm should get worse. Her muscles should knot up harder. Instead, they relaxed! More prostigmin. Within two weeks she could sit up easily; her feet became straight; she said her back felt loose now and the pain was gone; she could actually walk by herself a short distance without support.

The discovery was pure accident. Kabat had found the opposite of what he had looked for. This is an affront to pure scientists, especially those suffering from pride of intellect. This was a turning point in Herman Kabat's life. Medicine, at that moment, began to lose a brilliant neurophysiologist and began to gain a doctor. He had started out to hurt the woman and ended up by easing her torture.

Kabat, the new healer, did not toss away his scientific hard-boiledness. Though this woman had improved so dramatically under prostigmin, she was still getting the Kenny hot foments at the same time, even though for more than three months they hadn't helped her . . . yet! And good Sister Kenny was sure her hot packs were the answer, and who was Kabat to argue with Sister Kenny who was as terrific a woman as any in the world. Then there came the sad case of a little eight-year-old boy, unable to sit up or turn over in bed or even raise his head for five-and-a-half months and the Kenny treatment had had to be discarded after a week because of a severe crop of boils.

"Prostigmin?" muttered Kabat, questioning. Within two days the boy could raise his head under his own power. Within three weeks the little boy could sit up by himself and turn over easily in bed. His back was loose and he could do push-ups. Only because of prostigmin.

Kabat began asking himself a cautious question. Though polio's muscle-spasm can often be conquered (though slowly) by the Kenny hot foments, passive exercises, and muscle training, mightn't prostigmin speed up this long uphill recovery?

In the *Journal of the American Medical Association* in 1943 Dr. Herman Kabat and Dr. Miland E. Knapp reported that, on their series of 24 severe polio cases, only two failed to speed up their return to activity when prostigmin came to the aid of the

Kenny therapy. The speed of the relaxation of spasmed muscles was sometimes remarkable. The clawlike hands and fingers of one patient began loosening within an hour after the first prostigmin injection.

Prostigmin, of course, was no cure for poliomyelitis. It could not bring dead nerve cells back to life. From case to case there's a great variation in polio's damage to the spinal cord. But the painful, crippling muscle spasm of many of polio's victims is helped; and in at least one out of four the return to useful life was striking.

By his accidental observation Herman Kabat began probing deeper into the devastation of the polio virus in the human nervous system. Before Kabat began his adventure it had been suspected that the evil sub-visible microbe hit more than merely the motor nerve cells of the spinal cord that control voluntary muscle action. Deep inside the spinal cord there's an intricate pattern of nerve cells, the internuncial neurons—they're the switchboard controlling the tone, the timing, the co-ordination of muscles all over the body. These, even more than the motor nerve cells, are shattered by the polio virus. And right here, too, it seemed to Kabat that prostigmin came to the rescue, building up acetylcholine action, making new nerve pathways in the partially wrecked switchboard.

Whatever the machinery of it, Kabat was sure that prostigmin put a brake on nerve impulses that caused muscle spasm; it soothed pain; it increased co-ordination of muscle action; and it sometimes strengthened muscle contraction.

IV

Young Kabat—he was bright as a new penny at theories as well as experiments—believed he had discovered a new power of prostigmin. The internuncial neurons of the spinal cord switchboard were not only most sensitive of all nerve cells to the polio virus; they were most sensitive to boosting power of prostigmin. The drug put the brake on exaggerated reflexes that had been causing spasm;

it stepped up enfeebled reflexes and so increased normal muscle action.

What got Kabat his clear-cut results was his boldness in giving big doses of the powerful drug. Prostigmin in big doses produced unpleasant symptoms, super-stimulating the nerves that stimulate intestinal action. He guarded against the possibly resulting embarrassing accidents by giving his patients small doses of atropine along with the prostigmin. Kabat's bold dosing here was in a lesser way reminiscent of Leo Loewe's huge doses of penicillin to cure incurable sub-acute bacterial endocarditis. Physicians who failed to cure S.B.E. with feeble doses of penicillin were annoyed with Loewe because he cured it with big doses! It's well to ask those who question Kabat's work whether they used his doses.

Shouldn't the world now be Kabat's oyster? Good Sister Kenny—who had the aggressiveness of all crusaders—was definitely in the dog-house with many of the orthodox (and dominating) polio researchers and doctors. From celebrating her treatment publicly in print as a revolution in treatment of poliomyelitis, they began to deem her a foreign nuisance, and my undercover agents have even told me that an effort was made to deport the fighting Sister. Now here was Kabat who appeared to have greatly enhanced the power of the Kenny treatment and with polio B.T.O.'s and B.C.M.'s he should be the white-haired boy.

The director of a great foundation suggested to Kabat that he apply for a $30,000 annual grant for five years, which he did; and there had seemed to be, for our poverty-stricken youngster, not that much money in the world; but he was assured that his grant was in the bag. For Kabat the future seemed golden. He had married while he was in Chicago teaching and studying on a salary of $485 a year. Now he and his wife, Sara, were starting a family. He had worked his way through medical school toward his M.D. as a part-time instructor in neuro-physiology. It was Horatio Alger in real life. Then the big wheels started mysteriously turning. The grant did not come to Kabat but went to the head of his department. After all, wasn't Herman a bit callow to have the responsibility of spending so much money? Kabat was told that he could keep on working—but under direction.

Kabat left his University, got himself an ill-paid post in the U. S. Public Health Service in Washington, applied for a grant from the same great foundation to continue the work he had started. He was turned down.

v

It was the ordeal of Tom Spies all over. By the grapevine, it was hinted that there was something peculiar about Herman Kabat, "that Kabat might be brilliant but was not quite a man to be trusted." Then too, though he didn't look it, he was Jewish. . . .

Will it ever transpire that the searcher who makes a discovery will have some say about the money needed to bring the discovery to the help of suffering people? I do not have the answer. Why is it so frequent, in the high political ranks of science, that men who have not done the work have the power to frustrate, and feel it their duty to frustrate, the men who have done it? I do not know.

I only know there are some searchers who refuse to be frustrated. One of these was Kabat. He had a weapon that all power-loving B.C.M.'s in the world could not parry. His weapon was his knowledge (and he was the one man on earth who really knew) that prostigmin was an all-round trouble-shooter for impeded acetylcholine action in the nervous system. He had a far-ahead clairvoyance: that the repair of this impeded action of acetylcholine might be significant for more than those thousands spasmed by polio. It might aid recovery for hundreds of thousands wrecked by this or that damage to their neuromuscular systems, which might result in spastic paralysis.

Outside this knowledge and this clairvoyance, in his new job Kabat hadn't much more than a prayer, as they say in baseball. The Public Health Service, great though its tradition and experience in fighting microbic ills, had no personnel, no substantial funds to back Kabat in his attempt to rehabilitate all kinds of spastic cripples, with prostigmin.

In 1943 he began his adventure with about $4,000 a year to feed and house his increasing brood of youngsters. His budget for research was negligible and was eked out by a grant dug up for him by Ralph Shaner, but as against this poverty, Kabat had an entranced sureness that he was on his way. You couldn't tire him. He was externally very mild with energy boiling inside him translating itself into work with not much lost motion. He was a human bulldozer of which the tracks and the motor were almost inaudible. This type doesn't need priming with vast research money.

Kabat in Washington was a medical nobody. He was obscure among the pompous wartime medical buzzings-about of the Battle of Washington. He began scouting around for candidates for his chemical rehabilitation. What he found was appalling. He knew there were plenty of candidates among the residuals from infantile paralysis, but the number of these spastic polios was picayune compared to the spastic disabled from other diseases and by wounds and accidents.

Kabat made an informal, lone-wolf census. If what he found around Washington was all over the nation, how many hundreds of thousands, how many millions? Who knew? Spastic cripples were not reportable. Nobody had counted them. And who really wanted to know? Surely not many doctors would want to, seeing how little could be done for so many. Of all sick people these spastic disabled were America's forgotten. Anyway weren't we a strong-armed, straight-limbed, husky America going great guns winning his global war for our Commander-in-Chief? Not to regard these x million crocks was part of the American ritual—of optimism. Look at the husky lads marching.

Kabat lacked not for patients. They were a pain-racked residue— of broken bones set successfully, of joint injuries that had healed, of arthritis that had burned itself out, of paralytic strokes that had faded, partly, after the hemorrhages had absorbed. It was an incredible residue of the more or less permanently more or less disabled. By muscle spasm. By disuse atrophy of muscles.

Kabat's wide candid eyes narrowed to observe this curious phenomenon of spasm. He saw that it began innocently enough as a beneficent trick of nature. It was nature's splint against the insult of disease or accident. Then it often persisted as the deepening, the strengthening of a habit which, if not broken, might cripple its victims for life. Baths, passive exercises, hydrotherapy, short wave diathermy—all these were a boon to many muscle-spasm sufferers. Yet for many, physical therapy remained without effect.

These are the down-and-outers (cats and dogs some doctors call them) who drag themselves to spas, to quacks who thrive on them after respectable physicians have admitted themselves powerless. It was upon some 400 of such derelicts that Herman Kabat and Dr. Charles W. Jones mobilized themselves into a ridiculous two-man research army. They started to treat them in a clinic in Washington and in East Coast Marine Hospitals. Almost all were chronic cases disabled for years. Their ticket for admission was proved failure to benefit from all physical therapy, orthopedic surgery, osteopathic manipulations, or chiropractic violence.

Kabat began putting his prostigmin to a test that was stern and simple. When he began his injections, all other forms of treatment were suspended.

For fourteen months a man who'd broken his leg below the knee had suffered such cramps in his ankle that he couldn't drive his car or walk upstairs. After three weeks of prostigmin injections his pain had vanished and he was back at complete activity, with no relapse. In 51 fracture cases, 39 were significantly improved, range of motion increasing, fatigue diminishing, muscle strength soaring.

In arthritis it was a different story. It was plain to Kabat that prostigmin was no help whatever to arthritis in its active stages; acute cases were not benefited at all; and wrecked joints couldn't be replaced by prostigmin but might be mended if at all only by surgery. Yet even in arthritis—burned out—Kabat was a witness to strange happenings. An old woman whose rheumatoid arthritis had burned out many years before was still confined to her bed and wheelchair. She was deformed and in constant pain from muscle spasm. After two weeks of daily injections of prostigmin she could stand up and walk for the first time in six years.

Kabat had the happiness to find that he was no longer completely a lone wolf in his spasm-fighting adventure. Dr. Philip R. Trommer and Dr. Abraham Cohen, of Philadelphia, reported a case of a woman bedfast after burned-out arthritis for more than a year. Her hands were like claws, her knees were drawn up tight against her body. She was unable to feed or take care of herself in any way at all. Within an hour after the first injection of prostigmin her knees began straightening; she could cross her right knee over her left and swing her legs over the side of the bed. Her wrecked joints were not rebuilt, but before the improvement had reached its limit, she could get out of bed without help, comb her hair and take care of her needs—part way back to life as an independent human being.

But for arthritics where spasm was not a complicating factor, prostigmin was no help whatever. Kabat could only say that the drug opened the door that had been locked against any recovery for some of them, yet muscle re-education, nutritional, medical, and surgical treatment would be needed to bring most of them back to really active life.

Kabat and Jones found the same to be true of the disability following cerebral hemorrhage. This is the fifth cause of death in the United States. For every one dying there are at least six who live a long time, more or less incapacitated. When brain cells are killed by these cerebral accidents there is no hope of their resurrection, yet it's known that nature has a trick of making new nerve pathways, detours round the scene of brain tissue devastation, so that spontaneously usually there's more or less recovery.

Couldn't prostigmin—trouble-shooter for acetylcholine—help that master chemical of the nervous system form new nerve paths, faster?

Sometimes. One of the most hopeless of such stroke patients was a man who'd been paralyzed on the right side of his body for 17 years. His heel was two inches off the floor, his spine was twisted, his right arm powerless. Kabat started prostigmin. Within 24 hours after the first injection, the man could put a cigarette in his mouth with his right hand. After a month's treatment he could stand up straight with both heels on the ground; his twisted spine unbent somewhat; there was a surge of his muscular strength and marked improvement in his walking.

Yet again here Kabat saw that prostigmin—for the vast majority of stroke victims—was only the first boost upward on what would have to be a stern long climb toward rehabilitation. Prostigmin began their return to at least partial activity. It increased the strength of many. Yet again, as in the arthritics, it seemed only to open the door; some additional trick was needed to renew the lost strength of their muscles. Prostigmin was tantalizing. It *started* many spectacular returns toward life. Kabat and Jones could report that the majority of their more than 400 sufferers from the crippling consequences of polio, fractures, arthritis, cerebral hemorrhage (and even the tragic athetoid victims of cerebral palsy) were improved significantly by prostigmin. And the improvement was maintained after prostigmin was discontinued. Yet prostigmin action taunted Kabat. Prostigmin was cruel to many of the victims, really. It brought so many part way back to the old use of their muscles only to leave them—dangling.

Something more was required of Kabat. Something more was demanded of his patients. What was it?

VI

When Ralph Shaner brought him to meet us for the first time at the Hotel Gotham in New York on a rainy morning in October, 1945, Herman Kabat thought he had it. He was beginning to sense what these wrecked people needed beyond this first boost back towards life by prostigmin. And what they needed, beyond prostigmin, seemed absolutely out of reach of the vast majority of them— it was a new type of muscle re-education so long, so delicate, so arduous, requiring such expert aid from specially trained physical therapists (who did not exist) that Kabat's plans seemed to be, to understate it, Utopic.

It was a stirring and a sad day that Sunday all day with Ralph and Kabat. Rhea and I had never met anybody with so much to give to so many people but with such an utter lack of facilities to give it. Kabat was a pleasantly open-faced man, Italianish-looking, with luminous eyes and looking much older than his then 32 years. Well, he had been through plenty. He had left the Public Health Service and was now some sort of consultant to the Health Department of the District of Columbia, and he was doing his rehabilitation work in a grubby clinic in a grubbier hospital. Three years ago he had been a promising Assistant Professor in a great medical school. Now he had no academic standing. The B.T.O. of a great foundation had as good as promised him an excellent position; when he had come to New York to close the deal (he thought), Kabat had been stood up by the foundation's medical director who failed to see him. Kabat's black hair was prematurely gray over his ears and his shining wide-open eyes were sad though hopeful. He told of his work with absolute clarity and confidence obviously backed by immense neurologic knowledge; and in his voice there was a hint of querulousness. It was as if he was asking what was wrong with his work on neuro-muscular dysfunction. It was as if he was asking what was wrong with Kabat.

I asked him if anybody had tried to duplicate his prostigmin researches and published a refutation? On the contrary. His work on the spastic complications of polio, arthritis, and cerebral palsy—all of it had been confirmed by publications of other investigators. No controversies.

That rainy day we beat our brains out, all of us, trying to think of foundations, medical schools that might support Kabat. Or industrialists—there was a wide-open field for neuro-muscular rehabilitation in heavy industry with its toll of accidents. We felt hopeless that day. Time was when we would have grabbed the long-distance telephone asking Boss Kettering or Henry J. Kaiser to let Kabat tell them his story. Kabat had convinced me, yet at this time I had no confidence as a research promoter.

"But you'll try to write Kabat's work for *The Reader's Digest*, Paul," said Ralph Shaner, leaning back and looking at me with his Mona Lisa smile.

"Yes, by God, I'll try it," I said, "and then, maybe—"

Just before leaving, Herman Kabat told us of a case—it was pre-

mature and far too early to publish—that brought me to the edge
of my chair. In August, just about Hiroshima day, a lady had been
brought in a wheelchair to Dr. Kabat. "Multiple sclerosis, no less,"
said Kabat, smiling.

"Multiple *sclerosis?*" I protested. "But that's a progressive, degenerative disease, absolutely hopeless!"

"Is it?" asked Kabat. "Well, anyway, for 16 years this woman
had been completely unable to walk, even with support," continued Kabat, "and with great difficulty she could stand for a little
while, holding on to a chair."

Kabat had seen me raise my eyebrows when he had mentioned
"multiple sclerosis" and had noted my voice when I said "absolutely hopeless" and knew I was thinking "this fellow isn't going
to try to do anything about *that* one." Kabat remained perfectly
calm about my going off half-cocked on a subject about which I
knew nothing. Then he revealed the curiously original, sort of
mentally left-handed trick he had of beginning to unknot a tough
problem, even a notoriously hopeless one. "You see," Kabat went
on, half-apologetically as if to justify his having had anything to
do with such a derelict at all, "what struck me about this lady
was that she hadn't gotten worse. Her multiple sclerosis had remained stationary all those years after her first attack of it."

Kabat remembered better than I that all the books taught the
disease was hopeless. He forgot the books, now, asking himself a
left-handed question: How much of her bedfastness is due, not to
her original multiple sclerosis, but to a mere disuse of her nerves
and muscles? Promising her nothing, he had begun giving her
daily shots of prostigmin. In a couple of weeks the terrible tiredness, that's one of the diagnostic hallmarks of multiple sclerosis,
began to lessen. That was about all Kabat could say for prostigmin's
action. "But that opened the door for us," explained Kabat. "My
physical therapist began to give this woman systematic exercises,
not passive but active, and longer and longer. Of course we kept
shooting in prostigmin too."

Kabat became a bit excited. His usually low drawling voice rose.
"You should have seen her trunk and leg muscles when we started!

They were nothing. Wasted! As good as gone! It's been only three months she's been on prostigmin and our new exercises," he said. "You should see how a muscle can come back, after 15 years. She's even walked a few steps. Supported. But for the first time after all those years."

I was skeptical, having heard vaguely that some cases of multiple sclerosis have their ups and downs, remissions and relapses. Then too, wasn't Kabat a bit of a hypnotic personality? Mightn't it be, well, suggestion? Mightn't there be some of that Lourdes business operating on this woman? I was too polite to say it.

"That's all, so far," Kabat answered. "I wish I had another case of it to try. But you won't use what I've just told you in your story?" Of course not.

Herman Kabat was a gallant man who would try anything to help any spastic down-and-outer. He was lonely, medically and it was sad not to be able to get money to help him.

VII

At the end of January, 1946, the story of Kabat's rehabilitation of sundry spastic cripples was published in *The Reader's Digest* and, for me, a bit of minor hell began popping. Not a word had been written about the multiple sclerosis lady, but the leadership of the American Medical Association was as skeptical about Kabat's rehabilitation experiences, in general, as I had been about that one lady. It seemed that, countrywide, fathers and mothers and sisters and brothers and sons and daughters of spastic paraplegics had clamored in doctors' offices and spastics who could still drag around had come dragging to the doctors. It was scandalous; that damned de Kruif again. The cases were most of them so hopeless that who could blame physicians for being indignant at a story entitled *Many Will Rise and Walk?* Many embattled doctors wrote to the *Journal of the American Medical Association* (or so the Editor said) and the Editor said he had written back to the complaining doctors, comforting them to the effect that, so far as he knew, *The Reader's Digest* made no attempt whatever to check the scientific accuracy of the material it published from de Kruif. This is what you call the super-smear.

The denials by the doctors, it was curious, didn't stop the embattled relatives. The authoritative (I mean very highest authoritative) denials didn't stop the crippled victims, either. They swarmed to Kabat's old house in Washington. They camped on his doorstep. Kabat was working full time at his clinic which took care only of District of Columbia spastic paralytics but now he had to toil half the night at home with these pitiful supplicants from all over. He was lucky to get the help of an expert, strong, very gentle physical therapist, Maggie Knott, just out of the army.

Maggie had a crinkly smile around as kind and understanding eyes as you've ever seen on a woman, and she was definitely not averse to trying to help people for whom medical authority said no help was possible. Maggie quickly got the hang of giving these people Kabat's exercises against heavy resistance, her resistance, so that it was lucky for Maggie that she was strong. The jam of patients all but pushed Kabat's family out of the house and finally they had to wheel the new baby's crib into the hall and use its nursery for treatments. Kabat's lovely wife, Sara, besides taking care of their four children, answered thousands of letters. The block in which the Kabats lived filled up with patients who hired rooms so they wouldn't have to drag themselves far to get to the treatments.

"We were buried under every kind of cripple," explained Kabat. "It was a madhouse. We ourselves got wacky. Maggie got us three more physical therapists. Even then we were all crazy tired."

Kabat had brought it on himself, partly, no doubt, because of this story in *The Reader's Digest*. He was red-eyed from not sleeping and sore-armed from giving heavy resistance exercises and sad to have to turn people away who weren't spastics and happy to have the chance to help people who were spastic paralytics. "Those poor people began teaching me something I'd never realized," said Kabat. "It wasn't what I, the doctor, thought I could do for them. It was *their* life. They were going to decide whether I'd help them. They were going to say whether they'd live or die."

This was a really novel inversion of the time-honored "doctor-patient relationship" in which the doctor's prerogative has been to try to dole out life to this one and let that one die because there was nothing to do. Not because the doctor wanted that one to die but because it has not yet become the right of the patient to tell the doctor that the doctor had simply got to keep him alive and get him better. This was a curious, fourth-dimensional relationship which his patients imposed upon Kabat; and I'd never before met a physician who had felt this as a command, not a supplication, from his patients. Kabat bowed to it.

VIII

Amidst all this hubbub that first multiple sclerosis lady—a series of one case about which some "scientific" doctors make such merriment—kept on getting better. Her trembling was fading. It was seven months, now, since she'd begun her prostigmin and special exercises and now she was less and less tired and she could now (after 16 years of not walking at all) walk with two canes 700 feet. Kabat, encouraged, knowing that all empirical science is a series of one case when you start it, despite being busy with every kind of muscle-spasm sufferer—polios, stroke victims, arthritics, and cerebral palsy and athetoid children—peered round for more multiple sclerosis.

He was foolhardy. Your far-advanced multiple sclerosis case is moth-eaten, physically and often emotionally. To make it clear that he was asking himself for a headache, let's leave him for a while working days in the grubby District clinic and nights in his hectic one-man institution for the rehabilitation of the spastic derelicts of America. We must try to get hold of this horror called multiple sclerosis.

Its diagnosis by the neurologists has been generally feared as worse than a death sentence. It is the prediction of life on a trembling, more and more feeble downgrade to helplessness. It is a disease of the central nervous system that usually strikes between ages 20 and 40, the most productive period of life. At its onset it may hit devastatingly or again it may seem no-account because its first signs and symptoms may be transient. For a few hours or days the victim may see double or have blurred vision or blind spots before the eyes. Knees may suddenly buckle. Balance and sense of direction may be lost while walking so you'd say, if you saw such a victim, "That poor souse has certainly had a few too many." The victim's legs may feel weak and heavy; fingers may feel numb and tingle; incontinence of bladder and bowels is frequent; many sufferers experience fits of uncontrollable crying; most of them tremble.

These signs and symptoms may occur singly or all together. They may vanish as suddenly as they came, and are often misdiagnosed as hysteria. You do not blame a doctor for not wanting to say it's multiple sclerosis. Rarely these first sinister signals of doom never do return and only the minutest examination by a nerve specialist could detect that the patient had had multiple sclerosis. Usually the attacks return, and with greater violence, so that rank-and-file physicians are finally in no doubt of the grim diagnosis.

The pay-off in about 80 per cent of cases is spastic paraplegia (a stiff paralysis) of the legs, and often paralysis of arms and trunk muscles. From this fell blow, recovery to any marked degree has been uncommon.

Contrary to popular belief the death-rate from multiple sclerosis itself is not high. It kills all right, but usually indirectly. Kabat has a new word for it. "What kills them is bed-sickness," he explains. The bedfast victim of multiple sclerosis has a much greater than ordinary chance of dying from pneumonia. Usually sufferers live for many years. For them it is not so much a question of live or die as of being dead though alive. There are records of people hit by multiple sclerosis while young who have lived till 70. But when the disease has progressed to spastic paraplegia, stiff paralysis of the legs, the outlook for a comeback is dim.

Dr. L. C. Kolb and his co-workers, of the U. S. Public Health Service, have made a study of the fate of 176 multiple sclerosis sufferers. They lived nine years on the average, from onset; 80 per cent were no longer able to work within five years of the beginning of their sickness; 75 per cent had to quit their jobs within one year from the onset and did not work again any more.

A cure? Do not make us laugh, answer the best scientific authorities. In his famous textbook, Sir William Osler who for many years was the final authority on hopeless human afflictions, sums up the prospects for those stricken: "Ultimately the patient, if not carried off by some intercurrent infection, becomes bedridden."

Prevention? Do not make us smile, answer the public healthmen. How can you prevent what you haven't a notion of the cause of? There's no hint of its being contagious but, to the contrary, it can't be transmitted to laboratory animals (though there have been experiments that produce a replica of the disease, in animals, making it look like some sort of allergy). It is pretty certain that the bewildering complex of signs and symptoms is due to a patchy destruction—random—of the white matter of this or that part of the brain and spinal cord. Dr. Tracy J. Putnam, the distinguished Beverly Hills, California, nerve specialist, has a theory that the spotty havoc in the nervous system is made by clots of blood in little veins, blocking the blood supply of these delicate tissues. Why the clotting? God alone knows.

Early in the inevitable downhill march to doom, some—but not by a long shot all—cases have remissions and these mysterious let-ups have fooled many an earnest scientist into thinking, aha, here's a cure. The universal medical belief that there is no way to check or cure multiple sclerosis doesn't stem from doctors not trying, but from trying dozens of angles and failing. Artificial fever treatments, X-rays to the spine, quinine, liver shots, massive vitamins, histamine, sympathectomy operations—all have seemed hopeful, then wash-outs. The joker has been that, since the ups and downs occur spontaneously, any treatment of the early stages may seem to produce good results *if that treatment happens to coincide with the spontaneous remission.*

On this rock many a medical big name (and not only in the field of multiple sclerosis) has been wrecked.

At present Dr. Tracy J. Putnam is experimenting with the drug, dicoumarol, which slows down clotting of blood and he is trying to check the progress of the malady in the early phase of the sickness. He is a brave investigator, and we wish him much luck with this treatment which is certainly still experimental. The sad sum-up is that there is yet no drug, serum, vaccine, or physical force on earth that can prevent the formation of those mysterious plaques of spotty deterioration of the nervous system.

In the face of the inexorability of M.S. (as we shall now abbreviate multiple sclerosis), what do doctors do when faced by this horrible devastation? In general, they refer the victim to a neurologist who refers the victim to bed. To rest in bed all the time. To rest till death do them part from the victim. Dr. Walter Freeman, of Washington, D. C., reports a list of early cases, rested for some months, then getting up more or less better, even able to work for months or years without a relapse. Were those remissions simply spontaneous, rest or no rest? Maybe. Dr. Freeman has also seen the rest-cure rest its victims into permanent incapacity.

Herman Kabat has asked hundreds of dilapidated hopeless victims what the last treatment was that their doctors recommended and the almost invariable answer was—rest in bed.

We are now at the low point of this bleak M.S. saga, and the upturn is led not by neurologists or any other variety of M.D.'s, osteopaths, naturopaths, or chiropractors but by obscure citizens who had been advised to rest themselves out of this world. A glimmer of hope—not for cure of M.S. but for rehabilitation—came from two far-advanced hopeless sufferers who up and fooled their doctors and they will have immortality as Herman Kabat's precursors.

Wilford Wright, veteran of World War I, was stricken with M.S. in 1922, slid downhill into spastic paraplegia, became completely incapacitated in 1937, his doctor reporting then that he believed he had heard the last of this man—excepting for an obituary notice. Wright went on a stretcher to the Veteran's Administration Home, Bay Pines, Florida, and was there given up by government doctors. But in 1941, the Washington *Evening Star* carried a headline: "HOPELESS CRIPPLE CONFOUNDS DOCTOR IN TRICYCLE TRAVELS."

While the doctors weren't looking (you must rest, Wilford!) this human hunk of nothing began self-treatment, very feebly but very systematically moving his stiff, wasted muscles. Many months that way, smiling to himself more and more broadly till at last—"to the amazement" of his doctors—Wilford grotesquely heaved himself under his own steam up on to an adult tricycle. He has since driven his tricycle from Florida to Nova Scotia and from Florida to the West Coast and has rehabilitated himself economically by making tricycles for M.S. and other cripples who also refuse to let their doctors let them rot to death in bed.

By his own deed Wilford has perhaps over-simplified the pathogenesis of this frightful sickness. "It's all in the mind," says Wright. "If you've got the stuff it takes, you can win out."

In Cleveland, Ohio, a young woman, Betty Bard, lay paralyzed, deaf, and blind from M.S. Absolutely on her own she began giving herself the silliest, feeblest, fluttery, almost imperceptible exercises that grew noticeable—for heaven's sake see Betty *moving!*—then stronger, and then up and walking and vision returning, at last powerful. Till Betty Bard is now a world-famous medical curiosity, or maybe it's best to say Betty Bard is a world-famous phenomenon demonstrating a new medicine—guts, grit, and will-power. Yet the doctors must be given the credit: they admit that Betty contradicts their science, that she was an unquestioned far-advanced case of multiple sclerosis now free from incapacity.

In the far future, if the A-bomb boys allow us a future, when the medical profession will have progressed in wisdom to a degree of humility making it possible for them to learn from the laity, in that dim future in front of the marble portals of some medical school there may be a statue of Betty Bard or of Wilford Wright on his curative tricycle. However, I do not expect to live to see this.

Yet, let us be fair to the physicians. Weren't Betty and Wilford happenstances? Weren't they mysterious exceptions to a horrible rule of the total inability of M.S. victims to climb back up out of their trembling, stiff-muscled, lethargic desuetude? Some future Tom Spies, or Al Coburn, or Herman Kabat may find the chemical machinery explaining the reviving spark of life that made Betty Bard and Wilford Wright generate the will-power to fight back to activity. Let's hope so. Let's look at it that way, sticking to the strictly materialistic. Or might the Christian Scientists really have something?

Bard and Wright have this in common that they furnish a neat answer to doctors who frown on self-treatment as dangerous. They could say, speaking for themselves, that it was on the contrary salubrious.

I X

In February, 1946, a letter holding great news for Herman Kabat came to us at Wake Robin. It said, in part:

"Dear Paul: Imagine my surprise on picking up the current *Reader's Digest* and seeing your article on prostigmin. I've been taking it for a month and it's made a new world for me. Last May in Denver I became quite ill. The doctors all say it was the multiple sclerosis flaring up again. . . . Anyway, my legs became quite numb and I lost all sense of balance so I couldn't walk without help. Believe me I was scared stiff. In addition I was really tired out and had . . . lost 50 pounds . . . I couldn't stand any physical exertion . . . I was getting very low. . . . At Xmas, Sid Garfield suggested prostigmin. Well, it helped an awful lot. Instead of being shot by noon, I was good for a full day. I've got so I carry my own syringe and stick myself. . . . You can imagine what this means to me . . . Sincerely, HENRY JR."

This spectacular reversal of a downhill toward doom had happened not to an anonymous American but to Henry J. Kaiser, Jr., son of America's master-builder. My thoughts flashed back to that rainy Sunday in New York when we could think of nobody who might help expand Herman Kabat's project. This letter seemed Providential. It was Providence operating through Dr. Sidney R. Garfield, the director of the Kaiser health plan. Garfield had never met Kabat. Just on the strength of hearing the remark that Kabat had seen remarkable improvement in one case of multiple sclerosis, following prostigmin, Garfield had gone ahead and tried it on young Henry.

This beginning rehabilitation of young Henry would surely

mean more than all applications to Foundations, to rich people, more than all the promotional prospectuses that could be written for Kabat. At this moment, Herman Kabat was more in need of help than ever. He was overwhelmed with every sort of spastic paraplegic. His little home clinic in Washington was seething with muscle-spasmed cripples. His practice was now prospering at the rate of an income of $50,000 yearly. His facilities were totally inadequate. He had no medical assistants and he was short of physical therapists while at the same time it was becoming more and more plain to him that his new nerve-muscle training was even more important than the first boost with prostigmin. Though eligible, Kabat had not taken the trouble to join the District Medical Society, and you must definitely be one of the organization boys if you're going to have such an income, or you're in danger of denunciation as a medical racketeer. Though, mind you, the patients who were rising and walking weren't putting Kabat in that category.

Garfield now asked Kabat to join forces with Henry Kaiser's Permanente Foundation. Kabat, lone wolf, was cagey. First of all, young Henry needed more than prostigmin. "It's a gamble," said Kabat, "it's still an experiment. We've treated only one case up till now. He's got his first boost from prostigmin. Let's see what nerve-muscle re-education will add to it."

In this life among the doctors I've seen many a reversal from despair to hope, but few more striking than this now experienced by Henry J. Kaiser, Jr. In 1945, his prospects of ever working again seemed dim. Histamine, dicoumarol, and other treatments had failed. His trunk muscles were wasted. He staggered when he tried to walk. His knees would suddenly buckle under him. He would start to walk and fall on his face. He sagged under a growing weakness. I'll never forget the elder Kaiser's look when he first told me it was M.S. and that this meant curtains, almost for sure, for his son's productive life. That was about a year before Herman Kabat told us of the first woman, walking, after 16 years in a wheelchair and in bed.

It was a gamble, no doubt. That first woman's disease had been stationary for a long time, while young Henry's sickness was rapidly progressive. But now, by midsummer, 1946, you would not have known him. At 5:30, every morning, Henry Jr. was up for a rugged muscle-training workout with his personal physical therapist who had the build and strength of a light-heavyweight prizefighter. Against heavy resistance by this husky man, young Henry began systematically to try to move, then to move a little, then to move more vigorously, every weakened group of muscles in his body—fingers, toes, hands, feet, arms, legs, trunks. Aided by the boosting power of prostigmin these workouts brought new sap to his wasted muscles. His tremor vanished. He no longer fell. He gained in balance and co-ordination. By autumn he could walk a mile with little fatigue. He still staggered some when he started moving. But he could run half a mile, and he could dance.

His experience with these first two cases made Herman Kabat see that the tragic helplessness of M.S. is not all of it due to destruction of nervous tissue in the human brain. He knew that neither prostigmin nor the new exercises could repair that devastation. When a nerve cell is dead, it's dead. But Kabat believed he had now spied another, an added reason for the inexorably growing incapacity of these victims. It was loss of nerve control and muscle power—*through disuse*. Through inactivity.

In short, let's face it, the rest treatment actually added to the disability of M.S. sufferers and finally completed their total incapacity.

Kabat had the optimistic clairvoyance to act upon a fact that was known to all pathologists learned in multiple sclerosis. In this awful disease the destruction of brain tissue is spotty, patchy. The unknown destroyer seldom wrecks all nerve pathways. And the return of these two patients to more and more active life forced Kabat to a hopeful conclusion: It seemed as if prostigmin combined with systematic nerve-muscle re-education was forming new pathways from brain to muscles. They seemed to be nerve detours. They seemed to by-pass the patches of nerve destruction.

They were new pathways through despair.

It was stirring to listen to Kabat describing this curious new science, but you had to be skeptical. If you were a neurologist—

remember neurologists are the most skilled diagnosticians of doom in all medicine—you were sure to point out that Kabat had brought only two cases back to activity. I could see the deprecating raising of shoulders and outward gesture of their hands and droop at the corners of the mouths of these experts. Two cases. Indeed. So what? So he defied the neurologists; and he defied multiple sclerosis.

"We do not have to accept the low level of activity," he said, "decreed by the nerve damage. We can make new connections!"

If Kabat was correct, then it was a new morning in the drab defeatist history of multiple sclerosis. It was a first medical revolt against the inexorable. It was defiance of defeatist science. It was as if Kabat said to this damnable devastation: "Let's see the worst you can do. Bring on the derelicts you've made forlorn the longest. Bring 'em all on."

In July, 1946, Kabat gave up his booming practice. It wasn't easy. From his earliest boyhood he'd lived in a couple of little rooms above his father's various little neighborhood shoe-stores which, the old gentleman explained, were not successful because they were in the wrong location. He gave up the big money that makes medical specialists the most prosperous of professionals. With Sidney Garfield, he organized the Kabat-Kaiser Institute, non-profit, and became its director at a merely decent salary. He began his battle against every type of neuro-muscular dysfunction in a high-ceilinged old house—it had been the ministry of a Caribbean Republic—on 16th Street in Washington. He started without foundation, rich man, or government grants, or any sort of philanthropy. He equipped the new institute and expanded his staff of physical therapists and doctors on a bank loan backed by Henry J. Kaiser.

x

It began to seem as if the distinguished nerve specialists might be a bit premature when they shrugged off Kabat's first two rehabilitated cases of multiple sclerosis. The first woman who hadn't walked for 16 years could now go several blocks with one cane and could walk a short distance without any support at all. She was improving steadily. It was now 1947, and Henry J. Kaiser was tanned, heavy-muscled, and could beat everybody at push-ups. He could walk two miles. He was working the regulation Kaiser 16 hours a day. You had to watch close to notice his remaining slight lack of co-ordination. "Herman Kabat has saved my life," said Henry who would not have lived long if he could not have worked again.

Prominent neurologists were still not excited. Remembering the reputation of M.S. for hopelessness, you could not blame them. This was reminiscent of the newspapers of the world ignoring the Wright Brothers' first heavier-than-air flight at Kitty Hawk until four years after they had made it. Men would never fly. M.S. patients would never walk again. The big nerve specialists were not yet referring multiple sclerosis cases to Kabat. These forlorn began to come by themselves, having heard of him over the grapevine of the afflicted.

October, 1947, at the Kabat-Kaiser Institute in Washington, I saw 13 far-advanced M.S. victims learning to sit up, to stand, to use their hands and feet, to walk again. They were at every milestone on the rugged trail toward rehabilitation. They had all been going downhill for from five to twenty years. They were, when they came to Kabat, all of them, past that stage of multiple sclerosis where there are still spontaneous remissions, let-ups in the severity of the disease. They all had the spastic paraplegia from which there is rarely any return at all.

As I watched them working, it was curious how they made me forget Kabat. It was their battle. They were the doctor.

Twenty years afflicted, for five years completely bedfast, I watched Mrs. Henrietta Spatta learn to walk, alone and unsupported. Each step she took seemed to demand the energy a normal human being would expend to walk a mile. She had to think her walking. She clenched her fists in super-human concentration. Her endeavor seemed to be fanning new sparks of nerve impulses in the new nerve paths that were still only dimly blazed from her brain to the muscles of her trunk, legs, and feet. Her set jaw, her intent look at the line on the floor in front of her, those desperately clenched fists

—all were her pep-talk to her new nerve-muscle patterns. Mrs. Spatta was taking five steps, unaided, more than she had taken the day before. At the end of this record 30 steps she relaxed and leaned on her physical therapist.

Her plain face was lovely with a slight smile of triumph.

Kabat's M.S. patients, one and all of them, showed me how fiercely people can want to live. Mrs. Pauline Tannenbaum had come to the Institute after having been completely disabled for six years. Lying flat on her back, she hadn't been able to lift her feet half an inch off the examining table. Now she could raise both legs straight up in the air. On her arrival, her physical therapist had found it almost impossible to work with her because of her prolonged fits of crying. Now Mrs. Tannenbaum smiled with a sort of defiance as she walked steadily round the room, just holding onto her husband's guiding finger.

In the pitiful progress of these lost ones back to activity I saw a new kind of happiness. Gordon Tolman, afflicted with multiple sclerosis for years and totally disabled since 1945, had come for a last-ditch stand against his illness after all other treatments had failed. After three weeks of prostigmin plus muscle training by heavy resistance exercises, he could come to a sitting posture, unaided. The sixth week he surprised himself by finding himself standing without support while he combed his hair. Then a few weeks later he could stand alone to dress, which he had not been able to do for years. He was making slow but steady progress in walking.

Gordon Tolman had words for the uphill toil of the heavy resistance exercise treatment. His physical therapist was strengthening his quadriceps, the muscle that makes your leg kick out toward a straight position. Tolman was sitting on the table, his legs dangling. The therapist put her hand on his ankle and commanded, "Push as hard as you can!" Tolman's leg went up slowly till it was straight out. He felt himself pushing, at first, against her resistance. Then the therapist had taken over at the point where Tolman's strength failed and carried his leg through its full quadriceps range. "Now hold it there, don't let me push it back," said the therapist. Then she slowly pushed his legs back against all the resistance he could muster. Three times. Then Tolman was fatigued, completely. One minute's rest. Then the nerve-muscle power returned so he could go through the exercise three times more. No more, no less. A few weeks later he could do the exercise seven times. A few weeks more, 22 times . . .

"Do you wonder I jumped into my wheelchair and trundled off to my room, rather happy," asked Tolman.

Gordon Tolman who is a thin-faced, kindly-eyed New Hampshire Yankee, remarked on the curiously exuberant atmosphere among the patients in the gymnasium at the Kabat-Kaiser Institute. "The answer came to me after a month of treatment," said Tolman. "Not much improvement. Even now it is not tremendous, though it still continues.

"But the fact that any improvement at all should occur after a great many years of increasing disability, seemed wonderful, indeed."

That's what gave the Kabat-Kaiser Institute the esprit de corps of a military unit, the verve of a mining town, and the crusading faith of a pioneering church, explained Tolman. He knew it was really Kabat. Shortly before Tolman left the Institute, Herman Kabat tried a new exercise on him. "I sat on the table," said Tolman, "and Dr. Kabat pulled my head down between my knees. Then I straightened up against resistance. After one try I felt weak as blotting paper."

Kabat whispered in Tolman's ear as he encouraged him to try once more, "Boy, it's your battle."

Gordon Tolman and his 12 M.S. companions at the Kabat-Kaiser Institute were upstream swimmers, and Kabat, in his low-voiced, gentle way, called out of them reserves of gameness that probably exist in most human beings. I have seen these people grit their teeth to move a hand or foot inches against the physical therapist's resistance. Their faces illustrated Kabat's conviction that inactivity is death and activity is life. That was Kabat's unmysterious medicine.

At the same time, the patients testified to the boosting power of the prostigmin shots, which seemed to give them a first lift of energy to replace their long horrible fatigue. It seemed to begin a loosening of the spastic bands that had bound them. It stirred the first flicker of that chemical nerve spark, acetylcholine, to begin to activate muscles for years disused and wasted from that disuse.

Are most human beings inherently lazy? These M.S.'s gloried in their effort against resistance, the heavy resistance (to them)—pressure which they could barely overcome to move a finger, a toe, a hand, a foot, a leg or their whole body against the opposing pressure of the physical therapist's hands. It tired me, physically, just to watch this work of these people who had been totally tired for years. Applied to single wasted muscles, then to muscle groups for the total activity needed for sitting, standing, walking, the doggedness of these people at their heavy resistance exercise made this clear: in this new medicine it is the patient who is the hero.

At the Kabat-Kaiser Institute I saw the intangible medicine, morale, in action. Diagnosed M.S., five years ago, Mrs. Elsie Worch had drifted downhill to utter helplessness. She couldn't take a step alone and only a few assisted. She was sleepless in a whirling confusion of worry. Her pessimism got its first defeat when one day, after weeks of prostigmin shots and muscle training, she found she could stand for a moment, unaided. For years she had been unable to do any housework. Now she forged ahead and, in a few months, she surprised her husband and children when they came home in the evening, by having their dinner ready for them. She'd got the dinner, unaided.

"That victory," said Georgiana Windham, her physical therapist, "gave Mrs. Worch new confidence, and, oh, what drive."

Maggie Knott, the chief therapist, is at the head of as devoted a group of women as any who've worked to bring doomed people back to life. "Here's the way Dr. Kabat does it," explained Maggie. "He praises them all for each little flicker of muscle they haven't had before. That makes them proud. That makes them regain the wish to live."

And that made the physical therapists work, too, said Maggie. "Every one of us will work till our uniform bursts out, for every patient. The results we see talk us into almost anything," continued

Maggie with her photogenic smile. "We all begin dreaming of a bright future for them, with excellent walking, even running.

"They're the heroes," she said. "Their spirit keeps us on our toes."

In their superhuman concentration, these M.S.'s gave me the feeling they were trying to remember activities long ago forgotten. Imagine what it must mean to try to remember how to walk. They fought to recapture simple acts of living they'd learned without thinking, as babies. Here's what was wonderful about those farthest along toward recovery: once they'd set the new habit pattern by months of repetition, at last those patterns became automatic.

Kabat could coax activity into some muscles which had seemed completely dead. "Zero muscles," they'd been called, hopelessly. Here, for example, was a patient with no voluntary motion in the toes of one foot, yet when the whole leg was moved downward from the hip, those same toes went into a violent involuntary reflex. Now this motion from the hip is made again and again, while the physical therapist by resistance builds up voluntary control of the exaggerated toe reflex. Weirdly then those toes begin to show power of voluntary movement. The wild reflex is harnessed. New connections have been formed between the brain and long-disused muscles.

XI

If this demoniac fight by these M.S. patients from complete help-lessness toward a first flicker of self-help were all, then this game would hardly be worth the candle; but here at the Kabat-Kaiser Institute in October, 1947, were people who'd fought all the way back to rehabilitation. Here was Louise Tobey Dean, the lovely daughter of Senator Tobey from New Hampshire. Dark-eyed and vivid, Mrs. Dean walked up and down the examining room without a trace of the hesitating, dragging, staggering, stumbling, feeble, increasingly paraplegic gait with which she'd come to the Institute the year before. She had come in despair.

It had been 17 years since multiple sclerosis had aimed its first sinister blow at Louise Dean's happiness. For 16 years its weird signs and symptoms had come and gone, waxed and waned, gradually becoming more ominous. At first, she found herself walking into a flower bed, unable to keep on a path in the garden. This frightening sign vanished. Then she began to see double, traffic lights saying GO-GO instead of GO, eight people coming toward her on the sidewalk where there were only four actually. Her vision returned to normal, and she seemed in perfect health. Then she lost control of both bladder and bowel action and went into a black melancholy. From this again she recovered. Though she had been to many physicians, none made a diagnosis. At the war's beginning she was again well enough to marry. Her husband was away at the war for almost four years. The day of his return she was walking with him in the evening to a movie, and was terrified suddenly to feel one of her legs dragging. Then, one after another, those first signs and symptoms of a terrible nervous trouble returned. Her husband took her to Boston to one of the greatest hospitals in the country where she was examined thoroughly. They were given no diagnosis nor any hope, but her husband overheard a muttered mention of "multiple sclerosis" by one of the examining doctors talking to another.

Together Mr. and Mrs. Dean went to a medical library and sat down to read all they could find about multiple sclerosis in bound volumes of journals of neurology. Yes, that's what she had. In the silence of the library they read: "The average expanse of life for multiple sclerosis victims is nine years." Mrs. Dean's eyes wouldn't focus for further reading. She had already long outlived that death sentence. How much longer? When her husband closed the big bound volume, they went home. They couldn't mention what they both had read till some days later when they found it possible to speak calmly about the future. The big book had given them the grim diagnosis. Multiple sclerosis, no question.

During the next year Louise Dean became weaker and weaker with a slowly advancing spastic paraplegia. All the original symptoms were back now with no let-up, and to her double vision, incontinence, staggering, dragging weakness there was added a deep depression with outbreaks of uncontrollable crying. Then at a chance meeting Henry J. Kaiser, the builder, told her father, Senator Tobey, what had happened to Henry J. Kaiser, Jr.

"After one week at the Kabat-Kaiser Institute," said Louise Dean, "I felt like a different person. Any question I asked was answered fully. The treatments (prostigmin plus heavy resistance exercise) were thorough and regularly supervised by the doctor in whose charge I was put. I felt steadily stronger and life stopped slipping from me.

"I was beginning to recapture it, and although we had no children, I even dreamed of the time when we could adopt at least two. . . . I have been rejuvenated at the Kabat-Kaiser Institute. . . . Now I can keep in step with my husband. There is in my mind no longer a time limit to our life together. We're living as if eternally."

About Louise Dean (who was not cured, mind you) who again might have to face attacks of the sickness, who, just the same, was so obviously healthy and rehabilitated as she walked proudly round that room, lithe and graceful—about her there was something out of this world, unreal, dreamlike.

It was not until we shook hands good-bye that I was sure she was really there.

XII

Why do some medical discoveries, as for example those of the sulfas and penicillin, spread rapidly among physicians, while others remain confined to the discoverer, their validity being denied by "authorities" who, at the same time, have made no attempt to confirm or refute them by testing them on their own patients?

Why was it at the end of 1947 (with 51 out of 56 sufferers from chronic, advanced multiple sclerosis notably improved at the Kabat-Kaiser Institute) that there seemed almost no interest in Kabat's work upon the part of neurologists, Dr. Tracy J. Putnam excepted?

Of course the neurologists might answer that this had nothing to do with the finding of the cause or the cure of multiple sclerosis, that this was merely a matter of physical therapy, of more or less rehabilitation. In this the neurologists were right.

But why was it then that Herman Kabat, now besieged by throngs of far-gone M.S. victims, was refused space to advertise for physical therapists in the leading journal of physical medicine?

When the leaders of physical medicine had never claimed to be able to rehabilitate victims of this hitherto hopeless multiple sclerosis, and when, in fact, Kabat was rehabilitating many of them, why was it that Kabat at this time was refused membership in the Congress of Physical Medicine?

Was there a greater feat than Kabat's in physical medicine's entire discipline?

To these questions I can only guess the answers. This has been my observation: when the performance of any new treatment is technically very difficult or risky, or when it demands great patience, and takes a long undramatic time to get results, when it is not published from some big-time medical school, then physicians tend to be slow to go for it. They may even pooh-pooh it without so much as testing it, especially when the disease against which that treatment is directed is considered hopeless. Well, you see, it's hopeless anyway.

On the other hand, prescribing sulfa pills or giving patients shots of penicillin—these are easy. They spread like wildfire.

Kabat was very much alone against multiple sclerosis and it seemed safe enough for neurologists and experts in physical medicine to give him the brush-off. How much did this rehabilitation amount to, anyway? How long would it stick? Multiple sclerosis was well known (was it really?) to be an inexorably progressive sickness, an inevitably downhill nervous degeneration. Wouldn't you rehabilitate victims, jerk them up, fire their hope only to let them down lower than ever when they went to pieces with further nervous degeneration? Wouldn't it be more merciful to let them rest themselves to death, really?

Kabat's roster went to 100, then 200, then over 250 M.S. patients. Together with Dr. Sidney Garfield he opened new Institutes at Oakland and Vallejo, California. If the great men of neurology and physical medicine weren't excited about this new hope, rank-and-file doctors were alerting to it. Within a month after publication of Kabat's new treatment of multiple sclerosis in *The Reader's Digest*, more than 1,500 physicians sent him inquiring letters. His now three years of experience with hundreds of cases of this supposedly progressively downward nervous degeneration gave Kabat a new slant at this sickness. It was revolutionary. It had always been assumed that the progressive character of the ill is due entirely to the more or less continuous formation of new patches of destruction in the central nervous system. There *were* fresh attacks while his patients were fighting back upward under prostigmin and heavy resistance exercise. But not too many. Didn't the disease often burn itself out? It would seem so. Kabat was becoming more and more convinced that a major part of the complete helplessness of M.S. victims is due to *disuse*. Inactivity is death; activity is life. Disuse drains away both muscle and nerve function. Activity restores it.

Kabat now began experimenting, thumbing his nose at unanimous neurologic opinion, which was to the effect that, when there's any sign of an active attack of the disease, you must especially rest the victim, absolutely. To do otherwise would be harmful. Now Kabat began treating actively right through active attacks and so-called relapses.

The owner of a botanical nursery, long-time victim of M.S., just able to walk with a staggering gait, came to the Kabat-Kaiser Institute at Oakland, California. For a month he made good progress. Then he went downhill in a fulminating attack, getting rapidly weaker to the point where there was complete paralysis of both legs and terrible tremor of both arms. He became completely blind. He cried continuously and didn't know where he was—disoriented. He vomited almost every meal. He was under constant care of special nurses and had to be fed by vein to keep him living or barely alive. Kabat kept up the prostigmin treatment right through the poor man's imminent dying. Physical therapists gave him passive exercises. They found flickers of voluntary movement in his eye muscles and in one arm, and they urged the dying man to move that arm and to keep turning his eyes from side to side.

Kabat and his physical therapists grabbed at every feeble flicker of voluntary movement and used it and opposed light, then heavier resistance to it, fighting a hundred local muscle group deaths due to disuse. In two months this man who had been as good as gone could walk again between parallel bars. His vision cleared and returned to normal. He could feed himself again. He was perfectly oriented. Most of this recovery was due to a remission of the disease. But disuse had been prevented and vital nerve connections maintained. And, what's more, the exertion had not prevented the remission. On the contrary, recovery was unquestionably speeded up. The terrible attack had left residuals but these were treated successfully by prostigmin and heavier and heavier exercise. The patient is now walking with crutches, has regained a great deal of strength and endurance and is rapidly improving to the point where he will soon be able to return to work.

Here was Kabat's new, hopeful slant at this sickness so universally thought to be downhill, degenerating, inexorable. It was not so much inevitably progressive, as it was a gradual accumulation of residuals left from repeated, isolated attacks. It was irregularly recurrent with a piling up of residuals. These residuals, left untreated, left to the danger of rest, gave the false impression of inexorable downward progress. "It's often a progress of disuse," said Kabat.

Four years of Kabat's stern fight have passed now. Of his 250 M.S. patients, none has died at this writing; 150 are still under treatment. The vast majority are on the upgrade. Many are back to self-help and are walking. Many are back to work—rehabilitated.

All of Kabat's cases had passed that early stage of the disease where they might have expected to enjoy spontaneous let-ups, remissions. It was Kabat's treatment that brought them back to life.

XIII

Why did Herman Kabat go on with this rugged rehabilitation, so tedious, so undramatic because it was so slow not only among multiple sclerosis victims but among all the hundreds and now thousands of sufferers from every sort of neuro-muscular dysfunction—from athetoid cerebral palsy children to polios and far-gone victims of post-encephalitic Parkinsonism? From day to day, from week to week, Kabat and his physical therapists could see only dribs and drabs of progress. To realize what they were doing, you would have to see a given victim brought in on a stretcher or wheel-chair one year and then come back to see him walking, slowly, hesitatingly, the next. Then too there were hundreds of tragedies—of sufferers partially rehabilitated having to go home, for lack of money. Why did Kabat choose this rugged discipline so different from lightning-like cures of microbic infections by the new anti-biotics or the quick saving of life from the threat of brain tumors by neuro-surgery?

He chose it because his patients made him.

They were humanity's flotsam and jetsam, physically; they were mankind's remnants thrown up on the shore of the river of life. He chose them because he heard their low-voiced supplication, "You must save us."

Now, co-working in group healing with the doctors and surgeons of Permanente Foundation Hospital, Kabat went beyond prostig-min and heavy resistance exercise toward what he called a new synthesis.

A young woman was brought in, neck broken high up at the level of the seventh cervical vertebra, helpless for 5 years. A doctor was going to turn her down for admission. "You're not going to pass a death sentence on me," she said, in a fierce whisper.

Her spinal cord had been cut clean through. She could slightly move a shoulder. She had no movement or feeling in her hands or fingers. What good are arms without hands? But now resistance exercises built up her arm and wrist muscles. And, then, utilizing some of the wonderful techniques developed for amputees during the war, they are harnessing this newly-won muscular power to specially designed apparatus so she can use her hands. So she would be able to feed herself and wheel a wheelchair. So she would have a part of life. Other similarly hopeless victims of accidents are being rehabilitated by a combination of carefully planned orthopedic surgery, neuro-surgery, muscle-re-education training and prostigmin.

In his mild low-voiced manner Kabat kept telling his doctors they were giving up too easy. Kabat told them to listen to a patient who kept saying: "I won't stay this way. You know how to make people better, and I want you to try to make *me* better."

He began tackling nerve diseases more desperate than multiple sclerosis. A Dakota farmer brought his wife to California to Kabat. She was in the last stages of absolutely incurable amyotrophic lateral sclerosis—Lou Gehrig's disease. She had choking spells, couldn't write, couldn't feed herself, couldn't blow out a little candle. And she was slowly getting worse.

After eight weeks of prostigmin and exercise of her tongue and other speech muscles, she could talk so that her voice could be heard across the room. Her husband sold out everything he owned in North Dakota and came back to help his wife try to shove back death, in California. Kabat had promised them nothing. "You must try to save her," the husband had said. "I can promise you nothing," answered Kabat. "But you *must* try," said the man. "Sure I'll try," said Kabat. He could do absolutely nothing about the mysterious degeneration in her central nervous system.

Yet now the wasting in many of her disused muscles has improved. She is staving off death. She can talk and feed herself, and no longer has trouble swallowing. She can write again. She can get in and out of bed herself and is able to walk a little without support. She is not quite so near dead and isn't that something? It does not matter if neurologists don't think so, if you do not think so. It matters only that the woman and her husband will fight to the man's last dollar, to the woman's last breath.

Here Kabat worked in a strange other-world. For this woman it was not only a question of to live or to die but of being dead while still alive. She could breathe. Her heart kept on beating. She was not living. But now after a year at the Institute, she could talk, could feed herself, and begin to walk. She could move again. She was happy fighting for life.

This case is unusual. But it is difficult to predict which patient will improve and which one will fail despite the best efforts.

In this other-world of these hopeless, pathetically hoping, Kabat groped for a new philosophy of healing. He said: "If the doctor knows nothing can be done for a patient he should say so frankly. But the doctor is often not sure. If the patient wants him to try, then he owes it to the patient to do so if there is any possibility of recovery."

Herman Kabat continued, saying: "Too many doctors say this won't be important enough, this little I can do. It is not up to the doctor alone. It is the patient's life."

Kabat infected me with his cool courage. A boat-builder in my own neighborhood had been suffering for 20 years with that terrible trembling spasticity known as Parkinsonism—supposedly post-encephalitis. He lived in a shaking, flexed posture. His tremor was so terrible that it was hard to look at him. He couldn't straighten up. He could not move his neck. He couldn't straighten his knees. His fatigue was constant, yet he could hardly sleep. Kabat promised me nothing when I suggested he take on this man who was surely going to die. From bed sickness. The man was jittery, a naturally highly nervous type. Good neurologists had tried all they knew and failed, and the boat-builder was the most discouraged, the most skeptical man I've seen, only he still wanted to live with a small, feebly glowing dull red spark of hope. He wanted to go to Kabat.

Prostigmin. Exercises. The man could not lift his arm. Kabat pulled it up. Then the man couldn't get the arm down easily. Yet, here was a trace of muscular strength in that holding-up position. Then Kabat and the physical therapist began moving the arm up and down like a pump handle and then let go, telling him to go on with it and, by God, he kept moving that arm himself, against resistance, having caught the rhythm. For the first time in a long time he began to take a few shuffling steps, his physical therapist holding him, walking by his side. She started to keep step with him, then suddenly he stopped shuffling, strode in step with her a few steps, then fell back into that feeble shuffle when she let him go alone. Gradually he could stride along with her and keep on going, striding, alone, and in a while he could start striding by himself without her help, then without any cane and in a few months he could walk by himself . . . three miles.

Before he left, as he strode down the halls, he had the whole hospital (they'd seen him come in helpless in a wheelchair) buzzing. "Is that Kenny Campbell?" patients asked each other. Will he get still stronger? Will he go back to his boat-building? Who can say? Will he relapse? Who knows?

Herman Kabat says: "Campbell was as hopeless as you can get. You do not know what you, the doctor, can possibly do for a man as far gone as Campbell. But the patient wants you to try. The patient says, 'Help me. If you don't know how, find out for me.'"

It was natural that Kabat's young doctors might be intimidated by the failure of the most renowned clinics to help patients who came demanding help at the Kabat-Kaiser Institute. A 53-year-old man, wheelchair, rheumatoid arthritis, came, suffering contracture of both knees, knees bent 90 degrees in sitting position, couldn't stand. Bad muscle spasm. Twice at the most renowned hospital in America this man had had those knees straightened by simple traction and was then told to go home and walk. But he couldn't. His knees shook, his muscles were wasted and painful.

"We'll try to help you," said Kabat.

First, surgery, lengthening tendons and ligaments. Then months of prostigmin and heavy resistance exercises to the wasted muscles of the front and back of his thighs and his buttocks. In a few months he could stand on his feet and walk a little. In seven months he easily climbed five flights of stairs. He was a jolly Santa Claus at the hospital's Christmas party and with a cigar in his mouth he danced a jig; he is now back at full-time work on his feet as much as necessary, as a contractor.

That was a man to whom doctors had said: "No use to try." But he had said to Kabat: "You *must* try."

Herman Kabat says: "You say these patients are the heroes. They're more. They are our teachers. They've taught us the fatigue phenomenon, how fatigue lasts just so long, to the second, then vanishes—it's undoubtedly a precise chemical reaction—so that they can exercise immediately, as strong as ever."

Herman Kabat then said: "We learn from the will of the patients that we really don't know how many can be helped. What have seemed hopeless, are now working. You know what the patients are doing for us? They're rubbing out the line that used to separate hope from hopeless."

XIV

The worst hurdle for patients is the expense of Kabat's neuro-muscular rehabilitation. Every patient needs one or two hours at least, daily, of the personal, individual attention of a highly paid physical therapist, then individually supervised exercise in the gymnasium, then individually supervised occupational therapy. For the seriously ill and helpless nursing care is needed; and then for all there's the cost of room and board—so that the expense of treatment may run from $5,000 to $10,000 a year.

To cut down this financial load unbearable for the great majority of people, wife or husband, son or daughter, father or mother, often accompany the sufferer to the Kabat-Kaiser Institutes, learn heavy resistance exercises from physical therapists and then continue them on their dear ones, back at home.

I've heard physicians sneer at Kabat's science as being only for the rich, but he would have to shut down completely if he were not paid as he is for his treatment. The Kabat-Kaiser Institutes are not-for-profit. The small sum of money left over is put into a fund to help a few patients who run out of money part way through their treatment and a few—pitifully—who come without money at all.

Of course this is deplorable. For one patient lucky to get this charity, there are tens of thousands, yes, hundreds of thousands, who need it but cannot come by it. You see, there is no foundation to pay the treatment of these crippled ones, as there is for polio. There is no rich man in the world with enough money to pay for the rehabilitation of those who could be brought back to self-supporting life. The federal government is not yet interested. A newly organized society against multiple sclerosis does not endorse Kabat's work, when answering the letters of thousands enquiring about it

. . . though experts sent by the society to examine this work have approved it highly! . . . The medical head of this society has spoken contemptuously of the Kabat-Kaiser Institutes as rich man's clubs.

I have seen just two patients from families which might be called rich. The vast majority come from families that make stern sacrifices to give their dear ones, usually, less than enough treatment. May God sharpen the eyes, strengthen the brains, and steady the hands of the researchers looking for prevention or cure of multiple sclerosis with money supplied by this new society. May God speed their discovery, while a few hundred are being rehabilitated by Kabat and scores of thousands are waiting in trembling weakness, stiff paralysis and pain, ghastly inco-ordination, withering of muscles, and in dark melancholy.*

For a while, at the end of 1947, in the excitement of writing and going to press with the Kabat multiple sclerosis story in *The Reader's Digest,* it did seem as if there might be hope for a nation-wide spread of Kabat's science and financial hope for those who needed it to come back to active life.

My friend, Curtis Rockwell Gray, a pharmaceutical industrialist in Holland, Michigan, is a sad-faced, disillusioned, even cynical citizen whose secret hobby—on a scale commensurate with his modest resources—is to help underdogs and especially to make underdogs self-helping. Gray-haired Farmer Gray (we call him so because he is one of those not too successful gentleman farmers) listened to the new hope for M.S. victims with his usual pessimistic resignation. He listened deadpan, and then suddenly took fire.

A fiscal wizard, a financial lightning-calculator who does not really care for money, Farmer Gray excitedly sketched a practical way out of this dilemma.

"You say the disease in the majority of cases strikes between ages 20 and 40?" he asked. "Ver-r-ry well," said the Farmer in his Boston

---

* The amazing new vitamin, B-12, is the first chemical molecule to be found active against degeneration of cell, of the central nervous system—in pernicious anemia. There is a hint that B-12 may also arrest the progress of the nerve cell degeneration of amyotrophic lateral sclerosis—Lou Gehrig's disease. May this new vitamin also prove effective in multiple sclerosis? Here's hoping!

accent. "This means that the victims—if rehabilitated—will have many years in which to repay the cost of their treatment."

Farmer Gray was far ahead of his time with his insight into the economics of chronic illness. He said: "From a dollars and cents standpoint, alone, it's cheaper to invest immediate cash in treatment than to maintain and wait upon these victims to the dreary end."

"So what?" I said, reminding him that economically death always has priority. "The government—" I began.

"To hell with the government," Farmer Gray interrupted. "These M.S.'s, fighting back, are courageous, you say?"

"The most pathetically brave I've ever seen," I said.

Farmer Gray said: "You can always finance courage—locally. Relatives and friends can organize themselves into underwriting groups, maybe with the help of local banks. Rotary, Kiwanis, Lions, and Exchange clubs are generous—notoriously. For a pittance apiece for each of their members they could undertake to carry some local afflicted citizen through to recovery."

Now Farmer Gray became expansive and saw a vision. He said: "In a national way an over-writing group could be organized to lend financial aid by way of endorsement to local group bank borrowings. The patient could put up his 'recovery note'—so that the money paid back by him after rehabilitation will be recirculated for the benefit of those who are to come."

Then this kind-hearted man showed the faith that underlay his cynicism. "The man or woman with the courage to fight back up out of helplessness is the man or woman with the character to *pay* back," he said, his sad face now glowing.

This plan was presented to a big banker on the west coast and a big banker on the east coast—nothing doing. The farmer's plan was published in *The Reader's Digest,* reaching millions. The result was instructive. One little city, Woodland, California, contained a girl grievously stricken with multiple sclerosis. The citizens took fire. It would need $5,000 to bring their girl back to self-supporting life. Quickly the citizens raised $8,000. The girl is now under hopeful treatment. One girl, one city, one human being among scores of thousands. The response to Farmer Gray's plan was notable. He received hundreds of letters; they did not offer help. They were from victims and families of victims who needed it.

XV

The brush-off he has got from the public multiple sclerosis organization—strangely—has not discouraged Herman Kabat. "Don't be down in the mouth about the thousands needing help and not getting it," Kabat told me in a voice as always mild and patient. "Come and look at the hundreds we *are* helping."

It is hard to lick a silly optimist like Kabat. He keeps grabbing at every straw that indicates recognition. He isn't in the least bitter about neglect of his method of rehabilitation of polios by a great foundation. He is grateful because citizens of one of its local chapters are paying for the treatment of many polio victims at the newly opened Kabat-Kaiser Institute at Santa Monica, California. It does not hurt his pride that these polio patients came to him because there was no room in other hospitals in the Los Angeles area.

He'll show them. And then maybe some day the news might get to the foundation's main office at New York City. Kabat is patient. The Bureau of Rehabilitation of the State of California is paying for the treatment of multiple sclerosis victims at the Kabat-Kaiser Institutes and then helping them to get jobs when they've recovered.

"They're doing that because they recognize that M.S., even if it can't be prevented or cured, can be licked," said Kabat.

The patience of his patients seems to have infected Herman Kabat with a special, tough-fibered ability to work and wait. He is curiously not the typical highly scientific or highly prosperous doctor. He is humble, serving his clients with the deference of a masseur or of a barber, yes, the barbers who were the precursors of the great surgeons of today. Toiling, sweating as he evolves a new type of heavy resistance exercise for a man you'd swear would never again make a useful voluntary movement, Herman Kabat—for me—recalls the good Samaritan in the painting of Vincent van

Gogh's where the good Samaritan is bulging every muscle, straining every tendon to heave the helpless wounded man aboard the mule to get him to the inn after the Levite and all the others have passed him by.

From his patients Herman Kabat has learned to be satisfied with very small rewards. He has learned from Louise Tobey Dean. Louise told Herman Kabat that she didn't realize how fully she had recovered from multiple sclerosis till one day her husband, coming home unexpectedly, came up behind her, startling her. She wheeled, facing him. She wheeled suddenly perfectly steadily. A few months before, if she'd tried that, she would have fallen to the ground.

"Isn't that something?" Kabat asked me, and I will not forget his slow smile.

Kabat, you may remember, was refused membership in the somewhat august American Congress of Physical Medicine. They have now let him in. It is a triumph from the standpoint of medical respectability. It was only indirectly on the basis of Kabat's medical merit. The B.C.M.'s of the Congress sort of had to let Herman in, because they were really on a spot. You see, the Chairman of the Congress, for 1948, had gone to work for Kabat at the Kabat-Kaiser Institutes that same year . . .

Herman Kabat seems to be on his way now. His staff is now treating 400 patients at a time at Vallejo, Santa Monica and Oakland, California, and in Washington, D. C. New Kabat-Kaiser Institutes are to open soon in Vancouver, Washington, and later in Florida and the mid-west. These are growing resources of hope for the heretofore hopeless. The cost of the treatment remains murderous, but more and more patients are getting financial help— from private donations, federal and state agencies, foundations, insurance companies, United Mine Workers Welfare Fund. Kabat points out that the care of TB patients is also long and costly, and technically difficult. This is Kabat's faith: once people know what can be done for paralyses of various types, they'll demand treatment as their right. Kabat believes financial assistance will not be long in coming from the overall generosity of Americans more and more sensitized to suffering.

CHICAGO,
ILLINOIS   LATE AUTUMN, 1945

It was an honor when the grand old man of American medicine asked us to see the cancer Institute and write about hope for the cure of accessible cancer, in 1944. It was comforting to write under his sponsorship; the medical sharp-shooters might lay off us for fear of potting the grand old man. So we thought. Our story brought the Institute many more patients, helped save more lives; the news was astounding.

But in 1945 the local medical political powerhouse called officers of the Institute on the carpet for this undue publicity. Throat surgeons tried to smear the Institute's X-ray treatment by innuendo. The low-down? The treatment was cutting into surgery of cancer by throat specialists.

We had planned to sketch the grand old man in this book, telling how he figures that 50,000 victims, now dying, could be saved yearly from accessible cancer. Now he has had to ask us not to mention the Institute by name, nor his own name any more. We agreed, because if there's one person we respect and love, it's the grand old man.

Are we free to write the truth to help save human life, giving the credit where it is due? Not if certain medical toes are stepped on, commercially. Life-saving is business! So this will have to be the grand old man, anonymous.

CHAPTER XII

Old Man Against Cancer

※ ※

LET'S not be too starry-eyed about the practice of medicine and surgery. Let's look at it for what it is, a good business. And why shouldn't it be? What's more valuable than vitality? What do we want more than to cheat the old man with the long beard and the scythe who is coming to take us all? If we have the money, we're glad to pay, even through the nose, to stay strong and keep alive.

Though doctors and surgeons in general treat each other free, they usually still have to pay for the new miracle drugs used on themselves, and you can't blame them for squawking a bit about prices. (Mind you, these elixirs all get cheaper the more they're put into production for the millions who need them.) Recently a keen and prosperous surgeon I know was laid low suddenly by a great killing ill. For this there had been no chemical succor. But now? Marvelous, there was magic that not only might aid him in his present peril but might even prevent the death threat for years to come, giving him a new lease on life to go back to making an excellent living as a surgeon. He was being cared for by a keen, scientifically progressive internist who was willing to put his surgeon-patient on the new, possibly life-saving therapy.

"But it's awfully expensive," the internist protested.

"My God," I answered, "you don't consider that when it's live or die."

"But it may cost $18 a shot," he said.

"Maybe we can get the stuff free," I encouraged him. "Please do consider it."

The next day the internist phoned me, saying: "Since you say you can get it for nothing, we'll try it."

Now I ask you. If you were going to die, would you not spend your money or beg, borrow, or steal it? Would you stop trying to save your life unless you could save it economically or gratis? It shows how cheaply life is still held, among highly competent doctors, even when it concerns their friends and themselves.

The late famous healthman, Dr. Herman M. Biggs, said, sententiously, that "public health is purchasable." That puts it on a sound American business basis. And not only public health but individual life itself can now, to an amazing extent, be bought by all of us who have the money. Doctors have to live and they must not be expected to impoverish themselves to keep us alive. In the practice of medicine, good Samaritans are like diamonds—valuable, as Herman Bundesen says, because of their rarity.

Yet in this matter of buying life there is room for improvement. There remain aspects of medical commerce that stink. As, for example, when doctors try to thwart new science that might guard our lives for a pittance but that at the same time will rob them of business. Example: radiologists fighting cheap mass X-ray films to detect early tuberculosis. Example: surgeons trying to scuttle new radiologic science when it is ready to put powerful conservation treatment in place of expensive mutilation by the surgeon's knife.

That's what the grand old man of American medicine (whose name we may not mention!) is fighting and that's the story of this chapter.

In the practice of medicine and surgery as in other branches of free enterprise, the more things seem to change, the more they remain the same. It is now, at least to a degree though less crudely, as it was in the days of *The Adventures of Hajji Baba*, in which is told the fury of a physician at the smallpox vaccine discovery of William Jenner:

". . . Worst of all, he pretends to do away with smallpox altogether, by infusing into our nature a certain extract of the cow, a discovery which one of their philosophers has recently made. Now this will never do, Hajji. The smallpox has always been a comfortable source of income to me; I cannot afford to lose it, because the infidel chooses to come and treat us like cattle. We cannot allow him to take bread out of our mouths."

This satire on medical economics was given to me by America's grand old man of medicine. He is seeing the cancer Institute, the proud project of the evening of his life, endangered. Why? Because the cancerologist directing the Institute is using an X-ray treatment which—voice-saving and even life-saving—might take champagne and caviar money out of the pockets of certain surgeons.

II

Regarding these threats to a high standard of living our grand old man has never been concerned at all. Though a doctor, he has not practiced medicine. He has been essentially an academic, a pathologist and bacteriologist, moderately paid, living modestly like your typical professor, only supplementing his not ample living by testimony in forensic medicine and consultation as a laboratory man. Our grand old man has surely been no radical regarding medical economics. It is inspiring that ten years ago, at 75, in the late autumn of his life, he became one of the few doctors to be really bothered about fighting all possible death from cancer. He is now 85. Despite his age, he is on the front step of new science. He is still working to broaden X-ray and radium treatment because that will allow many to be cared for *who otherwise would have no chance for life.*

In his new battle, our grand old man exhibits a disregard for the type of medical economics that puts life on a business basis. At his cancer Institute this is the religion: every cancer patient is entitled to the best that can be done, no matter what the stage of his cancer, no matter what his income. This is the Institute's rule: no patient who can be helped at all is refused treatment, regardless of the stage of the disease or financial circumstances.

About the grand old man there is an informal dignity that, whenever I'm with him, has operated to quiet my profane boisterousness acquired from a somewhat rough life among rough men. He makes me measure my words; he calms me down. In the front line of the rough-and-tumble of the cancer fight, the grand old man seems other-worldly. He shows the fragility inevitable in one so very old, yet he retains the strength of finest alloy steel in his brain and a warmth in his heart. His hair remains thick and silky white. His wrinkles are hardly noticeable except when he smiles. His skin is smooth like that of a man of 50. His color is faintly rosy except when a medical rebuff makes him sad; then suddenly he may turn pale and look very old. His gray eyes are kind but look directly at you in a way that says, Do not give me any hokum, we haven't time. He has shrewd eyes that light up and become round like a boy's with delighted surprise when his immense sifting power, acquired over 60 years, tells him that here is something new in medical science—something possibly life-saving against cancer.

In his faintly Scandinavian accent, which has a trick of making American speech less strident, more gentle, and more impressive, his words are few, never trivial, and they're the product of an exquisite economy of thought that seems to have preserved his cortical neurons and left his brain the sharp-cutting instrument that it remains today. He is constantly generalizing, but always close to facts. The grand old man looks benign, unquarrelsome and gentle, yet his generalizations, most of them, deal with the horror of cancer and the scandal of not removing much of this horror when there is no scientific obstacle to its elimination.

To a biographical sketch of our grand old man, published ten years ago, I beg leave to take just one exception. The sympathetic biographer says: "It would be easy to glorify him, to hail him with excitement and frenzy, as what Paul de Kruif calls a 'death fighter'; but with [the grand old man] such diction would be wholly out of character."

This may really not be an inaccuracy on the part of the biographer, because the grand old man, at 75, had really just begun to fight. The biographer says that the grand old man "is a calm man, never given to overstatement." If that is true, then many of his understatements make up a terrible indictment of American citizenry, including the American medical profession. The best fighting is the coldest and the calmest. Until I was told so by the biographer just quoted, I did not know that, to be a death fighter, you have to be frenzied. I'm sorry if I have written of death fighters as frenzied; I shall try to be more calm from now on, especially about our very calm grand old man.

America's toll of 175,000 yearly deaths from cancer is hardly being dented despite our medical profession, unquestionably the best in the world, despite the world's best technical facilities and engineering skill, despite our know-how and new science. In regard to this tragic mystery the grand old man permits himself certain pithy observations. They are instructive; they are simple.

"Every cancer passes through a stage when it is curable," says the grand old man. He makes you ponder. He makes you want to know why, then, are so few cancers found in that hopeful stage? Why are they not cured, with a resulting lowering of the cancer death rate?

It is good to know from the grand old man's biographer that he is not guilty of overstatements. *"Accessible localized cancer is the most easily curable major death with the exception of pneumonia."*

By accessible cancer the grand old man means cancer that you can detect before it has all but killed its victims, cancer that you can practically get at with X-rays, radium, or the knife. Is there much of that? I asked him. *"If all sufferers from accessible cancer had a chance at the best treatment now available, not only in the early stages but when their disease is more or less advanced, 25,000 could be saved yearly,"* he answered.

But, if cancers are accessible, it is by the very fact of their accessibility that it should be easy to discover them early, and if they were all discovered early, what then could you do?

"If all accessible cancers were caught early and treated competently," he said, *"50,000 who now yearly die, could live."*

The grand old man was explicit about this possible immense saving of life depending not upon theoretical, conjectural, not-yet-existing science but on weapons *now* sharp and ready. He made no excuses for the persistence of this shameful needless death toll;

he didn't hedge; he didn't guard his challenges to our murderous neglect by careful if's or but's. He cleared his throat, swallowed, and in precise, r-burred Scandinavian-American, the grand old man made it stronger still:

"If localized accessible cancers were found early (which they could be) *and were treated competently* (which they certainly could be) *accessible cancer could be made largely a disease of historical interest."*

These careful words, well-chosen, meant that our grand old man belonged with the eradication boys. These are the radicals, the wild boys, the drastic and even somewhat fanatical boys in the medical and public health camps. They are boys who tend to go off the deep-end and boys who in their impatience about death may upset the prevailing medical order. They should be watched; let's be reasonable; let's be practical. Isn't it asking a bit too much to save them all? It isn't too much if it means saving your own life or that of your wife or children or father or mother or your dearest friends. But saving *all possible?* That smacks of totalitarianism.

In the grand old man's face there is a serenity that could only have been stamped there by a very long life of sympathetic under-standing of human woe, of giving without expectation of return—in short, by love. He is for getting rid of this needless dying, all this needless dying, right now.

The grand old man has dry humor. He says: *"You cannot satisfy the cancer victim* (and he doesn't mean rich victims or socially or politically prominent victims but every victim down to the for-lornest) *by proving to him that research in the future may bring the cure of cancer. You've got to treat him with the means at hand."*

The grand old man's calm, shrewd, cool, gray eyes lost the wrinkles around them, opened wide, looked through me:

"And those means are really magic," he said, and then sat back as if resting his case, as if finishing an indictment of medical neg-lect that was unanswerable.

A shiver ran down my spine. Magic is a strong word and many a time the defenders of the medical status quo have tried to gag me for saying far less. The iron in the grand old man's voice as he said "magic"—his biographer to the contrary—revealed, if not frenzy, at least a certain lack of calmness, an excitement, even indignation at our failure to mop up this sector of the front of the cancer battle.

If you want to go in there and wipe out eradicable death, aren't you a fighter? If fighter is an uncouth term to apply to the medical great—though I've heard the grand old man himself use it with relish—then maybe he can at least be called, less frenziedly, a man against cancer. Though he has worked in medical research and science for more than 60 years now, he rarely seems tired, and I've come to think of him as literally immortal. And he remains brave.

To be truly against cancer and not simply against it with your mouth means that you may have to be bravest of the brave. You'll have to point to needless deaths due to your own ignorance and neglect and that of others. You must accept it as your recompense that, in a fourth-dimensional manner, cancer is the most satisfactory of all curses of humanity to be against: untreated or treated bunglingly, the victim always dies of it; but if the victim lives, you can be satisfied that what you did saved him.

This black-or-white, live-or-die, makes the cancer game a tough and definitely young man's activity. Of all men in the field, our grand old man is the youngest and most optimistic of any I've met—at 85!

III

The grand old man is president of the Institute's board of trustees but he's also its active pathologist in charge of cancer diagnosis. He gets to work at eight in the morning, passing on the biopsied tissues of every patient coming with fear and hope. There has been no money for steel-and-concrete, glass and white tile edifice and the Institute is housed in an old school building in a midwestern city. Though grimy outside, it contains the last word in X-ray apparatus; its ten-gram radium bomb is one of the two most powerful in the world.

The Institute has no endowment; it has no beds and treats only patients who can walk or be brought in from near-by rooming houses. It confines its attack on cancer to irradiation but takes special care to route victims to hospitals if surgery might save their lives. No human being, no matter how poor, is turned away. Started on a shoestring, it runs itself on what patients who are not indigent can pay. A few rich people make up its annual deficit by a modicum of money. Society ladies do not get their pictures in the newspapers by conducting luncheons or charity balls for it. Is cancer too grim for such gay philanthropies? I don't know. The local chapter of the American Cancer Society has given the Institute the brush-off. In its beginning its unique development of radium and X-ray treatment was aided by grants from the U. S. Public Health Service; these have now been withdrawn.

Obscure though it is, the grand old man's Institute is the direct offspring of the famous Curie Institute in Paris, where X-rays and radium were first transformed from agents of death to givers of life; for in their original form, X-rays caused the cancers they now cure. Experimenting physicists, engineers, and doctors were burned by this silent atomic energy; and these burns broke down into slowly ulcerating, gnawing, boring tumors that hideously ate away fingers, hands, arms in a torture that could last 20 years before it ended its cruelty by killing. In America, 27 men died to make X-rays safe weapons against death. Madame Curie herself paid the final price for her scientific curiosity; radium cancer death caught up with her 40 years after she'd helped her husband discover what finally killed her.

In the 1920's came the first reward—for most of them it was posthumous—for these X-ray martyrs. To the Curie Institute in Paris, at different times and as a last resort, came six sufferers from cancer of the throat. On their hospital charts the surgeons had written one word: "Inoperable." This was their death sentence. The Curie doctors had learned to pull the vicious teeth of X-rays and radium. The patients came to the Curie without even being told to believe that here was a last straw of hope; they were made experimental human animals on a *conviction* of Dr. Claude Regaud and his co-workers, Coutard and Hautant, that cancer cells were more sensitive than were non-cancerous cells—to X-rays. So they irradiated these six sufferers from cancer of the throat. Why not? They were going to die anyway.

They did not die. The X-rays did damage the normal tissues surrounding the cancers, but only temporarily. They killed off the cancer cells completely, all of them and for good. These first six inoperable cancer victims were saved from death.

Alas, this batting 1,000 in that first deadly game did not turn out to be the average. The rays were powerless against cancer after it had spread through the body; and their trial against every kind of tumor brought the Curie searchers many disappointments. Tumors of the stomach and intestines, of the lungs, kidneys, bones, and prostate in those early days all seemed invincibly resistant to irradiation and the Curie men warned that such patients must not be robbed of a chance of life when surgery could save them.

In our own country the fear of the two-edged power of X-rays and radium died hard. While doctors at New York's Memorial Hospital confirmed the Curie reports of cure by X-rays, of many cancers of the skin, mouth, and uterus, yet—for mysterious and possibly not the most worthy reasons—the word, I mean the Ominous Word, the whispered Word of Warning, kept going about the hospital doctors' coat rooms that you just about had to kill a patient to cure him with X-rays and radium. Since human beings tend to be prejudiced to their own commercial advantage, and since surgeons are, like all the rest of us, just people, the perpetuation of this Word has not seemed to displease many surgeons.

The new treatment had another hurdle: in those early days radiologists did not rank medically with surgeons but were considered to be glorified laboratory boys, mere technicians. So radiologists ambitious to test the Curie magic were sent the "cats and dogs," poor devils rotten with cancer that would only spoil the already not too high cure rates of the surgeons. This situation persisted long after the sensational cure of the first six throat cancer cases at the Curie Institute and it persists to a large extent even today.

IV

As in the case of those far-gone multiple sclerosis patients of Herman Kabat's, cancer victims willing to be painfully burned, desperate to take any rap if there was a million-to-one chance for life, were the heroes who came to such X-ray and radium pioneers as Dr. Henry H. Janeway and Dr. Douglas Quick in New York, to the despised hope of radiation. In the early 1930's a doomed Greek, named Gust Econopulos, came with far-advanced cancer of the throat to a young mid-western cancerologist named ——. I'm sorry. As with that of the grand old man, we are asked not to mention names on threat of medical reprisals. This cancerologist anonymous lived in the grand old man's city and was trained by the country's top cancer specialists and pathologists (James Ewing no less); and he had got his X-ray and radium science at the source, from Regaud and Coutard at the Curie Institute in Paris. His education against cancer was probably the best of that of any doctor in America.

Poor Gust came at the fag end of a day that had been grim with nothing but "terminal" cancer. Gust could hardly swallow; he could whisper; he could just breathe; he had had several big hemorrhages; he had lost 30 pounds; to cure his cancer, surgeons would have had to all but cut off his head; there were metastases to the glands on the left side of his neck; Gust could only look at the cancerologist and whisper: "You fix me, Doc?"

Examination completed, the cancerologist said to his assistants: "Don't show me any more hopeless cancer today."

But that night he slept badly. He called Gust back next day. He gave him no hope; there was nothing to lose but life already lost for sure. Gust was dog-like, anxious to try anything no matter how terrible. Okay. Rx: telecurie therapy (radium) daily; enormous. Dangerous? Certainly. Murderous? Maybe. But as it turned out not quite murderous, not quite.

It was amazing. Daily for six weeks, Gust was exposed to a terrific dose of radium, two-and-a-half times greater than any administered in the annals of radiation therapy.

"If this had been a prominent citizen," admitted the cancerologist, "I would not have dared to have given him such heroic treatment."

This throws a curious light upon what we call democracy but it puts Gust (though he had no such aspiration) in the category of the servants of mankind. With Gust this terrible radium wallop made his skin peel alarmingly, then heal completely. And the hopeless cancer healed. Gust Econopulos lived nine years after that with no return of his tumor, with his voice restored, to die of heart disease near the age of 70.

This and other miracles, even though they were still infrequent, raised a plain question. Various cancers had been divided into radio-sensitive and radio-resistant. Till you actually tried it, not on the dog but on the man, how did you know? The cancerologist asked himself: "Do I dare tell any patient his condition is hopeless till I've tried—everything?"

Who dares guarantee that a given patient is going to die? The cancerologist remembered a medical symposium with a compilation of 25 cancer cases in which sure death had been predicted by various doctors. Years later all 25 condemned patients were living while many of their doctors had died.

Really to fight localized accessible cancer, free-swinging and all-out, the cancerologist knew he would have to move his base of operation from the general hospital where he had organized a tumor clinic, and start all over. The grand old man, then 75 and ready to begin his life all over, was truly interested. He agreed that, in a general hospital, any specialized fight against a disease like cancer is in losing competition with the hospital's major services of medicine and surgery.

He saw the reasons for the young cancerologist's defeat: cancer is the preserve of the major service of surgery. And wasn't our cancerologist (himself an excellent surgeon) naturally considered a traitor to surgery by dabbling with rays and radium?

The grand old man boiled down the need for a special Institute to a few words, characteristically: "General hospitals cannot give cancer the consideration it requires and deserves. Cancer demands teamwork—surgeon, pathologist, and radiologist working as one."

He said with his sly humor: "Working together they are not so apt to overestimate their own method."

v

So the little cancer Institute was started, founded by the cancerologist with the old man's support. Though his biographer correctly describes him as a calm man never given to overstatement, the grand old man began stating facts that were dynamite. They had the calm you find in the middle of a hurricane. He didn't make these statements to aggravate surgeons or the staffs and boards of general hospitals; he was simply putting the spotlight on a sordid situation existing in the cancer battle; he was calmly high-lighting the need for special cancer treatment centers.

He boldly made invidious comparisons between this kind of hospital and that one, in the grim matter of life or death. He began comparing cancer death rates, what percentage lived or died in general hospitals as against special institutions treating cancer. What's a better yardstick to measure medical conscience and competence? What do we want, if we have cancer, if not to be cured and live? Why should it be dangerous to publish comparative death rates—if staffs of all kinds of institutions are about equally competent to save life?

It's a curious circumstance that there is no great publicity about death rates in general in hospitals. It's usually only in some happy situation, such as a very low maternal death rate or the now possible low pneumonia death rate, that hospitals are beginning with pride to make such records public. Could it be that there are skeletons—this is figurative—in the closets of a good many hospitals in regard to other death rates? Or that, among themselves, doctors are gentlemanly enough not to make comparisons? In respect to cancer death rates the grand old man spilled the beans.

Item: Patients with cancer of the skin had one chance in five for cure in general hospitals and four chances out of five in specialized cancer institutions.

Item: Patients with cancer of the tonsil had no chance for cure in general hospitals not especially equipped to treat the disease, as against 30 per cent chance for cure in special institutions.

Item: Patients with cancer of the female organs had a miserable ten per cent chance for cure compared to 40 per cent in special cancer hospitals.

Now if some crackpot or fanatic had made these comparisons . . . But this was the grand old man, whose conservatism and meticulous honesty were impeccable, beyond question. Then he threw the Sunday punch. He said: "Careful studies show that the patient suffering from cancer has, on the average, four times as great a chance of being cured if treated in establishments specially organized, equipped, and staffed to treat this disease (cancer in general) compared to the general hospital in which these special facilities and experience are lacking."

That meant murder. It meant the loss of many thousands of lives, yearly, needlessly. It was a new medical honesty, real pioneering, but it made no special sensation publicly. It helped, years later, to get the officers of the new cancer Institute bawled out by the local branch of the medical union.* The grand old man foreshadowed a criterion of competence that plain citizens will soon be demanding. "Don't beat about the bush, Doctor," they'll say. "We know we've got cancer. Where's the best chance to get rid of it?"

In the end this may be the grand old man's greatest life-saving contribution.

VI

In their institute the cancerologist and his staff sharpened new radiologic weapons, making a drive especially against cancer of the larynx, which presents a combination of hope and horror. More than two weeks of persistent hoarseness should arouse suspicion of

---

* It is to the credit of the leadership of the American Medical Association that he has loyally supported this cancer Institute.

it, so that a laryngologist (throat specialist) should be consulted; and its diagnosis, yes or no, is easy and can be made very early. What's more, its spread is usually slow, and a limited surgical operation in its early stages can cure eight victims out of ten. But in its later stages the only hope is a total cutting out of the larynx so that the victim is left, for life, without a natural voice.

The fear of this probably accounts for today's failure to dent the larynx cancer death rate—more than 1,500 sufferers yearly choke to death in long slow pain.

At the Institute they now began to fight this choking death by science that was not so much medical as biological engineering. The requisite high voltage X-ray apparatus was determined and its installation supervised by Nobel Prize-winning physicist, Dr. Arthur H. Compton (we may mention his name because, as a physicist, he could hardly be subjected to medical reprisals). Instead of hitting cancerous and healthy tissues indiscriminately with the two-edged weapons of X-rays or radium, the cancerologist and his staff became marksmen, finding the bull's-eye of the cancer. Their rays became a high-powered rifle against the strangling terror.

This new precision underwent a stern test in 1942 when our sharpshooters saved the life of a young professor of law, from Brazil. The malignant tumor of his larynx was found to be so advanced that several laryngologists had advised "total laryngectomy" —complete removal of the larynx. This was no obscure Gust Econopulos. The Brazilian was a brilliant public speaker on the way to a great public career. To the laryngologists' advice he said, simply, no, he would rather die than live voiceless.

The Institute's Rx? How curiously different from the Latin mumbo-jumbo of medical prescriptions: Rx:

"X-ray therapy from June 15 to June 26, 1942 . . . 400 KV; 5 milliamps; filtr.: 5 millimeters copper; distance 84 to 115 centimeters; single left lateral port 5 × 5 . . . diminished to 3 × 3; intensity 4 to 3.3 roentgens per minute; 2 equal treatments daily with 100 roentgens 2 × daily to 425 roentgens 2 × daily—total 5,400 roentgens measured on skin . . . 12-day interval . . . Then 500 roentgens 2 × daily 2 days 3 × 3 cm. port 2,000 roentgens grand total 7,400."

Though the larynx lies deep in the throat, the penetrating power of the Institute's 400,000 volt X-ray apparatus reached it easily. Under this giant cannon the young professor lay propped up comfortably by sandbags so that he couldn't move a fraction of an inch. On the outside of his neck the exact site of his cancer—deep inside —was marked precisely. The point to be hit by the invisible X-rays was first outlined exactly by a beam from a light-centering device in the X-ray machine.

Twice a day for twelve days the Brazilian's cancer was bombarded by an intense irradiation, gradually narrowed down toward the very heart of the cancer, the precise path of the rays outlined by the light-centering device that you can focus down like a spotlight. The cancerologists knew precisely where they were shooting, so that the delicate, healthy tissues around the cancer would get a minimum amount of the rays' devastation. On the final days of treatment, the heart of the malignant growth—the most stubborn and resistant cancer cells are there—got a terrific concentration of the gradually stepped-up X-ray energy.

It was a super-delicate dissection. It was far more precise than the best surgeon's knife. It was a dissecting-out of murderous cancer cells —weird and subtle—leaving surrounding healthy cells comparatively undamaged.

Like other patients treated by this concentration method of irradiation at the grand old man's cancer Institute, the young Brazilian experienced none of the formerly dreaded irradiation sickness. There was a mild, red reaction on his skin while his throat healed completely. Within four weeks his voice had lost its huskiness; within six weeks all signs of the cancer had vanished; two-and-a-half years later he was well and practicing his profession and orating in the best Brazilian style.

In the six years it took them to perfect this hitting of the cancer bull's-eye, the Institute's cancerologists lost only two patients because of X-ray damage to their normal tissues. Among patients with cancer advanced so far that the only surgical hope was total removal of the larynx with loss of the voice, 52 per cent are now five-year cures; and if larynx cancer has not recurred in that time, the chance of its return is remote.

Best of all—among larynx cancer patients so far advanced that they were beyond all hope of operation—20 per cent of this rear-guard are free of disease after five years' time.

The cancer Institute began to become a Mecca for sufferers from larynx cancer. They came from every part of the U. S. A. and from many countries world over. They came as a result of the life-saving grapevine that so magically and quickly sends news among all types of the afflicted. Some began to come, referred by throat specialists, even though there was still chance of operation!

In the early years of the 1940's it seemed to the grand old man that this new concentration system of irradiation might reach out far beyond its spectacular curing of larynx cancer. This, if caught early when it was entirely inside the larynx with the vocal cords still completely movable, was now so curable that, in his words, "it could be made a disease of largely historic interest!" Irradiation seemed to promise a revolutionary upset in the grim picture of many another type of accessible cancer.

VII

In these years of the middle 1940's it seemed to me that, fired by this new hope, our grand old man was actually growing younger. Wouldn't the cure rate of many another kind of accessible cancer be going up now?

What makes the vast majority of people hide their cancers so long from their doctors? Why are eight out of ten cancers discovered late and most of them too late? Largely because of fear of the X-rays that used to burn people and even kill them. And because of fear of the knife.

Now something new had been added. "But now," the grand old man said, "when advances in radiation have reached their present stage, when we can offer such hope for cure *without fear of mutilation*"—and his face flushed, his voice rose, his gray eyes gleamed—

"when people know that, then patients will not be afraid to come early."

Yet, strangely, the ghastly words, "if they'd only have come earlier," kept echoing in doctors' offices and hospitals. Advances against accessible forms of malignant death remained isolated. New York's Memorial Hospital, for example, records 55 per cent of radiation cures of early cancer of the cervix of the uterus; and the Curie Institute in Paris reports a cure rate of 75 per cent. Yet in the U. S. A. 16,000 women were dying yearly from this disease.

What was wrong about the grand old man's optimism?

From Germany, Sweden, from his own cancer Institute and the pitifully inadequate number of other special cancer centers came great news of the high cure rate of malignant tumors of the skin, lip, mouth, sinuses, and throat. Yet between eight and nine thousand victims continued to die yearly from these causes in the United States.

What was the deadly bottleneck?

"It's expert cancerologists we lack," said the grand old man, keeping up his courage. When you watched him and the staff of the little cancer Institute, it is true it portended the need of a new breed of doctor. A handful of them had been specially trained for years, not only in the pathology and surgery of cancer, but also in the subtle, dangerous, and super-precision biological engineering of irradiation. But watching them at their preliminary examination of cancer-riddled patients, you saw how they needed more than technique and science. They had learned the stern discipline of hope against death that came to them, hopeless by all old standards, in nearly four cases out of every five. The grand old man kept them buoyed up with a slim, yet grim, expectation. For every single one of these hopeless who does live, they knew it was not luck, or an act of God, it was only their own stab at a new unorthodox treatment that had saved the victim from an otherwise inevitable progress to the grave.

Such satisfaction was counterbalanced by an awful responsibility. The first course of their X-ray or radium therapy seals the patient's fate. It can't be repeated. From it there is no recall. It is decisive for cure or death.

I began to see why young doctors weren't exactly flocking to the cancer Institute to enlist for this adventure. Wasn't it that the cancer radiologist's discipline was a bit too tough—or seemed so—to the new young M.D.'s? Tediously putting patients under X-ray machines twice a day for weeks, then waiting months for the result—was this as exciting as a brilliantly executed operation? Where was the drama in the dingy radiotherapy room with its low-humming X-ray cannon? Compare that to the men-in-white business of the surgical amphitheater!

The results? Comparing the results? Remembering the far-gone inoperables the X-ray cannon was saving, curing? Death rates are still far from the first consideration in the fetching-up of our boys in colleges of medicine. For maximum low death rates to be an index of the best medical care, we need a few more Herman Bundesens.

The grand old man had rewards, though. For example, a man came to the Institute, frightful with a cancer of the nose and lip. He had been referred to one of the most famous clinics in the world, where he was advised that an operation *might* save his life— but with the loss of most of his face.

He refused it and came to the cancer Institute. The cancerologist and his staff inserted radium needles into that tumor and now, years later, the man was free of cancer, his face almost as good as ever.

For the grand old man there was a salt of life in saving victims given up by the surgeons. There seemed a dignity in his knowing that so very few of their patients coming for radiation were cases which surgeons would welcome to their amphitheaters. Discards. Cats and dogs. Lost ones. Marked for the ash can. The disfigured. The ulcerous. Begging life in a whisper.

Fundamental scientist that he was, the grand old man was proud of his cancerologist's follow-up, probably more complete, thorough, and accurate than any in the field of cancer treatment. Bending his distinguished head with its silky snow-white hair over these records, he pointed. Look, a list of 22 victims of larynx cancer beyond all help of the knife. To be irradiated, so many a surgeon thought, for palliation not for cure. Of course not. Not only their voices but their lives as good as gone. Look! These 22, alive, talking out loud—singing if they felt like it. Free of any sign of cancer, after X-rays or radium.

It was after all a record in which the Institute and the grand old man could take a calm and quiet pride. Not, of course, frenzied.

"Pr-r-r-rogress," said the white-haired veteran, with a heavy burring of his r's for special emphasis. "A gr-r-r-reat str-r-r-ride ahead in irr-r-r-r-radiation." Every one of these 22 was alive because of new irradiation so powerful, so terrific, that a few years ago all radiologists would have predicted that the cure itself would kill.

One lack, because of its poverty, prevents the Institute from multiplying these miracles. Because of its poverty, it has no beds, no hospital where these doomed people could have every type of nursing and nutritional care while they get their super-radiation. It is pitiful how these very sick people, living nearby in rooming houses, drag themselves daily toward the radiant energy that gives them a bit more than a straw of hope. One of these, a little old lady to whom I had the honor of listening, told her story while her eyes beamed through her spectacles.

"I'm going *home* today, just imagine," she said.

Why was that remarkable? Remarkable, that was an understatement, she explained. A few weeks before, a malignantly spreading cancer of her pharynx had all but stopped her ability to swallow.

"Have you ever found you couldn't swallow?" she asked. "Have you ever been so it was harder and harder to swallow, till at last you couldn't at all?"

When she arrived at the Institute the X-ray film showed an almost indiscernible opening, hardly a line, leading down to her gullet, an almost obliterated opening through which with terrible pain she could take a little liquid.

The cancerologist explained that the greatest surgeon in the world would not have dared to operate to cure the cancer and rebuild her pharynx. She had been bedridden with a mounting weakness for three months—semi-starvation. She had to be helped up the steps of the Institute to the biopsy proving her cancer, a malignancy far beyond operation and surely fatal; then to the X-rays, increasing their fierce energy of more and more thousands of roentgens, formerly deadly, now harnessed, tamed into gentleness to this little old lady. Two times daily for twelve days . . .

"Show him my throat, Doctor," she urged the cancerologist.

"When the doctor saw my throat, yesterday," she said, "he just couldn't *believe* it." Her dark eyes flashed their own rays, sparks of new life through her spectacles.

VIII

These were the Institute's halcyon days. The grand old man did not say the rays were cancer's final answer. He had been a great immunologist in his own active laboratory days. He was keenly following new science hinting that some new type of mysterious virus might be sneaking into our healthy body cells, turning them cancerous. To him it seemed hopeful that cells so changed behaved as if foreign to their human owners' bodies. This gave hope for an antibiotic, some super-penicillin might be found to kill them.* Or a serum. The grand old man smiled, repeating:

"But that doesn't satisfy the present cancer patient. You've got to treat him with the means at hand," he said. "And those means are r-r-r-r-eally magic."

Now I had seen this magic working and knew that what he said was true. He was the youngest of any of them at the Institute. He kept prodding the cancerologists to extend their attack on other mass-killing cancers. To other desperate ones. Mightn't cancers deep in the body, heretofore remote from rays, be made accessible? Cancer of the lung was killing 10,000 or more Americans yearly and seemed actually to be on an alarming increase. Many sufferers were in no condition to withstand operation for removal of the entire lung or even a lobe of a lung—very slim hopes. Others refused such operations. In such, mightn't the accurate and penetrating power of

* Intense search for a cancer anti-biotic is now in progress. Its discovery is far from impossible.

concentration radiotherapy by X-ray hit the cancer bull's-eye? The depth of the cancer wouldn't bother now that super-voltage rays could strike so accurately and so deep. There is new hope that lung cancers could be found earlier than they had been, what with X-ray screening in chest clinics, with confirmation by the bronchoscope. This offers hope both for surgery and irradiation. The grand old man was excited.

Couldn't they start, just as they'd done with larynx cancers? With the hopeless ones discarded by surgeons as too far gone? And work up to the earlier ones as they'd done with the larynx?

This was the old man's dream. But for this they must have a small, highly scientifically equipped hospital.

I X

He was sure, by 1945, that they were ready for it. "Every cancer," he repeated, "passes through a stage when it is curable either by surgical removal or radiation." The grand old man serenely needled the Institute's staff. Did they really know, till they tried, how far that curable stage could be prolonged? Had they reached their limit in refining and raising the power of radiation? Already X-rays hinted promise of replacing the knife for many cancers. Look at their larynx cancer records—in two or three years they'd be publishing five-year cure records that should make the medical world sit up and take notice. Wasn't it something that tremendous and effective doses of rays could at last be given without fear of deadly radiation sickness or fatal burns? What cancers mightn't at last remain inaccessible? The grand old man was one of those rare human spirits who really believed in this new magic.

X

At this moment of the hatching of new bold death-fighting projects a blow fell on the Institute.

A meeting of throat specialists was held in September, 1945. This Institute! It was getting undue publicity! *The Reader's Digest* had published its hopeful story and the response had been tremendous. The Editor of the *Journal of the American Medical Association*, himself, had published laudatory articles about the Institute's success. How to put the bee on all this ballyhoo?

What about those two patients who had died of tuberculosis following treatment "by a famous tumor group" for supposed carcinoma of the larynx? So asked a throat specialist. No biopsy had been made. Tut, tut. The Institute was not named by name, but the implication was obvious.

The grand old man went into action. He wrote a polite letter to the throat specialist. If the Institute was meant, would it be possible to give the patients' names? The object in mind was the possibility of studying their records in order to guard against unwarranted claims for the value of radiotherapy of cancer of the larynx, and also to determine how these cases were listed in the Institute's follow-up reports.

The throat specialist replied courteously saying it had been till now impossible to check the records in the desired manner but that he would be glad to do so as soon as possible in order that the grand old man might compare these cases with the Institute's records.

Months went by; no answer. Four months, and the grand old man wrote again to this throat surgeon, disliking to bother him, but had he succeeded in finding any data regarding those two cases?

To this date, three years later, no answer.

There were still more serious charges, by another throat surgeon at the conference in 1945. Three patients had been mentioned as dying within six months of the time they had been presented in a certain clinic as cured. The grand old man again wrote, asking: If these were patients of the Institute, would it be possible to have *their* names? For clarification of the Institute's records?

For three years—no answer of any kind at all.

These accusations—as the late Adolf Hitler knew so well—even though nailed the way the grand old man had nailed them, leave a residue. They sneak out of hospital coat-rooms into the minds of physicians and there they work their poison. For many it is as if they were true.

Meanwhile, the Institute's cancerologist had published its five-year cure records in *Radiology*, October, 1948.

In 107 consecutive unselected cases—meaning most of them far gone—of laryngeal cancer, treated by radiotherapy, the five-year cures were 35 per cent. Seven of these, who died from causes other than cancer before five years, were counted as cancer.

Among cases of laryngeal cancer where the only surgical alternative was total removal of the larynx, the cure rate for five years stood at 52 per cent.

Among similar cancers, beyond any operation, 20 per cent were free of the disease after five years.

In early cancer of the larynx, where the tumor had not completely fixed the vocal cords, the five-year cure rate was 60 per cent. In still earlier cancer of the larynx, an operation called laryngo-fissure—less drastic than total removal of the larynx—had yielded five-year cure rates of 80 to 85 per cent. Yet, in such early cancers where the vocal cords were not completely fixed, radiotherapy was preferable to the knife.

In this the Institute did not stand alone. Several other radiation clinics in America and abroad reported closely similar five-year cure rates—the Memorial Hospital of New York City excepted.

In view of the essential uniformity of these good end results by radiotherapy, wasn't it startling to read recent articles and discussions on cancer of the larynx in which radiation was mentioned casually as a palliative for inoperable tumors? Such is the boil-down of the Institute's cancerologist's scientific publication.

From here on the present writer will take over. Yes, it was startling—especially in view of the 20 per cent of larynx cancers, absolutely given up as inoperable by the throat surgeons—*and then cured by irradiation.*

Yet we had best restrain our indignation. Let's grant that, with irradiation—in competent hands—running neck and neck for five-year cure rate with operations that mutilate or remove the larynx, let's admit that irradiation will win out. If only because so many sufferers fear the knife and because all sufferers would enjoy retaining their voices if they have to go on living. But let us grant, too, that if the throat surgeons would dispassionately examine and analyze the comparative records, they would surely not, as some have done, try to kill this great new hope of non-mutilating cure of accessible cancer.

XI

For throat surgeons who try to kill irradiation therapy of larynx cancer this is an apologium. They do not know and, as Herman Bundesen says, do not know that they do not know. With due respect, men of the knife, wizards that some of them are, are servants of a crude ancient discipline inherited from barbers. The art and science of irradiation is a new, exacting, highly experimental discipline. It is biological engineering. It demands a new kind of man, expert in pathology, expert in physics, and yet having that physician's sixth sense of knowing whether a sufferer is going downhill or getting better. It lacks surgery's brilliant thirty minutes of drama. It is a stern game of weeks in which you sweat it out hoping your stuff will cure, not kill. Yet it has gained marvelous precision, the delicate exactness of a machinist fitting bearings to millionths of an inch. But it is more difficult, because radiation must deal with that subtle stuff called protoplasm. This is chemically shifting and variable, and in a given human being there are as yet no formulas for stress and strain or strength and resistance (as engineers have formulas to guide them in work with inert metals). It is super-precision, the final portal for the exit of rays from the machine against laryngeal cancer being only 2 centimeters × 2— a narrow terrifically concentrated shot at the heart of the murderous cancer, blasting it, tearing the sinister guts out of it, curing it—six times out of ten.

When a science and an art are so new and strange, it is natural that many do not like it.

XII

Imagine my surprise, in January, 1949, when the grand old man called me by long distance telephone, asking that his name, the name of the cancerologist, and the name of the Institute be left out of this story.

It seems that my writing about the Institute had aroused a definite antagonism to it and to its leading personalities. This was shown by the failure of approval of the Institute by certain Boards. The local unit of the American Cancer Society consistently ignored the Institute, though its trustees had tried to get the Society's friendship. The cancerologist is kept off scientific programs. The work of the Institute is ignored in reviews of cancer of the larynx, the very field where it has made its most splendid life-saving contribution. "It is intimated" that *The Reader's Digest's* undue publicity is the reason for this persecution.

That's why all this has had to be anonymous. What is going to happen to the grand old man's hope for a great life-saving surge in the war against accessible cancer? I do not know. What is going to happen to the Institute, which I had tried so hard to help but only succeeded in threatening with ruin? "Laryngologists are no longer referring cancer of the larynx to us," said the Institute's cancerologist. What is going to happen to the grand old man, who such a short time ago looked so much younger? He plans to retire soon. I for one want to ask who can come up to the grand old man— whose work has just started, even though he's 85—in hatred of suffering, in honesty, in fundamental vision of what now must be done to save 50,000 cancer victims yearly?

The Institute's cancerologist, apologetic for having to ask me not to mention his work by name, told Rhea and me how it was said that, when the grand old man died, he, the cancerologist, was going to be run out of the city. Though he has been foully set upon and abused, he is not the martyr. It is the cancer victims who are the martyrs. The Institute's cancerologist should take heart, remembering the conduct of Master Hugh Latimer and Dr. Nicholas Ridley,

Bishop of London, on that day they both were burned at the stake for heresy, in 1555, before Balliol College, by Bloody Mary:

"Then they brought a faggot, kindled with fire, and laid it down at Doctor Ridley's feet, to whom Master Latimer spake in this manner: 'Be of good comfort, Master Ridley, and play the man. We shall this day light such a candle, by God's grace, in England, as I trust shall never be put out.'"

Let our cancerologist, who after all will not be set alight with faggots, play the man. If they do run him out of the city, let him start over. His X-rays and radium have saved hundreds of lives, and thousands and hundreds of thousands know it. Let him begin again. He is only 50, against the grand old man's 85.

It is the victims of accessible cancer, now being kept from the Institute's healing rays, who are the martyrs to medical envy and obfuscation. They too, by their needless dying, will light a search-light. It will help future sufferers to look for truth about all means available for use in time to save their lives. It is fighters like the grand old man (like Herman Kabat he has the gift of feeling the pain of others) that some sufferers can thank for their voices and their lives. It is thanks to the last of our mavericks, whose story I shall now tell, that future victims of accessible cancer may—I'm italicizing it, *may*—cross the economic hurdle now barring so many of them from life.

PART FIVE

THE LAST MAVERICK

*Sid phoned us long distance, with no preliminary ex-
planations, asking us how quick we could get out to the
Coast. Three days later, at seven in the morning, he met
us at Mills Field, San Francisco. It seemed the boys—
medical politicians—were getting set to give Sid's health
plan the business.*

*It seemed Sid's crime was that of building a pilot
plant for good medical care within the means of the
ordinary citizen, paying its own way without charity or
government socialization. For this, Sid was to be tried
by the doctors as unethical, which medically is only
slightly less heinous than performing abortions.*

*Why is it odiously sinful to keep folks from dying at
a price not straining their pocketbooks? By a system cir-
cumventing government medicine, when government
medicine was what Sid's accusers hated worse than poison? The goofiness of the smears of those doctors against
Sid was what made those days between June 2 and 13
such fun and so astounding.*

*It seemed comical—provided that you could avoid
thinking of the hundreds of thousands who would be
sick and might die—if medical plots like this one against
Sid should be generally successful.*

CHAPTER XIII

What Sid Did

-》》 《《-

DURING all these years of life among the doctors we had been
looking for a type of medical maverick different from any we have
written about. Was there a man who had found the economic trick
of putting medical science into universal action? We were looking, not intensively, but out of the corner of an eye, for a master
maverick who had actually demonstrated a sound, sane, sensible
system (fine American words), a system not socialistic—we knew the
doctors wouldn't go for that—but a system strictly in the American
grain, a system that would bring all possible medical science within
the reach of every man, woman, and child who needed it. If we
could dig up such a genius, what doctors could possibly object to
him? What doctor worthy of that title would want anybody to die
who could possibly be saved?

What we were hunting for was a good Samaritan, model 1950.
We had to try to unearth him if for no other reason than to give
artistic rhyme and reason to this chronicle of life among the doctors. We wanted the book to have an optimistic, if not happy, ending. Hadn't we gone on record that our physicians—because of the
new awesome power of their science of live-or-die—are a brand-new
kind of human being, a new sub-species of *Homo sapiens,* promising
at last to show how we may fuse the power of science with the
faith of religion?

Hadn't we even suggested a timid hope, not directly stated, that
our doctors—fusing science with religion—might be the ones to
save humanity from threatened suicide? By making men neighbors?

By Good-Samaritanism? After the mellifluous promises of politicians had turned out murderous and the pious sermons of the preachers had turned out just words? At this book's start we had stuck out our necks on the proposition that this new human mutant, the doctor, with his terrific power over live-or-die, plus more of the tradition of the good Samaritan, could now at last multiply acts of mercy *ad infinitum*. That might make the preachers and politicians look ridiculous; and if the world survived long enough, medical stronghearts might take the lead.

We know that practically all doctors (including the most expensive chromium-plated specialists) perform many charitable and life-saving actions. For this we revere the doctors beyond any other servants of mankind; and to many an excellent physician it means more than his handsome income when we praise him for stopping and binding up the wounds and applying his modern scientific oil and wine to poor folks who have fallen among thieves and been given the brush-off by the priest and the Levite.

But here was the rub: this Good-Samaritanism was imperfect, undependable. We kept poking about for a medical Good-Samaritanism which might be automatic and all-pervading, and which would preserve the free enterprise of our doctors.

II

As long ago as December, 1942—in the Hotel St. Francis in San Francisco—we picked up a trail. The faint promise of such a Good-Samaritanism appeared in the person of a mysterious young doctor. He sympathized with our quest but was not sure that he liked our enthusiasm about what he was trying to do. In a seemingly timid manner, he said he was not too sure that he had what we were looking for, or that he had it ready to put across to the American people right now. It might still be Utopic. We weren't asking too much for the American people, he admitted, but we might be asking too much of their doctors. He was skittish about our writing him up, even though his boss, Henry J. Kaiser, had given us the green light.

"You'd better leave me out of it," he kept urging.

It was obvious from his health plan that he was a white hope against medicine's socialization, yet to our astonishment it turned out that many doctors in the San Francisco Bay region did not like him. Surely it couldn't be that they would object to being made better Samaritans, painlessly?

This young man, only 34, was Dr. Sidney Garfield. He was the director of the Permanente Foundation Hospitals and health plan which were taking care of about 90,000 of Kaiser's shipyard workers in the Bay region and, in addition, other thousands up north in the Portland, Oregon, area. Like most of our other mavericks, who had made their discoveries in fields outside those of their original training, Garfield had not been trained, *ad hoc*, as a medical economist but had begun his career as an especially promising general surgeon. He was enigmatic. How could such a seemingly mild young man have so spectacularly and rapidly (in six months) organized advanced, all-inclusive super-modern, streamlined medical care for over a hundred-thousand people—against the particularly savage opposition of the local medical fraternity?

He was definitely a young man of mystery. His finely-tailored clothes remained unwrinkled because of the economy and careful precision of the way he moved about. He seemed not medical and even a bit Hollywoodish in his elegance, but beneath that he was wiry and gave one the feeling that one had better not get funny with him. His face had high cheekbones and was chiseled in clean lines, photogenic. His hair, cut close, was curly reddish-gold and he was deeply tanned. His gray-green eyes told little because they were usually peering through narrow slits, especially when he smiled, which was often, and yet he seemed to be a sad young man and in repose round his mouth there were deep lines that had been made, I guessed, by some kind of pain, not physical.

In his talk there was no medical gobbledygook. He kept you straining to understand his low-keyed explanations which were without emphasis and had no dramatic inflections. He wanted to talk only about his health plan. He was hard to follow. Not that he was abstruse, on the contrary he was clear; but his language was like that of a man from Mars—technically new and almost entirely in figures which seemed fantastic. He talked a strange mathematics in terms of hundreds of thousands of people paying only a few cents-per-day for top medical care that cost many dollars-per-day to give—all this at a substantial profit to the health plan.

To us—medico-economically ignorant—this sounded like one of those things they can only do in California. But we weren't alone in our mystification; in history there had not before been just such language as that of Sidney Garfield's.

That first day of our now almost seven years of close co-working I did my share of the talking, trying to explain our hunt for all-pervading automatic medical Good-Samaritanism. He listened, deadpan, not batting an eye. Looking back on it now, Garfield must have thought me pretty high-flown. Would he subscribe to this credo: that human life is good; that for *medical* science there are no rich or poor, no high or low, no black or white, no Jews or Aryans, no race or creed, but only human beings all equally candidates for its salvation? Did Garfield believe that it was not for him to decide whether human life is worth perpetuating or whether certain levels of humanity are not worth preserving? Was the aim of medical science not only the conservation but the now possible mighty lengthening of the lives of all, down to the most forlorn of mankind?

Garfield smiled his slow, pleasant, slit-eyed grin and nodded a polite yes to all this oratory which must have sounded somewhat windy. How was this to be translated into practical action? I hadn't the foggiest notion. It must have sounded to Garfield like an H. G. Wellsian improbable future. The only proposals I had—and of these I was doubtful myself—were revolutionary, Utopic. In Garfield's smile as he listened there was pity. He agreed with all my beautiful objectives, only, you see (he explained hesitatingly), he'd been working for ten years, feeling his way slowly, to make those objectives come true, practically.

The immensity, the portentous promise of Garfield's discovery slowly dawned on me. He was actually solving one of the knottiest of all human problems, he was groping his way to the filling of the most tragic of all human needs—how to pay for the doctors, the laboratories, and the hospitals out of your own pocket so that you will not have to go to loan sharks and be ruined as a solvent citizen, to keep from dying. Like all problems, when solved (Boss Kettering's words), it turned out to be simple. Garfield was demonstrating that the solution involved just two changes in traditional medical practice. Both were practical and for both there were already proved precedents.

The first was prepayment. That was only what we all do in all kinds of insurance. Folks whose houses don't burn down all join together to pay for the houses that do. People who don't break their bones join together to pay accident insurance for people who do. People who are still alive join together to give security by life insurance for the families of those who do die. But in medical practice it's been the opposite. By direct fee for service to doctors it's only the sick who pay for their sickness, and the longer and the worse they're sick the more they pay. Why shouldn't the well, all the well, join together to pay for the sick? That's prepayment.

Garfield's second change was that of transforming the present solo medical practice into medical care by groups of specialist doctors all working as a team under one clinic and hospital roof. The waste of money in the present solo practice, the reduplication of doctors' offices, X-ray and diagnostic laboratories, was terrific. It pushed the cost of a serious illness—when the patient had to pay for it by direct fee for service to solo-practicing physicians, surgeons, X-ray technicians, and laboratory men—to astronomical figures bankrupting the ordinary citizen.

So here was what Sid did: he hooked prepayment by large numbers of citizens to practice by groups of specialists. This reduced the cost of medical care astronomically in an opposite direction. It made prepayment profitable. It gave the groups of doctors the opportunity to give everything needed and available in the latest and most scientific of medical care. The astounding profits, from the large funds furnished by such prepayment, to groups of specialist doctors, made it possible for them to build, and pay off the cost of building, their own hospitals. They could now practice the most

modern medicine in their own facilities. It revolutionized the practice of medicine. As medicine was paid for now, the solo-practicing
doctor made more money, the longer and the more seriously each of
his patients was sick—to the possible financial ruin of that patient.
But under Garfield's new system, the shorter time all the patients
were sick, the less time the patients had to stay in the hospital, the
less medical attention they needed—the higher were the profits of
the doctors, at a cost, because of the small prepayment of so many
cents a day, that was within the means of the working citizens of
the nation.

Under the Garfield system, the treatment of the sick would inevitably become a vanishing economy. It paid the doctors *most* to
keep all possible patients in the *best* health. The patients wouldn't
mind it. It was obvious. Alas, what is more obscure than the obvious? The people and the doctors didn't yet see it.

The pain lines around Garfield's mouth seemed to deepen. His
voice stayed low. His eyes occasionally widened in a cold blaze of
fury as he told us how a man gets ganged up on, how he's got to
take being smeared and lied about when he tries to get something
going that's new and good. What we liked was that Garfield wasn't
paranoid; he didn't take this personally; what encouraged us was
the impression Garfield gave of a sinewy indestructibility. All right,
he said, we were agreed upon medicine's great religious goal. But
did we want to see hospitals which were actually in operation, giving sick wage-earners modern scientific group medicine and unlimited hospitalization for seven cents a day deducted from all the
workmen's wages? Did we want to!

III

For most of the next two weeks we as good as lived in the Permanente hospitals. Though in our day we have been in many institutions, public, private, and voluntary, for rich, for middle, for
poor, in Garfield's hospitals something new had been added which
had been lacking in all we had ever seen. (There may be possible
exceptions—private sanatoria for rich alcoholics and psychotics—

but of these we have had no experience.) In the Permanente hospitals there was an atmosphere. Curiously, it at first escaped definition. It narrowed down to an olfactory sensation. Yes, this was it: your typical hospital—even a good one—gives you the impression that it needs a daily drenching with Airwick. In the Permanente hospitals there was a curious absence of that mephitic blend of stink of the products of disease and corruption and an aroma of antiseptic.

"It's because they're completely air-conditioned," explained Garfield. "If *anybody* needs air-conditioning—who needs it as much as sick people?" he asked as if this were the most sensible self-answering question in the world.

There were no wards; the rooms were private or semi-private, holding at the most two people, and the rooms were airy and painted a pleasant and restful light green. "We try to have everything as nice as possible for them," explained Garfield. Nice was his low-keyed word for his houses of healing and hope. His gray-green eyes opened wide as if defying us on behalf of his patients.

"If anybody needs pleasant surroundings, who needs them as much as sick people?" he asked.

The surgeries were gleaming and handy to the X-ray rooms and the laboratories. The physicians and surgeons were most of them young, highly-trained internists and specialists all working on salaries, full-time, under one roof, as a team, handy to the patients, to their healing gadgets, to the X-rays, to the laboratory, and to each other. First explaining the complexity of modern medicine and its subtly exact physical and chemical methods of diagnosis and the elaborate and widely varying techniques of chemical and surgical treatment, Garfield asked:

"How otherwise can you give people modern scientific care— excepting by this group medicine, teamwork?" It was another one of those questions to which there was only one answer.

We went back to what had seemed to us his Martian mathematics—"scores of thousands of people paying seven cents a day for this modern, streamlined, group medical care that cost many dollars per day to give."

"What is this arithmetic?" we asked him.

He slit his eyes almost shut in that enigmatic smile. He opened his eyes wide in astonishment at our fiscal imbecility. Garfield said: "There's nothing to it. On the simple principle of any insurance— haven't you heard of *insurance?*—the Kaiser shipbuilders pre-pay that seven cents a day. It's voluntarily deducted from their wages. The well pay for the sick. The sick alone don't pay for it. That's always been the trouble. The many chip in to pay for the sickness of the comparatively few."

Garfield made me feel silly, like Dr. Watson, the straight man for Sherlock Holmes. "But you say you're more than paying for your limitless care for these sick people. You say you're paying off the con- struction cost of this hospital, at a rate of $50,000 a month. You're actually practicing medicine at a hell of a profit," I protested.

Garfield's polite pity for me again showed in his slow smile. He said: "There's nothing to it. We've washed out the terrific waste of the old medical private practice here. In the old traditional medical practice, every doctor, every surgeon, every specialist runs his own little private individual cure store." Didn't I see the over- lapping, the reduplication?

Garfield waved his hand about in a gentle gesture. He said: "There's nothing to it. Here we've got a streamlined team under one hospital roof. All we've done that's maybe a little original is to hook up"—he hesitated—"to tie this Mayo Clinic type of care by groups of specialists to prepaid insurance from thousands of people."

"Is that all there's to it?"

"Not quite," said Garfield. "The prepayment of seven cents a day from the workers' wages gives us 60 per cent of our income— the other 40 comes from a flat fee paid by workmen's compensation insurance companies—for care of industrial accidents."

What obsessed Garfield was that the doctors, paying off the cost of their hospitals, could at last build them the way they wanted them, could really run them. "It's simple, there's nothing to it," he kept repeating.

IV

Now I saw it and it was really wonderful. Then I took the mental bit in my teeth and started to run away with Garfield's invention. "You've got the answer to medical care," I said, aglow with ignorant enthusiasm. "The American Medical Association should go for this. You shouldn't have any trouble with the local medical boys on this one. Prepaid medicine, health insurance, is becoming medically respectable. And who dares to say that group medicine by teams of specialists isn't the best medicine?"

Garfield looked at me with a faintly pitying smile as if to say it was wonderful how, having been in this for two weeks, I had all the answers. Then he said: "You're wrong. With a few exceptions, the local doctors are opposing us. They are conspiring to put us out of business."

But that was incredible. Organized medicine now approved of voluntary, prepaid health insurance. It approved of group medical practice. Here was the simple logic of it: If it's all right for the rich man to pay *individually* for group medical care by teams of specialists, why can't ordinary citizens pay for that same group specialist care, *jointly?*

"Yes, it is completely logical," said Garfield, patiently, "but do you think this fight is going to be settled by logic?"

He was, curiously, not angry with the doctors. The physicians in the Eastbay area had the hatchet out for Permanente Hospital and its health plan for the very reason that they saw the threat of the ordinary citizen paying for group specialist medical care, jointly. Didn't I see the doctors would have to be against it? If it spread, what would become of their individual private medical businesses? What would become of their little individual cure stores?

Then Garfield went on to tell the fantastic events of the past six months, from the time he had opened the Field Hospital at Richmond and the Permanente Hospital at Oakland. What had happened outdid Alice in Wonderland in its irrationality. From 1941 to the end of 1942 the banging, clanging, slamming shipyards had increased the Eastbay population by 90,000 workers, to say nothing of their families. There was medical chaos. Men hurt in the battle to build boats—learning clumsily to build them in the new, Gargantuan Kaiser manner—had to wait days for necessary operations that could not be performed for lack of doctors. Their wives had their babies anywhere, anyhow, and if they were lucky enough to get into a hospital, they were forced to get back to their homes or hovels or what-have-you within three days.

The doctors' offices became miniature insane asylums; appointments had to be made weeks ahead of time. How many people died, waiting for them? Nobody knows. In the hospitals there were frequently no beds available at all, not even for emergency operations. Vallejo physicians had to open wards in the dank and dismal basement of their utterly inadequate hospital. A U. S. Public Health Service officer recorded the sad saga of one Richmond mother. Her baby was sick and for three days she wandered, child in arms, from one doctor's office to another and from town to town, ending up at last down the Bay in Palo Alto where she found a doctor to attend her child who died, next day, of pneumonia. The heat, so reported Dr. A. E. Larsen of the California Physicians Service, on the doctors was getting so intense that some were running away from their practices. The doctors felt they were being killed, they were so loaded down that they had come to the breaking point. When Garfield had opened his health plan to the Kaiser workers, he was careful to submit it for approval to the leaders of the local medical society and gladly they gave him the green light; what else could they do, you couldn't let people die!

But then—when Henry J. Kaiser appealed to the War Production Board for priorities for materials for Garfield to equip his hospitals, to his astonishment the big builder was told that the WPB had been informed, by physicians in the Eastbay area, *that no additional hospital beds were needed.*

"The shocking records," said Henry Kaiser, "are available in Washington on the effort they (certain local doctors) made to prevent the hospital from being built."

The hatchet once more whistled close to Garfield's neck. The

Federal Procurement and Assignment Service—it had the say as to which doctors were to go to war and which ones were to stay home—was informed that Garfield's young teams of specialists were not needed for the care of the Kaiser workers, that these skilled groups of doctors should be inducted into the Army and replaced by what older ordinary doctors Garfield might be able to get. This would have wrecked Garfield's medical care and the Permanente health plan. Henry Kaiser and Garfield went to Washington. The bitter facts, the potentially murderous data on the threatened medical deprivation of the shipyard workers, laid before a U. S. Senate committee, got front-page newspaper publicity.

To counteract this, the *Journal of the American Medical Association* thundered, editorially: "Mr. Kaiser and other industrial leaders desire to maintain their individual empires without disturbance, regardless of the need of the armed forces for physicians." At this time the Army already had one physician for every 100 soldiers while in many a region there was one doctor for every 3,000, or 4,000, or 5,000 civilians.

The official medical editorial attack was supplemented by a far subtler and probably more effective official grapevine rumor: "Garfield's prepaid group medicine is wildcat medicine, unethical in principal and practice." No official of the A.M.A. had inspected Garfield's hospitals. But this word might scare off young highly trained doctors wanting to join Garfield.

"God alone," said Henry Kaiser, "will be the final judge upon the injury they could have done to thousands of people if they had succeeded in taking away our doctors or closing our hospitals."

But there were honest California doctors who did not want people to die; and Dr. Harold A. Fletcher, Chief of the State Procurement and Assignment Service, heading a committee of San Francisco's leading physicians, motored across the Bay Bridge to take a hard look at Garfield's Permanente set-up. It was novel and strange for Garfield to have a chance to be actually examined before being condemned as wildcat and unethical. The Fletcher Committee reported officially, in print, that it found "an up-to-date medical service . . . hospital and treatment facilities excellent . . .

a well-qualified and well-paid staff of physicians available for every kind of medicine and surgery."

The Committee even made an invidious comparison: "From the standpoint of the present emergency"—who had been lying to the effect that there was no emergency?—"this complete industrial and health service is doing a necessary job which could not have been done nearly so effectively with the medical facilities existing when it was set up," concluded the Committee.

Privately Dr. Fletcher was still more emphatic. "Dr. Garfield and his staff are doing a very good job with the Kaiser workers," he told Edgar Kaiser, son of the big builder.

During the remaining war years Garfield expanded his operations in comparative tranquillity, only mildly annoyed by medical talk that he was running a highly profitable "peanut concession" at the shipyards and personally making millions of dollars.

At this time and for six years in all, he took not a penny in salary. He lived on his own capital.

v

In his relations with the doctors of the Bay area, Garfield had a possibly regrettable shortcoming. He was no back-slapper, no hail-fellow-well-met, no salesman, not one of the boys.

"I don't care about talking a health plan; I'm interested in doing it; any competent medical man, taking the trouble to see what we've got, will go for it."

That summed up Garfield's promotorial proclivity. Though the late Clarence Day, Jr., pointed out that we act like human beings because we are descended from Simians, Garfield was in many ways cat-like rather than monkeyish. He was always landing on his feet when figuratively thrown out of a tenth-story medical window; by his multiple lives he survived what should have been fatal medical attack; he had an indolent grace of movement that I've seen flash into blinding speed in emergency. He was impersonal like a cat, looking at you while you talked to him and then often turning and walking away, seemingly indifferently, as if you did not exist. In the Permanente Hospital the patients did not know who this quiet, smiling, red-haired young man (never in medical white coat) was.

The traditional bedside manner, for Garfield, was replaced by arithmetic such as this: "So far, from $500,000 received from the workers on the health plan, we've actually given them $1,500,000 worth of care. That, conservatively, is what they'd have had to pay to individual doctors on the old fee-for-service basis."

I saw nurses—peremptorily—order him out of the Permanente Hospital's obstetrical division, for fear that he might break the aseptic technique by entering; they did not know this was Dr. Garfield. He was definitely not the distinguished Dr. Garfield; he was the farthest remove from your big director, your pompous front man. But he knew to the penny the profit and loss account of his hospitals and health plan. Give it time. Prepaid group medicine would speak for itself. No need peddling it around. Such was his austere, un-American salesmanship.

Garfield's prepaid group medical care spoke plenty to the Kaiser workers, it spoke vividly to one tough ex-Marine I especially remember. For the privilege of meeting him I must thank Virginia Jackson—now Virginia Garfield. He had his arm shot off at Cavite just after Pearl Harbor, he had nearly died, he had got back to the States, and had been turned into a one-armed welder at the Kaiser shipyards. This was Corporal Wilmer Patrick Shea (rhymes with shay). He'd slipped on the deck of a landing boat they were building and had broken his other arm badly.

"They kept me at the hospital much longer than I thought they ought to," said the Marine. "But that's the way they do everything here. They said not to worry—all they wanted was to be sure this wing I had left would be okay."

Shea had the run of the hospital and, convalescing, became a student of Garfield's medical care. Back at his dormitory, his arm in a sling, he came to the hospital for three excellent meals a day fed him by a trained nurse; and he hobnobbed with patients.

"They don't *bargain* about the care you ought to get," said Shea. "Knew a guy got clipped on the bean. X-ray. No fracture. Most places they'd say: go back to work, you're okay. But here? They took him to the hospital and put him under close observation."

This lean youngster with a pain-marked phizog had a curious insight into a certain potential of Garfield's new medical care—a power that, ultimately, may sell it without fine words or promotion, that may put it across to the citizenry despite every medical smear or obfuscation.

"You see," said Shea, looking me straight in the eyes, dead serious, "the way they treat us fellows at the shipyards keeps a lot of us from dying."

I pricked up my ears. There was a point. That was the nuts of the whole business, as Herman Bundesen would say. "How do you mean?" I asked the Marine.

"Well," he said, "out of the pneumonias, over half of 'em wouldn't have got any treatment if we hadn't had the health plan— or they'd stall around till it was too late before going to the doctor. You know, costs a lot of dough to go to an ordinary doctor," said Shea.

"Half of that 50 per cent would have died," he went on. He was up on his statistics of pneumonia mortality rates, when untreated.

"But at the yards, when we've got a sneeze and a sniffle and a little fever," he went on, "do they just give us a handful of aspirins and tell us to get back to work? I'll say they don't."

"What do they do—it might be just a cold," I said.

"They take us in. X-ray our chests. At the first sign of pneumonia we're in bed and being treated with this here new sulfa-"—he hesitated—"diazine, isn't it?"

At this moment I determined to follow Permanente's pneumonia mortality statistics for the next few years, and for this tip-off— which you will later see had its own significance—I'll always be grateful to Wilmer Patrick Shea.

The observant Marine had caught another nice angle of Garfield's new medical economy.

He expounded it in his own crude words: "The ordinary docs've gotta try to make plenty of dough off of every sick man," he explained. "Here, they examine you carefully, and if you don't need an operation, you don't get it."

He would write me a word about what he thought of this new medical care. Clumsy but legibly with his left hand, just out of its sling, just learning to write, he scrawled it:

"I, as a shipyard worker, think the Field Hospital and the Permanente Health Plan are tops. Because you get the best that science can give. I think the rest of the shipyard fellows feel the same." Signed, *"Shea."*

He was a saturnine boy whose every remark had hit a bull's-eye. Life had been rugged with him, and he judged everything that happened to him on that basis. Words meant absolutely nothing to him, events everything. His face was thin, deadpan and cut deep with very long pain, and now it was eerie as it lighted up with the first smile I'd seen on it, in many hours of talking. He handed me his testimonial, smiling.

"I don't see why this can't be done everywhere, for everybody," he said as he gave me his left hand for good-bye.

Wasn't the Corporal kidding himself? He was only a Marine, and even though he had experienced Garfield's streamlined medical mercy, even though he'd seen it operating on hundreds of his fellow shipyard workers, what did Shea know? Could he judge it as well as experts in medical economics who passed on it adversely though they'd never been within 2,000 miles of it? What did any patient know of it? How does anybody know anything about medical care unless he is an M.D.? You know nothing about it unless you're on the giving end of it instead of the receiving. Someone ought to tell Shea that Garfield would soon be washed up.

You can only give this unlimited medical care when you get your seven cents a day from 90,000 Sheas. Collections automatic. Not having to sell the plan. One of those war babies. Wait till *that's* over. Watch Permanente blow up with a loud report. Watch these beautiful hospitals shut their doors and their gleaming gadgets gather rust. Thus and so I was told by medical men, insurance and medical economic experts, sociologists, economists, bankers from coast to coast. It seemed as if most of them—though men of average good will—were awaiting the collapse of Permanente health plan with glee commensurate with their pride of intellect, their deep instinct of *we* didn't-do-it-so-it-can't-be-done. It not only couldn't work anywhere in normal times, but it simply wouldn't work at all in ordinary communities where most citizens already had a family doctor to whom they were decidedly loyal. Garfield and his teams of doctors? As against the age-old institution of the family doctor, that grand old man with the beard sitting by the bed of the dying child?

In April, 1945, I tried to write a story to show how Garfield could transform his special prepaid group industrial medicine into home town medicine to lick the threat of government medicine; I was sweating it out, commuting to the Coast, convincing almost no one, getting nowhere fast. Finally the chips were down when Mr. Louis H. Pink put Garfield to this test. Mr. Pink, the director of the largest pre-paid hospital plan in the country, the Associated Hospitals of New York, Blue Cross, looked me in the eye not unkindly but with maybe just a trace of pitying incredulity. Mr. Pink measured his words:

"If Garfield's plan can survive the shutting down of the ship-yards, the case for voluntary, full-coverage, prepaid group medicine will be proved."

I read what he had dictated back to Mr. Pink. Check. I filed it away carefully and must confess that my heart was in my shoes. Nobody had faith in it, except Garfield, and he was a bit inscrutable. Maybe Mr. Kaiser, too, believed in it, but then Mr. Kaiser was busy at his own job of surviving, industrially.

Then came V-J day. In the autumn the booming, bellowing, banging, slamming clangor of the Eastbay shipyards died down to a grumbling rumble and, as it died away, as the workers faded back to their homes all over America, and as the hammerhead cranes and the hysters and whirlies gathered rust, the Permanente health plan enrollment slumped down from 90 to 60 to 40 to 25 and finally to only 15 thousand . . . Garfield's miracle of medical care couldn't stay alive on that. Then the *Bulletin of the Alameda County Medical Association* indulged in a bit of editorial self-congratulation: The government should present Permanente Hospital to the City of Oakland!

Hadn't it been built by government money paid to Henry Kaiser? No, it had not. It had been built by the faith in Garfield's care, the seven cents per day deducted from the pay of 90,000 welders, riggers, flangers, and sweepers. But only partly—Garfield was in hock to the Federal Works Agency for hundreds of thousands of dollars for his tremendous expansion, not yet amortized. With Garfield washed up at last, was the government going to have to whistle for that money?

Now came help from an unexpected quarter. A great many of the workers who remained in the Eastbay area bellowed for a continuation of their health plan, Kaiser or no Kaiser. Many new groups of people influenced by the migration of former health plan members into their ranks—clamored for an opportunity to join. It was the demand of these ordinary citizens—not Garfield—that saved the Permanente Health Plan.

VI

Garfield smiled. He closed down the smaller Field Hospital no longer needed for shipyard emergency care. He cut down his staff. Like the cool businessman he was, he rationalized his operation. He grinned like the Cheshire cat but, unlike that pussy, he did not disappear. He threw open his 330-bed Permanente Hospital, almost empty and running at a murderous loss, to the physicians and surgeons of the Eastbay area. But with the Kaiser workers gone, the emergency was over, and there would be plenty of beds in the regular hospitals. Or so Garfield's enemies had said, you remember. Only it turned out that there weren't plenty of beds, and Permanente Hospital kept its head above water by residents of the Eastbay area clamoring for hospitalization by their own physicians and surgeons who very soon were filling up the Permanente beds left vacant by the now pitifully skeleton Permanente health plan.

I have never seen Sid Garfield so imperturbable. He grinned so you could hardly see his cool gray-green eyes at all. He began canvassing all kinds of Eastbay groups, the city police force, C.I.O. and A. F. of L. unions, the faculty of the University of California at Berkeley, workers of all kinds of little industries, employees of the city of Oakland. He began building his prepaid group Permanente health plan back up from next to nothing at all out of groups of substantial citizens "who had family doctors to whom they were decidedly loyal" but who had also heard of how Garfield's prepaid group medicine might guard you against the economic disaster of illness.

This was in the late winter and early spring of 1946. These were memorable months, because now the chips were really down. It was a knock-down-and-drag-out between the new group specialist and the old solo medical care. It became clear that this was the real issue, not prepayment. The national organization of the doctors had had to swallow prepayment because a decision of the U. S. Supreme Court had convicted the organization's head men of persecuting prepaid health plans. It is said that certain of those head men of the medical power-house had narrowly escaped jail. Prepayment had now become official medically, and many state medical societies were offering their own prepaid health plans—but not like Garfield's, tied up to group specialist medical care. Group specialist medical care? Leaving aside big group clinics like the Mayo, Crile, and Lahey—mainly for well-off people—group specialist medical care, for ordinary citizens prepaying for it, now became the villain the American Medical Association must expose and attack.

From the marble-fronted, white stone national headquarters of A.M.A. in Chicago now came a devastating statement:

"Eighty per cent of medical care—the actual investigations show 85 per cent—can be rendered by a competent general practitioner with equipment available in an office or handbag. . . . Group practice is inevitably more costly than general practitioner service."

This was official. This was authoritative. Group specialist care was a luxury! This was from the editor of the *Journal of the American Medical Association,* himself, in person, the leadership of organized medicine. This was the beginning of the attempted excommunication of Sid Garfield from the church of medicine. This made Sid Garfield out a gypper of the public.

"It looks as if they've got you, there, Sid," I said. "It looks as if you're out to sell 100 per cent of the people an expensive medical care that only 15 per cent of them need!"

Garfield's eyes hid behind the slits made by his grin. "The editor is absolutely correct—that is, if he wants the American people to accept medical care at a low level of quality," he said.

Then Garfield expanded what he meant by that low level of medical care. Sid said: "If you have hemorrhoids are you going to have a general practitioner take care of them, or a proctologist? Of course a proctologist can take care of them better, but general practitioners take care of a lot of them." (Here Sid was getting down to fundamentals.) "If you've got a compound fracture in an accident, do you want a general surgeon or the best kind of orthopedist to fix you up? Do you want a general practitioner to handle your wife's childbirth, if it's complicated? They handle a lot of those cases, and you know what may happen. When your kids are mysteriously peaked and not gaining and sickly, would you ask for something out of the good old family doctor's black bag, or would you look up a pediatrician? You yourself are at the age where your plumbing is likely to get plugged up—are you going to a general surgeon for a possible transurethral resection, or to the best urologist you can find?"

Sid—usually so laconic—was warming up now. "Let's grant 85 per cent of the diseases are so trivial they can be taken care of by the practicing doctor, how do *you* know, I mean you, the ordinary citizen, which symptoms are the ones that need only a general practitioner?"

If Sid had one characteristic, it was fairness. "Maybe I'm prejudiced about this group specialist medical care," he said. "Why don't you ask one of your medical friends who doesn't know me, a man of broad vision, for whom you have the highest respect?"

So we called up Dr. Max Minor Peet, professor of neuro-surgery at the University of Michigan. Max filled Sid's bill. He had begun as a brilliant biologist and was still one of the great ornithologists in America. He had taken his first training in internal medicine. Then in general surgery. Now he was one of the greatest neuro-surgeons in the world, internationally famous for his operations for the cure of tri-facial neuralgia—*tic douloureux*—and for his sympathetic nerve operation that was saving many lives from the consequences of malignant high blood pressure. Best of all, on top of his breadth and high competence, Max Peet was simple and honest and never played his cards close to his chest and never talked out of both sides of his mouth and always called them as he saw them. He had no political ax to grind nor any ulterior motive and he didn't give a damn—not for anybody. So we called Max Peet and asked him to give us his judgment as between solo medicine from the little black bag of the good old family doctor and group medicine by teams of specialists.

Max snorted at our question. He laughed as if he thought I was ribbing him. "No—seriously, Max," I protested. "Give it to me and I'll write it down and read it back to you."

"All right," Max said. "Take high blood pressure. Plenty of doctors from all over the world send me patients from all over the world for that one, don't they?"

"Hundreds from the world over," I admitted.

"All right," Max said. "You know high blood pressure is one of the most common conditions. It may be nothing to worry about. Or again, it may be one of the most *potentially* deadly. It's the first sinister signal of nearly all cases of Bright's disease, for hundreds of thousands of victims of enlarged hearts and ditto of cerebral hemorrhage. Millions of people have high blood pressure. Of course the family doctor can detect it. But then—"

Max waited ominously like the superb teacher he is.

"But then," he went on, "how's the general practitioner to know if it's serious? The moment he finds it as a sign, *instantly* it's his duty to call in the experts. An eye man to find out how hard that hypertension is hitting the arteries. A heart man and an X-ray man for orthodiagrams to see if there's dangerous enlargement of the heart. An internist and laboratory man for blood chemistry to determine possible high blood pressure damage to the kidneys.

"And then—" Max hesitated—"only then can it be decided whether the neuro-surgeon offers hope with a sympathectomy, an operation that may give the patient years of life. Yes, a new lease on life."

That was only one example, and Max cited many another covering the gamut of the signs and symptoms with which millions of people come to their good old family practitioners.

"You have a persistent cough and are spitting a little blood, not much, and you're losing weight," he said. "Is your family doctor going to tell you it's TB or maybe early carcinoma of the lung? Or will it take medical teamwork to save your life?

"Or you're burping and have epigastric pain and are losing your appetite or can't keep your food down and you are or are not losing weight. Is it your family doctor out of his little black bag or a gastro-enterologist that's going to tell you whether you're suffering from a nervous stomach, or a peptic ulcer, or a gastric cancer—early, this last one, when there's still a slim chance, but a chance—for a surgeon to cure it?"

Though Max allowed as how he was running up the long-distance telephone bill unduly, I told him to go on, he was going strong.

"If you've a persistent hoarseness and tickling in your throat and the family doc pulls this or that out of his little bag and says this may give you relief but it doesn't. If he strings you along and you get hoarser and hoarser. Till maybe it's too late for an expert radiologist or laryngeal surgeon to save you from carcinoma of the larynx that's going to kill you, sure as hell, if you come too late. What then?"

For Max Peet it was no argument. "Don't make me laugh," he ended. Of course medical teamwork was the only modern medicine.*

Sid Garfield said nothing, only grinning enigmatically at Max's proof that, at their onset, the deadliest ills—with few exceptions such as pneumonia—may not seem serious. It's precisely at the onset that the family doctor needs the help of group specialist medical care, of specialist teamwork. I was no longer alarmed about Sid's insistence on the universal need of groups of specialists.

---

* Dr. Max Peet personally checked the accuracy of the above passage on the evening before his untimely death, in April, 1949.

But Garfield wasn't satisfied. In his self-effacing way, he was a killer.

"I'd like to ask the editor of the *Journal of the A.M.A.* just one question," said Sid. "Here are maybe a hundred thousand general practitioners in the country—how are they *taught* medicine? They're taught at modern medical schools that are the highest form of group teaching, of teamwork teaching that is. Who ever heard of a one-man medical school, of solo medical teaching of all the branches of medicine, in modern times? What modern medical teacher would have the gall, the brass, the presumption to teach all the medical disciplines? Then these medical students, these poor boys and girls, taught all these disciplines by the finest teams of doctor teachers in history, are supposed to go out and take care of 85 per cent of all of our illnesses—*alone.*"

When he got going, Sid was a holy terror, he wouldn't let go. "And the editor of the *Journal of the American Medical Association* says that group practice is inevitably more costly than general practitioner service?" Sid smiled open-eyed and enigmatically like Mona Lisa.

"I'm a nobody," said Sid. "But what does Dr. Ray Lyman Wilbur say about the economics of group specialist practice? He's a past President of the American Medical Association. Even the editor must respect Dr. Wilbur—"

"That's saying something," I said.

But what was Dr. Wilbur's opinion? Dr. Wilbur said: "Grouping your staff under one hospital roof, you've compelled them to work around these facilities. Your doctors no longer work for the automobile company or the real estate agent; they're working for the patients."

I myself had heard Dr. Ray Lyman Wilbur say that to Sid; congratulating him on his innovation of prepaid group specialist medical care.

Sid wouldn't let go. Who was he, Garfield, but an ex-desert doctor having a tough time staying in his county medical society? But let us consult Dr. Louis I. Dublin, Vice President of the Metropolitan Life Insurance Company and an internationally known authority on the economics and costs of medical care in general.

"It just costs too much in the way of equipment to make the general practitioner equipped with the necessary instrumentalities of his profession, and if he had them, it would be a sheer waste for the number of patients he has," said this brilliant man.

Dr. Dublin went on: "Great economies are possible both of time and money through the organization of group (specialist) practice in which men of various skills are brought together with the necessary equipment. This will help in better diagnosis and treatment and would reduce costs enormously."

"Sid," I said, "I guess that editor of the *Journal of the A.M.A.* hasn't got you, after all."

Among all of our medical mavericks we have never seen a more patient man than Garfield. What was the editor, in that marble-fronted white stone building that houses the American Medical Association in Chicago? He was the real brains, the leadership of the national organization of our doctors. The doctors' union. And how do doctors deliver their services to their more than 100 million customers? Overwhelmingly from their little individual cure stores—solo. And what should the leadership of the doctors' union do? Work for the doctors—for their *status quo.*

Such was the understanding and charity of Sid Garfield who smiled and deprecated all this heat of argument and said we could argue till we were blue in the face, we would never argue that brainy editor in Chicago down; he was the quickest-thinking, fastest talking argufier in the world who had the enormous majority of doctors in the hollow of his hand. He had the disgruntled, dissatisfied doctors buffaloed.

The editor could always talk them down.

"Only one thing I know to do," said Sid. "Not argue, but just go on trying to build a model of prepaid, group specialist medical care in normal times in an ordinary community. If it works, the ordinary citizen will go for it, and then—"

VII

And then Dr. Sidney Garfield would really get a kick in the groin. It was quaint the way he did not blame the opposing doctors of the Eastbay region for their animosity; towards them Garfield showed not a trace of paranoia. It was really only quaint till you understood Sid's understanding them. They had a lot on their side. As proprietors of their little individual cure stores, weren't they, the traditional doctors, individualists in the American tradition? Weren't they exponents of American free enterprise? Wasn't a solo doctor with penicillin, streptomycin, aureomycin, hormones and vitamins a better physician than most groups of doctors ten years ago? Absolutely. Weren't the solo doctors the defenders of the ancient and sacred right of the patient to choose his own doctor? Yes, to all these questions, that was Sid's tolerant answer. Weren't the doctors fighting to maintain the time-honored doctor-patient relation? Yes, but—

It was right here that the issue was clearly drawn, the chips really down between Garfield and the traditional doctors. It was here that Sid was cool, honest, devastating and definitely far ahead of his time. It was here, in his own phrase (always with an amused smile) that he made the traditional doctors "mad at Garfield."

Regarding this sacred doctor-patient relationship Sid asked: Is it to have him for a nice chum, a pal, that you pay your fee to your doctor? When you're really sick, what's more important, chumminess or the rapid, concentrated, teamed-up use of all the new power of medical science? Less than 30 years ago just about all the doctors had to offer was this personality stuff. It was nice and comforting but how much disease did it cut short? How many lives did it save? What kind of pal to a patient can a doctor be, when he X-rays that patient in the dark, when he operates on his brain, his chest or his belly under deep anesthesia, when he studies E K G heart tracings made by a technician, when he studies the dangerous or merely painful mysteries of that patient's bottom through a proctoscope? It becomes more impersonal, this medical science, as it gets more powerful. More and more, what a patient wants to know is not that his doctor has wonderful eyes or dextrous surgeon's hands or a sympathetic personality; what patients want to know is whether a team of doctors know their X-rays, their blood chemistry and liver-function tests, their anti-biotics and sulfas and the cold, advanced mechanics of urologic, neurologic, thoracic surgery. That, Sid knew, was the secret of the new medical power over live-or-die.

Of course you can and do get chummy with your personal family physician; it is one of the deepest of human emotions to worship him. Of course Sid had to admit that it's hard to establish this tender tie to a team of internists, surgeons and laboratorians. That has to be a pretty cool, mechanical impersonal business. Here I realized that Sid was walking on most dangerous ground. He was asking us to abandon the warmth of friendship for—life-saving efficiency. Three times in the past 24 years I've been rescued from exceedingly dangerous illness and even impending death not by a group of doctors but by a lone doctor or a surgeon, and for these three individual, traditional medical men I have an affection, peculiar and highly sentimental. What's that but the ancient doctor-patient relationship?

Here Rhea came in on Sid's side. "If you go into any doctor's office around here," she said, "and ask people who are really worried about their illness whether they'd prefer this solo doctor or the Mayo Clinic—if they could get the Mayo Clinic group specialist care for the same money they're paying their doctor—I know the majority of them would say get us to the Mayo."

It would be a lovely question for our pollsters.

But Garfield—aside from Rhea's opinion which remains only just that—was hard to keep down in regard to his conviction that group specialist medical care was coming, and solo medical care was dying. There were other psychological considerations besides this chumminess and the bedside manner between the doctor and his patients.

There was the little business of money. Garfield himself had detested taking money, personally, for this healing art which to be at its highest must be not only friendly and scientific—but religious.

From the days in the desert in his little hospitals along the Los Angeles Aqueduct construction job, in the hectic days at the building of Grand Coulée Dam, in the banging, slamming days of Kaiser's Paul Bunyan ship-building where his medical teams were handling the smashed-up and sick among 125,000 workmen—Garfield had watched the growth of a strange new spirit in his team of doctors. That prepayment of a mere seven cents per day had made their medical care economically painless to the patients. The doctors were on excellent salaries. Between them and their patients there was no money consideration—whatever. They could give the sick man or woman everything science had to offer—no restriction because of the lack of money-enough when you had to pay by the old system of direct fee for service. And when there was no money consideration between his medical and surgical teams and their patients, Garfield watched a new spirit blooming among his doctors. *It was the spirit of the good Samaritan.*

Exit dollars—enter God.

"Isn't that good doctor-patient relationship?" asked Garfield.

He was charitable about the fury of the Eastbay traditional, solo-practicing doctors. After all, they hadn't themselves experienced this, so how could they understand it? Isn't it what you're ignorant of that you fear? Isn't it what you don't clearly understand that you fight? So now there were Eastbay physicians who went out to wreck Garfield not by fair means but by foul. Who blames them (Garfield didn't) when they saw the Permanente health plan not washed up as they had predicted but growing, in 1946, back to 20, 30, 40 thousand subscribers—most of whom used to be the traditional, solo doctors' own patients?

Now in a local newspaper there appeared an ominous item that certainly damned Permanente's medical care—of a charity patient. Permanente had contracted with the City of Oakland to take care of emergency and accident cases. A man had been badly smashed up in an automobile crash. He was brought to Permanente Hospital. Then he was routed by ambulance as a charity case to County Hospital. Then, 15 minutes after he'd got there, he died. It was charged that the Permanente staff did not examine the man, that as soon as they found he had no money, they shot him to the County Hospital. Another example of Permanente's heartless, production-line medicine! Now, when a patient dies under the care of a given traditional, solo-practicing physician, it is distinctly not the custom of other physicians to make it public that he has been guilty of negligent homicide. On the contrary, doctors are not only very charitable but solicitous to cover up each other's lethal mistakes. At least they make no charges without investigation—and how often do they investigate? In the instance of this crash victim's death, the Eastbay doctors made no investigation whatever. They simply inserted the item in the city's leading newspaper.

"It was pretty nasty," said Garfield.

The charges were lies. Physicians from the Oakland Health Department checked all the events leading up to the tragedy. The badly injured man had been carefully examined when he'd been brought into Permanente; his blood pressure was O.K.; there were no other signs of impending shock; the records were thorough and nothing in his condition predicted that he was in danger of dying as he did.

"The Oakland health department officers called those charges in that newspaper item 'hasty and unwarranted.' They cleared Permanente completely," said Sid.

"Did the doctors who'd smeared you apologize?" I asked.

"Don't be silly," answered Sid, chuckling.

"Did any of the good physicians in the Bay region come to your defense?" I asked.

"Don't be foolish," Sid said. "Their approval of Permanente has been what you might call tacit."

The newspaper attack helped Sid, really. The C.I.O. members of the health plan were fit to be tied, got space in the newspaper, denounced the would-be character assassins, praised the quality of Permanente's care. The subscriptions to the health plan zoomed higher and higher.

What gave me a feeling that Sid was solid was his bending over to blame himself. "Even so," he reflected, "we shouldn't have let that injured man go so soon after the smash-up."

He explained it was episodes like this that made them learn at Permanente Hospital. Now, when a patient came in on emergency, they no longer sent such a patient to County Hospital. If the patient could pay, fine; if the patient couldn't pay, then the health plan paid for him. That was what kept Garfield going, what kept him winning, with almost all the doctors of the Eastbay region against him because even those approving did not speak up for him.

Then Sid chuckled and said: "We turned the tables on the smear boys a few weeks later. A poor guy was brought into the County Hospital, smashed up and in deep shock. The doctors there found an old Permanente health plan card in his pocket. It was out-dated. He was an ex-shipyard worker. You know what they did? They shipped him, shock and all, right down to Permanente. Well, our boys worked like hell on him. They saved his life."

Had Garfield put that in the newspaper?

"No," Sid said. "You see, we're *ethical.*"

How could they put the skids under Garfield? They didn't stop trying. Presently he was hit where it really hurt. The State Board of Medical Examiners of California—this is an official body—found Dr. Sidney R. Garfield guilty of employing unlicensed doctors, interns and residents, at Permanente Hospital. They suspended his own license to practice medicine for one year. They ordered the suspension withheld "provided Dr. Garfield abided by state laws." They placed him on probation for five years.

The medical powerhouse in Chicago nationalized this grave charge. The *Journal of the American Medical Association* under the heading of licenses suspended, listed Garfield's name, neglecting to state that the suspension was withheld. It simply amounted to every doctor and his brother, reading, that Garfield's license was suspended. This was not a lie. It was the technique of half-statement more subtle than lying.

Garfield fought it, keeping his temper. What were the facts? Simply that in every good hospital in California, qualified to teach interns and residents, during the first two years of their tenure these interns and residents are *not licensed.* This was true of the University of California Hospitals and the Stanford University Hospital.

In reporting this action against Garfield, the Oakland *Tribune* added that Permanente was the hospital recently charged by the Alameda County Medical Association with conducting "a production line type of medical care."

The attack by the Board of Medical Examiners was conducted with a certain degree of impartiality. Permanente Hospital was not singled out, not completely. Three or four hospitals in other localities were included as employing unlicensed interns and residents. But they happened to be hospitals which did not have approved intern and resident training programs. On the other hand, the license of no director of a hospital with an approved intern and resident training program was suspended—even though its interns and residents also did not have licenses during their first two years of training.

Among the directors of such hospitals, only Garfield's license was suspended. "You understand," said Garfield, "interns and residents during their first two years of training *are not allowed* to have licenses." So Garfield was attacked for not doing what he was not supposed to do.

"What was back of this attack?" I wondered.

Garfield was unsuspicious. "There is no evidence that the California Medical Association or the Alameda County Medical Association are conniving with the Board of Examiners," he explained. It was just coincidental . . . maybe so . . .

Now Henry J. Kaiser became a bit bothered. That genial giant sat up all one night cooking up a blast which was published in part in most of the Bay region's newspapers, and—to its credit—completely in the San Francisco *Chronicle*.

"Those who know Dr. Garfield will be forever grateful, as I am, to Dr. Garfield and his staff for the great service they have rendered the community at great personal sacrifice," wrote the big builder. (At this time Sid had not had a penny in salary from the Permanente health plan operations.)

Henry J. Kaiser wrote: "Now to Dr. Garfield's enemies and to the enemies of prepaid medical care I say, 'God forgive them, for they know not what they do.' "

The big man would leave forgiveness to God. The big man himself was furious now, and when he was stirred up, let connivers beware.

"Since the inception of this program of medical care," wrote Kaiser, "we have recorded over 10,000,000 patient-treatments to people in all walks of life, who, like myself, are indebted to Dr. Garfield and his staff."

Then the big builder took a bear-like backhanded swipe at the honest doctors, the good doctors, the doctors who knew Permanente's excellent medical care and gave it their *tacit* approval.

Henry Kaiser ended: "It is quite possible that there are those in our western cities who don't want to see Dr. Garfield suffer, but who are falsely represented by the small but vocally strong minority interests who are fighting to destroy our plan of prepaid medicine."

Then the kindly giant chided them: "They are really saying, as did Pontius Pilate: 'I can see no wrong in this man, but let us turn him over to the State.'

"Again I say, 'God forgive them, for they know not what they do.' "

There must now have been something of a buzz among the doctors in the hospital coatrooms. There may even have been sleepless nights among those—if such there were—who had connived at the suspension of Garfield's license. In the Bay region it is not well to get funny with any of Henry J. Kaiser's men if they are good men, which they are—as good as any I've ever met in any industrial organization—and who was a better, more straight-shooting man than Dr. Garfield? Henry Kaiser was fond of Sid Garfield and proud of him and of the doctors at Permanente Hospital. Henry Kaiser is slow to anger but the news of the suspension of Garfield's license— even though Garfield had been paroled—put the Permanente hospitals in danger. It naturally scared the young doctors on the staffs. Where would they be if their chief's license was really and finally revoked? How could they work under a director who had no license to practice medicine? If Garfield should be forced to resign, where would Permanente hospitals and the health plan be?

Sid Garfield was Permanente. That was maybe the weakness of this experiment in prepaid group specialist medical care.

These events took place in October, 1947, and it was strange how this hubbub affected the citizens of Eastbay. The number of subscribers to the Permanente health plan kept growing. There was less and less room in the Oakland Permanente Hospital for the privately practicing Eastbay doctors. The enrollment in the health plan was now between 50,000 and 60,000, from hundreds of different groups of citizens. Including only some 200 employees of Henry Kaiser—down from 90,000 of the ship-building days in the war. Garfield's prepaid medical care was no longer a war baby. Why hadn't his plan collapsed now that the big Kaiser payroll had vanished? Hadn't physicians, medical economists, hospital plan authorities predicted that Permanente health plan would blow up when the shipyards at last were down?

VIII

In May, 1948, Sid Garfield called us long distance asking us how quickly we could get out to the Coast. The State Board of Medical Examiners had not revoked his license, it's true. In a few months the case would be tried in the open. And the Permanente health plan was growing, more than 60,000 subscribers now, but it was definitely in competition with traditional, fee-for-service, solo medical practice. And it was now widely rumored that the time had come to give Garfield (and hence Permanente) the business: the Alameda County Medical Association—or so it was said—was going to charge Dr. Sidney R. Garfield with unethical conduct; and if the charges were proved, Garfield would be dismissed from the County Medical Association and the American Medical Association. And that would finally and completely cook Permanente's goose, because Permanente would not be able to get competent physicians and surgeons to work under a chief who was not a member of the A.M.A.

Within three days we were on the Coast. Wasn't it really silly of Sid to have sent for us? Who were Rhea and I but a couple of writing people? What could we do? Well, it would just feel good to have us around in a pinch and we might give him some new angles. And maybe we could report it, if they chucked him out; maybe the whole country might be interested, mightn't it?

Sid anticipated his possible coming martyrdom with amused detachment.

Did Sid know what his alleged unethical conduct, specifically, was supposed to be? No, but he had heard he was going to be really chucked out of the medical association, this time—for Permanente's not meeting the health needs of the patients—

"Wait a minute. Hold it!" I said. "What's the ultimate index of health needs, Sid?"

"Well, what is it, Paul?" he said, smiling and trying to look stupid.

"Death rates," I said. "What about Permanente's death rates in large series of cases of specific ailments, in large series of operations —do you have them?"

"Oh, yes," said Sid. "Isn't that a basic way to follow the quality of your medical care?"

"Yes," I offered, "and can you get comparative rates—between Permanente's and other hospitals' in the Bay region and California?"

"We'll get right after it," he said. I was excited; Rhea and Sid were amused at my ebullience, both of them very cool.

"You remember you told the U. S. Senate committee that when the Coulée workmen and their families got pre-paid group specialist medical care, so they'd get to the doctors early—*they stopped dying?*" Yes, Sid remembered.

"Doesn't that hold here, and if it holds here, you've got 'em, Sid, you've got 'em."

The week went by in a rush, getting death rates together, for Permanente as compared to the San Francisco County Hospital, University of California Service at that hospital, Los Angeles County Hospital. Maybe if the Bay region's doctors, the traditional doctors (Sid's enemies, or maybe we had better call them Sid's competitors), saw the figures on Permanente's death rates, they would call off the trial. Maybe they would compare Permanente death rates with those of their own hospitals, and if they did, what would they find? At least maybe they would send in a committee to investigate Permanente, which they had never done. That was not the medical way of doing it; you charge a man with misconduct first and don't investigate till afterwards, if ever.

On the 8th of June, 1948, the charges came, special delivery. They left Sid not much, if anything. Worse, they left Mr. Henry J. Kaiser next to nothing. Tough cookies, these doctors, when they set out to get you.

All that week, off and on, Henry J. Kaiser had been reminiscing to us about Sid, and it was clear Sid was to him as a son is to a father. Henry Kaiser—he is generally described purely as a big, bold builder and high-powered supersalesman who shoves everybody around till he gets his way—is sentimental and gentle, though maybe a bit impatient about getting what the sentimentality and gentility tells him people should have. All that week-end, banging us about in his very fast speedboats on Lake Tahoe, sitting before the big fire in our guesthouse at Homewood, or the next week in E. E. Trefethen's office in Oakland—Gene Trefethen is Kaiser's *alter ego* —the big man thought out loud, fumbling at the thorny problem of how we could get the doctors to lay off Sid Garfield. How could he fix it so that Permanente and solo medicine could live side-by-side . . . maybe even co-operating?

"You see, Paul," Henry Kaiser told me privately, "Sid's a genius at the organization of this pre-paid group medical care, but he's the poorest salesman in the world. He knows how to do it, but when he gets up to tell it, what comes out of Sid's mouth ain't music," said the big builder, laughing.

I have never seen the genial giant so serious or sad as he was that week, giving Rhea and me the story of what the care of the sick— or the lack of it—had meant to him.

"When I was a boy of 16, my mother died in my arms," he said, "because of improper medical care." He continued: "You see, she had not been willing to go to a hospital as a charity patient. She believed in giving, not taking, charity."

That was the marvelous discovery Sid had made—ordinary folks getting the best, most complete, most scientific care—but paying for it, and so easily.

The big man went on, saying: "Then my father went blind because he did not have proper medical care."

He tranced back into his rough life's yesterdays. Then he continued: "Mrs. Kaiser and I lost our only daughter in childbirth owing to lack of medical care. . . . Several of my closest associates died for the same reason."

Then his massive face—Gabriel Pascal has noted how it is grooved deep with the pain of years, pain not physical, the same grooves you see when you look close at Sid Garfield—Kaiser's face lighted up as he told us how he'd found Sid as a youngster, absolutely unknown among the big shots of medicine, operating a clean little hospital in the desert, saving the lives of construction workers.

"They'd never before been given decent medical and surgical care," he said.

Henry Kaiser was forever needling Sid to get along faster with his Permanente expansion, knowing well what Sid's hurdles were, and joshing Sid about his being such a poor salesman. Now Henry Kaiser said: "No one knows the number of lives Garfield saved as he moved his services to the big job at Coulée Dam. And then to our shipyards when there weren't enough doctors to go round, in Eastbay."

The giant was puzzled. Didn't the Eastbay doctors see that Permanente health plan was the hope against socialized medicine? Wasn't Permanente *proving* there are ways to provide medical care—greater and finer than any of the government could give?

Henry Kaiser was exasperated at all this smearing and knifing of Permanente. "Won't all thinking doctors agree that methods of spreading the cost of health—for those who can't afford their own private physician—are sure to come?" he asked. "What's wrong with a well-worked-out, privately operated system like Permanente?"

"If they kill a system like Sid's, if Sid fails," he said, "they'll get compulsory government medicine."

Henry Kaiser talked slowly, giving out with what was his religion: "What Permanente is doing is just scratching the surface," he said. "I propose to earn millions of dollars and put millions into hospitals and to devote my life—" and he swept his arm like an oak limb, around in a gesture as if to say let there be life—"I propose to devote my life to helping. . . ."

I X

Thus on the 8th of June, 1948, organized medicine's blow fell not only on Sid Garfield but on Henry Kaiser. The Council of the Alameda County Medical Association filed charges of unprofessional conduct against Garfield. Here were the accusations: advertising and solicitation of patients for the health plan; placing mass production ahead of the health needs of the patients; preventing patients having free choice of physicians; rendering inadequate service because the hospital was inadequately staffed—though the health plan promised hospitalization and medical care to thousands of patients; medical services rendered under conditions which made adequate medical care impossible; the Foundation and Health plan directly profited from the professional services rendered by Dr. Garfield and his associates.

This curious document, in effect, accused Henry Kaiser of fraud. Permanente Foundation was a corporation not for profit. It had been founded by Mr. and Mrs. Henry J. Kaiser. This strange document accused Mr. and Mrs. Kaiser of making money under the guise of philanthropy. This serious charge was made out of whole cloth, without any examination whatever of the books and the financial arrangements of Permanente Foundation and the Permanente Health Plan. The Alameda County Medical Association doctors had not asked to see the books; they had invented the charges. Nor had they ever investigated the medical care that Permanente Hospital and Permanente Health Plan gave its patients; nor had they requested to be allowed to make such an investigation. If the charges were unfounded, here was conspiracy to take action against the Permanente Health Plan and its doctors for the purpose of restraining the practice of medicine. Of what was this reminiscent? Of the American Medical Association's attack upon a prepaid medical plan in the District of Columbia. If the charges against Garfield were unfounded, what then portended? An action similar to the U. S. Government's when it convicted the American Medical Association under the Federal anti-trust acts, for conspiring to prevent the doctors of the District of Columbia Group Health Association from practicing their prepaid medicine.

The cases—if the Alameda County Medical Association's charges were unfounded—were exactly parallel, explained Todd Inch who was Gene Trefethen's right hand man. Todd's face which was round, open, and usually very pleasant, showed that now he was fit to be tied, now he was out for the kill. Todd Inch said: "If, as we believe, a conspiracy to restrain the practice of medicine exists, the State of California is by law obligated to proceed with the dissolution of the medical associations."

I'll never forget how Henry Kaiser took these charges—founded on no investigation—charges that assassinated his character, questioned Garfield's good faith, and denied the competence of the devoted medical staff of Permanente Foundation Hospital. He later explained how it hit him. "I was profoundly shocked. . . . I was astounded and horrified," said Henry Kaiser. He did not look it. Throughout the reading of those terrible accusations his face showed the serenity of a man who knows he has not done wrong.

Fight these doctors? Dissolve their medical association? That was not what Henry Kaiser wanted to do. Couldn't we sit down with those doctors, "and reason together"? The big man did not want lawsuits. Did we realize what an all-out fight on the issue of more medical care for more people could mean? Doctors fighting when they should be using their energy saving human life? The big man cooled us all down. "I do not believe," he said, "that wars are necessary either among nations or doctors."

I've never learned more than on this June afternoon in the office of Gene Trefethen, when we all wanted to fight, when we were sick and tired of Sid Garfield and his Permanente doctors being defamed, libeled, and generally shoved around. All of us wanted to fight, excepting Henry Kaiser and bright-eyed, kindly, good-natured, cool-headed Gene Trefethen. But look where Sid had them. "Look what they're saying about Permanente Medical care," I said, "and look what that care is, really." What was it, really? Henry Kaiser waited, interested.

Well, the little investigation we had been making might throw some light on the charge about Permanente contracting for the medical care of a large number of people and not having an adequate number of physicians to do the job; and about its policies and management placing mass production ahead of real health needs of patients. The simplest and toughest criterion of the quality of medical care and hospital services are, as we have said, death rates—mortality rates in disease conditions for which there is generally recognized effective treatment. It was this tough test that Herman Bundesen had used to alert Chicago's doctors to the scandal of the needless dying of infants, of newborn babies, of mothers —and the results of a new discipline against death, spreading out of Chicago nationwide, had cut the infant deaths by two-thirds and the maternal deaths by more than three-fourths. Now what was the rate of dying among the patients in Permanente Hospital—compared to the best hospitals in California?

Take, for example, the overall mortality rate for pneumococcal lobar pneumonia at Permanente Foundation Hospital in Oakland for the years 1944-1946. It notably fulfilled the prophecy of the Marine Corporal Wilmer Patrick Shea because, during those years, this pneumonia death rate had been cut to the amazing low of 1.1 per cent.

During the same years the pneumococcal lobar pneumonia death rate on the University of California service across the Bay in the San Francisco County Hospital—an excellent institution—had stood at 15 per cent point one.

In short, a Permanente health plan patient has about 14 times better chance of living in case of an attack of lobar pneumonia, at Permanente Hospital than at San Francisco County Hospital.

Now here was a question Mr. Kaiser and Dr. Garfield could ask of the Alameda County physicians who charged that Permanente's medical care was "inadequate." The overwhelming majority of those dying from pneumonia, die in hospitals. What, gentlemen, was the mortality rate from pneumococcal lobar pneumonia in the Oakland Hospitals in which you treat pneumonia, while that rate stood at 1.1 per cent at Permanente?

Other Permanente mortality records were outstanding when compared with those other hospitals, even nationwide. For example, the death rate for perforated peptic ulcer at Permanente Hospital in an unselected series of cases of that extremely dangerous condition, was 1.1, and that record stood at the top of 32 comparable series, nationwide. It compared well to the 15 per cent mortality rate for perforated peptic ulcer at the San Francisco County Hospital and 28.7 per cent at Los Angeles County Hospital.

Mr. Kaiser and Dr. Garfield might ask: "What are the mortality rates in Oakland hospitals, other than Permanente, where Permanente's medical enemies treat perforated peptic ulcers?"

The death rates in appendicitis with peritonitis, in childbirth including that by Caesarean section, were amazingly low at Permanente Foundation Hospital. Would the doctors on the staffs of the other Oakland hospitals welcome a comparison with their figures?

Did these stirring records of which the Permanente physicians and surgeons were so proud mean that Garfield's medical men were better life-savers than the physicians and surgeons of the Bay region, generally? Not at all, or at least not necessarily. It meant that the Permanente Health Plan's prepaid medical care by its group of specialists was better than the Bay region's solo medicine as traditionally practiced—and why? Only because the Permanente Health Plan people prepaying for their medical care could go to their doctors and hospitals without hesitating because they feared a looming large medical, surgical, and hospital bill. *They could go right now*.

The earlier you treat any curable sickness, the greater the chance of cure, the less the chance of dying.

If the Alameda County doctors insisted upon trying Dr. Garfield for alleged unprofessional conduct, if they persisted in trying to boot him out of organized medicine, if they were determined to wreck Permanente Hospital and Health Plan—how would a comparison of death rates look to California citizens? If published in newspapers of California? How would it look to the people of the U. S. A., if it went over the wires of the press associations?

How would the Alameda County Medical Association look—killing off the medical care that saved the most human life?

To my astonishment, Henry Kaiser did not want to take this action. Or not till he absolutely had to. "I don't claim that Permanente is perfect. I don't know," he said slowly. "I don't claim that Blue Cross is perfect or that the California Physicians Service"—this is the California Medical Association's prepaid medical care plan—"is perfect or that numerous other kinds of plans are perfect.

"I only know," he said, gently, "that encouraging them all will eventually prove which prepaid medical plan is best for all."

He smiled and said: "I only know that this war between doctors can only force a delay in the ultimate correct answer."

Then he made a generous suggestion. Even though the doctors had charged him personally with taking profits from a non-profit foundation, even though they had charged that Garfield's medical care was not good, would these physicians possibly now . . . maybe . . . peradventure . . . make an impartial investigation of Permanente Foundation Hospital? Would they investigate Permanente Foundation's books, which would be thrown open to them without restrictions? Mr. Kaiser would be happy if the Alameda County doctors would determine the true-or-false of all their charges —*after they had made them.* And no hard feelings.

That afternoon Henry Kaiser made me feel very small. The issue, he said, went far beyond this local controversy. If only the Alameda County doctors would investigate fairly, this might be the beginning of a real, conscientious effort on the part of all doctors to fulfill the objectives he was sure were common to all of them. Not only for group specialist medicine like Permanente's if it was lower in cost. But for that type of medicine which so many wanted, private, solo medicine, although it cost a great deal more.

"Regrettably," said the big man, "until the earning power of the nation is greater, all the people cannot participate in private medicine." He was sure the two systems could exist side-by-side. He was sure the Alameda County investigators—if they only would investigate—would find that Permanente had demonstrated how millions of Americans could be accorded infinitely better medical care than they were now getting—by a *voluntary* prepaid, group specialist medical plan. "Rather than by compulsory government socialized medicine," he ended.

That June afternoon in Gene Trefethen's office Henry J. Kaiser made me feel ashamed. And soon after that Sid Garfield's trial for alleged unprofessional and unethical conduct was postponed. Soon after that, the President of the Alameda County Medical Association—a physician of high competence, of integrity and good will—sat down to lunch with Gene Trefethen, telling Gene that he admired Permanente's medical work; that the main trouble, so he thought, was that Sid Garfield lacked tact, sometimes; that a committee of Alameda County Medical Association physicians would examine Permanente Hospital and Health Plan *before* Dr. Garfield was tried for unprofessional, unethical conduct.

Soon after that, Sid Garfield was cleared of the State Board of Medical Examiners' ridiculous charge that he was employing interns and residents without licenses to practice medicine. Superior Judge Edward P. Murphy ordered that Board to rescind all action against Dr. Garfield. The Judge in his decision stated that the Board's action was "arbitrary," that it had proceeded "in excess of its jurisdiction," that Garfield had been following a common practice of medical schools and teaching hospitals and that he had the approval of the American College of Surgeons and the American Medical Association in doing what he had done. Judge Murphy castigated the members of the State Board of Medical Examiners, saying that they "had denied the petitioner (Dr. Garfield) fair trial and had prejudicially abused their discretion in proceedings against the petitioner." Judge Murphy sharply reprimanded the Board, ordering that Dr. Garfield be reimbursed for all costs in prosecuting his reinstatement action and that he should be immediately reinstated to full practicing rights."

What it boiled down to, translated from legal language into the vernacular, was that Dr. Sidney R. Garfield had been the victim of

funny business by a board of California physicians who were in
a position of the highest trust, by physicians who had the grave
duty to license or not to license all physicians in California, by an
official body with the stern power over live-or-die.

Judge Murphy's decision was handed down on October 11, 1948.
That day good-natured Sid had reason to smile even more than
usual.

"But you mustn't think the Board was conniving," he told me,
over long distance, his voice raised in one of his very rare moments
of exultation. "It was just one of those coincidences."

X

How could they lick Sid Garfield? He did not deal in the fine
art of the smear. He did not argue. His books were open to any
responsible medical man who asked to see them. His medical care
at his hospitals was there to be seen. They kept trying to wreck him
and he kept beating them simply by what he did. What was the
answer to the wreckers and to all the objectors who for seven years
now were so sure he would fail? The answer was the Permanente
Hospital and the Permanente Health Plan in 1948 and 1949.
There they stand. All the wrecking and all the objections stand
refuted by the present existence, the lusty growth, the enthusiasm of
the people of the Bay region for Permanente. My own thoughts
flashed back to the measured words of Mr. Louis H. Pink of the
Blue Cross, uttered at our luncheon in New York in April of 1945.

"If Garfield's plan can survive the shutting down of the shipyards, the case for voluntary, full-coverage, prepaid group medicine
will be proved."

There stands Permanente. Its health plan drawing no longer
from shipyard scores of thousands, but from more than 200 varie-
gated groups of Bay region citizens, joining at a rate of 3,500 people
a month, membership now over 72,000.

Permanente's financial position is like that of the insurance company that advertises itself as being as strong as the Rock of Gibral-
tar. Its income at Permanente Foundation Hospital in Oakland,

Richmond and San Francisco, alone, is $320,000 monthly. The income from the aggregate of all Garfield's operations, including those at Fontana at the Kaiser steel plant and at Vallejo, is $625,-000 monthly—a gross of over $7,000,000 annually. Garfield is now operating in the black at a rate of $600,000 yearly, not putting these "profits" into the pockets of Mr. Kaiser or of himself and his co-partnership of doctors and surgeons—but into the expansion of his hospital and laboratory facilities and into their paying off, their amortization.

During the war the Federal Works Agency had loaned Permanente $1,200,000. Already it had paid off $300,000 and this, so far as I can learn, is the only hospital in the U. S. A. that is paying off the government for money advanced for its construction. Garfield's is a lone voice raised against government hospital construction handouts. Garfield's amortization is a faint gleam of hope against the nation's growing load of debt, sure to be enormously increased if the government subsidizes a great hospital building program.

After all, nothing succeeds like success. When the State Board of Medical Examiners had tried to kill Sid's license to practice medicine, Sid hadn't for a moment made himself out a martyr, he hadn't whimpered in public or even privately. He had at his trial simply proved, coldly, that in employing his unlicensed interns and residents he was only doing what all California hospitals—approved for intern and resident training—did. Now in the winter of 1948 Garfield received a letter from the new President of this Board of Examiners which, two years before, had charged that Permanente had no intern and resident training program, that it was only trying to get cheap medical help by employing these unlicensed medical youngsters. Now the President of the Board was most complimentary. He wrote that he understood Garfield's operations were making excellent progress—and there were certain young graduate physicians who wanted openings for their training. . . .

What were the subscribers to the Permanente Health Plan paying for their medical care? With the cost of living sky-rocketing during the war years and after, the cost of treatment to Permanente Foundation Hospital had risen to the high of more than $24 per day per bed—not because of a lack of economy but because of the completeness of the medical, surgical, nursing, and laboratory treatment which Garfield offered.

The prepayment of the Permanente Health Plan set each family back $5.45 per month, for a family of four or more—no limit to the size of the family. That came to a total basic prepayment of $65.40 per year per family.

What did the subscribers get for this modest amount of money, in the line of medical, surgical and hospital care?

The employed member of each family got *complete* coverage, getting 111 days in hospital—if necessary—for each illness, and no charge for drugs and medicines, X-ray and laboratory examinations. The remainder of each family got the same length of stay in hospital if necessary, for each illness, but paid half of the laboratory and X-ray cost. In addition, all members of each family paid a fee of $1 for each visit to the clinic and hospital—though each visit by a subscriber set Permanente back between four and five dollars. Garfield's reason for this modest $1 charge per visit was simple, i.e., that subscribers using the plan more should pay more, though slightly.

This little charge has not retarded patients from coming in the early stages of their illnesses.

Sid admitted that he had had to back off a bit from his 7¢ per day coverage in the war-time days when the shipyards were booming full blast. By now the costs of his operation had risen tremendously and he no longer had the cushion of 40 per cent of his gross income being paid by a flat fee from the workmen's compensation insurance companies. Even so, the overall, average cost to all families subscribing to the Permanente Health Plan was a modest one considering the superb quality and the completeness of their medical care.

The average, overall cost for complete medical, surgical and hospital care was still no more than $100 per family, yearly.

I remember vividly being told by medical economists, insurance and prepaid health plan experts—and especially by doubting doctors—that the average American family would never go for such a

prepaid assessment for its medical care. But here was their answer—
membership rising at the rate of 3,500 per month to a total, now,
of 72,000.

In the last months of 1948 and the first of 1949, Henry Kaiser's
amiable determination not to fight the Alameda County doctors
began to pay off. Again and again the committee appointed by the
County Medical Association met with Gene Trefethen; the committee actually went to inspect the Permanente Foundation Hospital and its books, opened to that committee without restriction.
The committee was friendly. "The quality of the medical care as
practiced by Permanente's co-partnership and its employees is the
equivalent of the average medical care in the community," said
the members of the Alameda Medical Association committee.

In view of the County Medical Association's charges in regard
to the inadequacy of Permanente's medical care, this was really saying a very great deal, even though not quite enough.

Apparently Sid Garfield was running no peanut concession at
Permanente, nor was Henry Kaiser making hidden money out of
what was supposed to be a philanthropic, non-profit foundation.
"We are in accord with and commend the motivations revealed by
the purposes of the Permanente Foundation and the Permanente
Hospitals," declared the investigating committee.

So, with no acrimonious argument, Sid Garfield kept winning.
Now at last they would let him begin to show them.

Of course there still were objectors, die-hard, implacable enemies
among the doctors of the Bay region.

In examining the Permanente books the investigating committee
of the doctors believed they had caught Garfield in an act that,
by the standards of traditional solo medical practice, was unethical.
The committee unearthed an item in the plan—"$61,000 for promo-
tion and selling." This, the committee said, gave Permanente an
unfair and unethical competitive advantage over the rest of the
doctors of the Bay region. The private doctors may neither advertise nor proselyte for patients, while Permanente's books showed
that it had indulged in these "shocking" practices.

We will not here defend Sid Garfield, though an entertaining
treatise might be written about the subtle, ingenious—if indirect—

manner in which many a physician and surgeon advertises himself
and peddles his wares, ethically. About this charge Sid Garfield was
candid.

"We slipped there, we made a mistake," he said. "In those rugged
days just after the war when our membership had gone down to next
to nothing, some of our people, I'm afraid, did do what you might
call sell the Permanente Health Plan."

But Sid went on: "We stopped all that long ago—and long before they began their blitz to kick me out of the Medical Association."

Now, Permanente officials are approached by various groups of
Bay region citizens interested in prepaid medicine. "We have it all
set up now," said Sid, "as a comparison of plans—Blue Cross, California Physicians Service, various insurance company indemnity
plans, and Permanente Health Plan. We simply ask them to study
what each prepayment plan offers, then make their decision and
take their choice."

Sid smiled and asked wasn't that reasonable? "The only way I
see to make Permanente succeed—is to explain it to people," he
said drily.

"But the Blue Cross and the California Physicians Service solicits
and advertises—in the newspapers and over the radio—big," I protested.

Sid laughed. "But, you see, that's different," he said. "It's a fine
theological point. Our rivals solicit and advertise for *all* the doctors.
That seems to be okay. But it's unethical to advertise and solicit
business for one doctor. And it's positively heinous to advertise
and solicit business—for a specialist group like ours."

"Oh, I see," I said.

"Don't let that fret you," said Sid. "Look at the way we're growing. And not by soliciting and advertising, just by explaining."

"You mean just by giving complete prepaid medical and surgical
and hospital care—for a lot less money than anybody else can give
it," I said.

It was a good thing I wasn't an M.D. Making such an invidious
comparison would surely get me in the doghouse as unethical.

There was now another comfort for Garfield, now that the heat

was off, at least somewhat and even if temporarily. Though Permanente paid its medical staff excellent salaries, though they had the
advantage of reasonable hours of work, though they had the fun of
practicing scientific medicine as a streamlined team, though they
had the pleasant emotion of being able to give their patients the
best scientific care, untrammeled by the patients' lack of money—
even so the medical kicking-around of Garfield had kept many a
keen young doctor and surgeon from coming to Permanente.

Now by grapevine spread the news countrywide that Permanente
was no one-man show, no Kaiser war baby, that it was on a broad
base and run by a co-partnership of doctors. Now from all over the
country young medical and scientific men of the highest type began
to apply to join up with Permanente.

It is amazing how his victories left Sid Garfield unchanged. He
didn't crow over the medical fuddy-duddies he had licked so often.
"I can't do much more of this than I'm doing now," he explained.
"All I can do is to hope Permanente will teach as many doctors as
possible to form themselves into these group specialist teams—hook-
ing them up to prepaid plans—then they'll run their own medicine."
He is no proselyter.

Sid isn't quite so diffident as that day I first met him in the
Hotel St. Francis. He looks a little heavier, though he hasn't gained
a pound, yet he seems not quite so sharply chiseled, and his red-gold
hair is graying; he's as much a cool fighter as ever, fighting, fighting
fairly, by doing, and about his first principle he remains implacable:
there should be no such thing as solo medical practice. So he'll never
be out of trouble, not in our lifetime. . . .

A couple of years ago, he hired a distinguished public relations
expert, Mr. Raymond Rich, to find out why he, Garfield, was such a
pain in the neck to the Bay region doctors. Among his many recommendations, Mr. Rich pointed out that "it doesn't seem likely that
the tendency of the average citizen to identify himself personally
with one doctor is going to change in the near future." Mr. Rich
was all for Garfield's trimming, making some kind of deal, some
kind of compromise with the traditional solo-practicing physicians
in whose sides he was such a nagging thorn.

"It's the old free choice hooey," said Garfield. "What's more important, penicillin or the doctor who injects it?" Sid smiled tolerantly and had reason to, since 3,500 new subscribers joining Permanente each month were evidence of a substantial number of citizens preferring free choice of a group of specialists to the hoary custom of identifying themselves personally with one doctor.

Sid knew very well his battle wasn't over; the trial for his alleged unethical conduct, despite its being postponed again and again, was still hanging over him despite everything Gene Trefethen and the friendly physicians of the Alameda County Medical Association could do. "I don't *think* they'll kick me out. The A.M.A. doesn't want a big stink right now," Sid said with a smile.

The trial has been held, but, as this book goes to press, a decision has not yet been handed down. "But if the local boys do boot me out, so what?" said Sid. "It's mostly me they hate; and if they get rid of me, my partners can carry on—it's too big to kill now."

He was probably thinking of the 72,000 Eastbay subscribers to the Permanente Health Plan. Just let the mossback doctors try to kill what was saving their lives!

"But why don't young doctors in many other places organize themselves into specialist groups and hook up such teams to groups of citizens, prepaying?" I asked.

Garfield was in no hurry. "The only doctors who really understand it are the ones who've lived it," he explained. "The trouble is their great backlog of experience with ordinary hospitals," Sid went on. "Who ever heard of a hospital ever amortizing its cost of construction? No doctor. Who ever heard of a hospital not in the red? And if citizens brought up our new-fangled Permanente idea, urging the doctors to try it? The doctors, knowing nothing about it, would naturally pooh-pooh it."

The crusader died hard in me. "But your boys are cutting short so much illness, saving so many lives, so cheaply," I protested. "You've got a knock-out—that's what Herman Bundesen would call it."

Sid's eyes went almost shut. Through their slits they peered at me more enigmatically than ever. "Oh, yes, we've got a swell idea," he

drawled. "But look at Christianity. That seemed pretty hot, too, in
the early days. But now look at it," and Sid permitted himself one
of his infrequent chuckles and waved his arm as if across the sin-
ridden world. "Christianity simply hasn't got across, not so you
could notice it," he said, now laughing. Then he woolgathered west
out the window, across Lake Michigan and way out west, out to
Permanente and I knew what he was thinking.

"There she stands," I said.

X I

What to me is finest about this really modest, seemingly indifferent and invincibly enigmatic character, Garfield, is that he is
no Messiah or even a bit of a John the Baptist. He is in no dither
or sweat to convert the doctors of America to prepaid medicine by
groups of specialists. He seems icily indifferent. Women and babies
might be dying like flies in some badly-run hospital, and fathers
might be dying for lack of money for medical care, with Sid knowing it and knowing too that Permanente-type medicine would put
an end to the murder, and I can see him saying: "Well, let the
doctors fix it. They could. But they don't seem to get around to it."
He has become so averse to propaganda that he's a bit creepy. He
has become . . . detached, that's the word for him.

In the first days of Permanente's glory when the 100,000 Kaiser
workers with their seven cents a day prepayment were showing how
incredibly easy it was to give marvelous medical care by gearing
group specialists to that prepayment, in those days, I remember,
Sid was in his low-keyed way mildly enthusiastic and much more
hopeful about spreading this discovery than he is now. Great physicians of the Johns Hopkins University, Cornell, Columbia, Pennsylvania, and other university Medical Schools were vigorously interested in the new sane and sound medical economy of this red-
haired young genius from the west. Hundreds of medical big shots
made pilgrimages to Garfield's gleaming hospital. They listened to
him eagerly. Their hospitals were in the red; their research funds
were dwindling; the pay of their young physicians, surgeons, and

scientific men was an insult to our alleged American standard of living.

"We have the specialist groups; we have the finest research men; why can't *we* gear that all up to prepayment?" they asked him.

"You can," Sid said. But they didn't.

Sid simply was no salesman. At Mr. Kaiser's request, Garfield met with Mayor La Guardia who was fed up to the teeth with the miserable medical care of the employees of the world's greatest city. The Little Flower, the Hat—dynamic—stopped talking long enough to listen to Sid's low-voiced suggestions.

"You can prepay their medical care," said Sid, "but it'll only run you into a big red if you give the money to solo-practicing doctors on individual fee-for-service," he explained.

"How would you do it?" asked La Guardia.

"It's how we do do it—at Permanente," Sid answered. "Organize groups of doctors, practitioners and specialists, and turn your collections over to them. The economy of their group practice will put you into the black," he said.

Despite open as well as hole-and-corner opposition from the organized doctors, La Guardia got together a sufficient gang of brave physicians (they defied threats of being kicked out of their medical societies) to organize the Health Insurance Plan of New York, "H. I. P." in today's vernacular. Half the plan's income came from the employee's payroll deductions; half from the employer, the City of New York. H. I. P. began growing like wildfire. Today over 600 physicians and specialists working in more than 30 streamlined groups are giving the only modern medical care—group specialist care—to more than 200,000 prepaying citizens. The director of H.I.P. has recently announced that the plan is already operating in the black. The groups of doctors are planning fully-equipped medical centers, with practitioner, surgical specialist, X-ray and laboratory services all handy under one roof—

If only their solo-practicing brethren do not put the skids under them. That's a disaster that might well happen, since they do not have a Sid Garfield. Even so, H. I. P. is now the largest complete prepaid group specialist medical service in the nation; it has the support of many of New York's most distinguished citizens; it has the guidance and sponsorship of some of New York's most competent and public-spirited doctors; and the overwhelming majority of subscribers are enthusiastic about it. H. I. P. should be a tough baby for the political doctors to kill; and there's a fighting chance that this prepaid group specialist plan can soon begin to build, and begin to pay off, its clinics and even its hospitals.

About today's hubbub over government medicine Sid Garfield is nonchalant, knowing that socialized medicine—as such—is no answer. As modern a physician as I've ever met, Garfield is old-fashioned. He believes in hard work; he is all for medical free-enterprise; for medical specialists. He is even for that grand old free-choice red-herring the political doctors keep dragging across all trails toward medical reform—only not for free choice of the dear old family practitioner with his wonderful worn black bag, but for free choice of medical groups.

"If the Government hands out the money, at so much a head—capitation—to individual doctors, it's going to cost the country from 15 to 20 billion dollars a year. The government's going to have to tax the daylights out of everybody—if it's simply a collection agency—if it doesn't insist on modern, economical medical care," says Sid.

"Where do the Murray-Dingell boys get this free-medical care stuff, anyway?" he asks.

Granted today's distribution of medical care is cruelly uneven, yes, murderous. "Making it free won't make it good," says Garfield. "The distribution of food, clothes, and houses is bad, too. But the ordinary citizen hasn't got to the stage of demanding free beefsteaks, free suits of clothes, free shoes and free houses as a remedy," says Garfield, mildly.

"If the Government begins paying the whole nation's medical bill," says Sid, "it'll control our medical service—that should be controlled by the doctors untangled in Government red-tape."

Sid is curiously detached from this idiotic argument that offers us only two choices—Communism or a continuation of today's inadequate, solo, little black bag, tin-lizzie medical care.

"If only," says Sid, bringing up the biggest if of all, "if only America's doctors would undertake to organize voluntary prepayment in trade areas, prepayment to groups of specialists, there'd be no danger of the government having to ram socialized medicine down the throats of the doctors.

"Even for the underprivileged populations in the blighted areas the government could subsidize, partly, these prepayment plans which could pay the Government subsidy direct to groups of specialists," explains Garfield. "They could practice modern medicine scientifically. With an economy that could build and pay off new hospital, clinic, and laboratory facilities."

Garfield for the long pull is optimistic. Like Henry J. Kaiser, he is sure that America is on the up economically and that even the down-at-heel areas aren't going to stay blighted.

"If the government would only help groups of doctors organize medical care where people can't afford it, the indigents wouldn't be dragging themselves to county hospitals as objects of charity. They'd get a new dignity."

How right Sid is. This free nationwide medical care propaganda is laughable. We are the one country in the whole world where people overwhelmingly do not need a medical dole handed out to them by a bunch of power-hungry little bureaucrats in Washington. But in Garfield's alternative the medical leadership in the medical powerhouse in the headquarters of the American Medical Association at 535 North Dearborn Street in Chicago—is not interested. They simply throw up a smoke-screen. He says look, 55,000,000 citizens in the country already have some kind of prepaid medicine or medical indemnity insurance. Yes, some kind of prepaid medical, surgical, or hospital care—but what kind? Not the kind that will make the maximum number of Americans strong, prevent their sickness, and keep them alive. With due respect to the Blue Cross and to the medical society prepayment plans—they are still tied up to an antiquated medical engine, to inefficient, solo, wasteful medicine practiced in old-fashioned facilities. Government medicine as proposed by Murray-Dingell wouldn't alter this deplorable condition. We, the citizens of the U. S. A. with no chance of the Garfield plan, are given the choice between two nostrums: the medical *status quo* upheld by the politicians of the medical powerhouse on the one hand and a government medical dole on the other.

Both are reactionary. Neither will mend our misery. The Murray-Dingell nostrum proposed to pay the doctors so much a head for our care when we're sick. What we need—and what Garfield has proved is practical—is a medical economy that will benefit the doctors and the hospitals if they keep their patients well.

Sid Garfield stands alone, like most of the other medical mavericks of this book about life among the doctors. He stands alone, nationally unknown and neglected. The forces now battling for power over the medical fate of the people act as if Garfield did not exist. On the one hand, the brainy little Ph.D.'s of the Government's Social Security Agency—who know nothing about practical modern medical care—have never to my knowledge consulted Sid Garfield. If any of them have seen Permanente in action they give no evidence of having been impressed by its glowing promise. Like all typical bureaucrats, what probably interests them is the power over the expenditure of from 15 to 20 billions of dollars it's going to take to keep us in our half-alive, run-down condition. On the other hand, the boys in the A.M.A. powerhouse and in the local county and state A.M.A. powerhouses—you have read what they have tried to do to prepaid medical care by specialist groups—notably Permanente. Their record is not pretty. We must not blame them. They themselves are proud of the fact that doctors are poor businessmen. It is the duty of the powerhouse boys to maintain the *status quo* of a hundred thousand little individual cure shops—a shop to fix up your sparkplugs, a shop to tinker with your carburetor, a shop to bump out your body—now threatened by the streamlined super-service station where groups of experts can give economical overall care to your machine.

They've fought Sid Garfield always; they'll fight him again.

Sid, bless him, betrays not the faintest trace of frustration. "It's just a business proposition," he explains. "In seven years at Permanente we've already amortized over $1,000,000 worth of new facilities. We've started outstanding research—look at our new Kabat-Kaiser Institutes for neuro-muscular rehabilitation. That and much more like it is what we're going to do with our so-called profits. I'd like to convince a few bankers that prepaid group specialist medical care is a sound investment. They'd get their money back with interest within 20 years, easy."

Yet, if Sid is to be criticized at all, it is on the ground that he could expand Permanente's medical research activities more rapidly and broadly. But he is more interested in building just one more model, a sample for the whole country to see. This is the way to put any really new discovery or invention over, according to Boss Kettering who has put over plenty. Sid wants to build a new Permanente Hospital and Health Plan in Los Angeles. It looks like a natural. Here the head doctors of the three medical schools are actually for Garfield. They'll not be smearing the quality of Permanente medical care; they'll welcome the powerful engine of Permanente's prepaid medicine that will pour desperately needed dollars into their research. There's a great shortage of hospital beds in Los Angeles. Many industries, the unions, many doctors—yes, the doctors!—are hot to try Garfield's medical care.

If only the bankers, or even some one rich fellow with a couple of million dollars to invest . . .

"I'll help you land one, Sid," I said with excitement—after I had sworn there would be no more of this crusading.

At my enthusiasm, Sid chuckled. "All right," he said, "but what will happen is that the bankers or the rich guy will have to consult the doctors."

And what, mathematically, were the chances of the bankers or the rich man consulting doctors who knew about Permanente? And if they did not know about it, then—without looking into it—what would those doctors say? That's where Sid had me. And, alas, I've not yet found him a banker.

So it's very fine for Sid that he is not a Messiah or a John the Baptist. Almost certain disappointments won't raise his blood pressure or give him a gastric ulcer. He'll just keep building his present lone Permanente model bigger and stronger and maybe some day some one will come along, who knows? But Sid is in no hurry. Of all of them, he is for me a super-maverick.

She pushed aside the oxygen mask, gasping: "Give me the injection, the needle!" She wanted a shot of papaverine. Those were her last words, a testimony to her experimenter's spirit. This was my mother.

She had hated her fears. Five weeks before she had conquered a big one, making her first airplane flight non-stop Los Angeles to Chicago. She was almost 82 and that was her great day. My father had died of diabetes, at 60; my mother had diabetes too, but insulin and other medical science had kept her vivid, alert, active and really alive up to her last moments, far beyond life's normal expectancy. None of that science was known when my father died in 1917.

The day my mother died it dawned on me that the 30 years since my father's death were the greatest decades in history. More life-saving science had been discovered in the past 30 years than in the preceding 30 centuries.

A very great deal of it had concentrated its power on my mother, to keep her alive so long and strong. How her eyes would have snapped to realize that she had been a participant in this most astounding of all revolutions. "Rest easy, mother," I said, looking at her for the last time.

✠ ✠ ✠ ✠

CHAPTER XIV

To Live or to Die

⇛ ⇚

WHEN you ponder the curious events in Sid's life among the doctors, his troubles are not that he is the innocent victim of systematic character assassination. Of this he has been the victim, but not innocent. He asked for it. He is an innovator who has invented a democratic system of medical care. But he has taken no pains first to convince the doctors that this is to their own great advantage. Instead he launched his health plan in the teeth of a social storm—stirred up on the one hand by the doctors who insist they'll retain their time-honored way of selling their science to individual patients; stirred up on the other hand by citizens more and more determined *they* will have a say as to how to buy the life now made possible by medical science. Garfield has had a rugged time of it because so many thousands of people clamor for his system of medical care before the doctors have decided to make it their own.

If Garfield merits criticism it's because he took no consideration of the rank-and-file doctor's fear of change. If he left another factor out of his calculations and plans, it is that organizations, if established, are rarely ruled by leaders who appreciate innovations. This is notably true about the organization of the doctors. With the A.M.A. it is today much as it was in the days of Florence Nightingale, when she was fighting for decent care in the stinking hospital at Scutari for the English soldiers wounded at Balaclava. Lytton Strachey explains what baffled our lady with the lamp; the English army head doctor, who tried to give her the brush-off, "was lost in the imbecilities of a senile optimism." Today our own medical die-hards are optimistically convinced that all is well with the system by which they sell us medical care. The evidence?

"You are an essentially healthful America." That flat statement by medicine's leadership explains everything.

The millions of Americans who are only partly healthy, other millions who are downright sick—and the majority of all these having a tough time paying for it—know that this A.M.A. slogan is balderdash. They are ready to go for any system—even the silly one of government alleged free medical care for everybody—so long as it promises relief from their medical economic miseries. Millions are ready for any change, while only thousands have experienced the dignity of Garfield's plan of prepayment to groups of specialists, the system that puts good medicine within the reach of all citizens who work for even modest wages. That system means plenty of medical care for nearly everybody.

It's unfair to blame the doctors, even the die-hards, for opposing this. Like all other unions it has been the duty of the leaders of the medical union to make the product of the union *scarce*. The least work for the most money—that must be their motto. The doctors are hardly to be censured because, as Professor Ernest J. Simmons happily puts it, "their profession has developed amidst the cleavages of our commercial, money-mad, security-seeking economic system." But after all, Professor, it's the only system we've got and even though we're living in a half-baked Utopia, isn't it way ahead of the future perfection promised by Communist crackpots?

The boys who run the medical economic powerhouse have tried to rest their case on good medical care but the people know that this is not good enough; they're tired of jalopy medicine and are clamoring for Cadillac medical care. But that's out of the question, it's so expensive? Even the true leaders, the medical élite—not the political powerhouse boys—are worried by the terrific cost of it. This concern is expressed by Dr. Edward S. Churchill, the great thoracic surgeon at Massachusetts General Hospital in Boston. Dr. Churchill has recently returned from a study—an impartial and friendly one—of the British Health Plan. Here in Dr. Churchill's own words are his doubts and worries:

"Is there no end we may ask ourselves to the increasing demands for more and more beds in hospitals? Is this really going to be the road to the bankruptcy of society? Have the doctors in their ambition to discover new and better ways of treating disease created a burden that will prove intolerable?"

To these questions Sid Garfield has given a comforting and practical answer: The more beds in more hospitals prepaid jointly by more millions of people to more groups of specialists, the easier the economic burden. The greater the production, the less expensive the product. But with the highest respect to Dr. Edward S. Churchill, he has not yet examined Garfield's medical care and cannot be expected to understand its promise and its answer to his economic fears. Dr. Churchill must not despair. To the aid of his urge to soothe all suffering within the range of his surgical wizardry, and to the support of Garfield embattled among the imbecilities of a senile optimism, I spy the coming of a champion.

It is not human. It is a force, as powerful as it is impersonal. It is the one good revolution in human history. It is the sudden emergence of medical science during the past 30 years—making more science available to more people than in the preceding 30 centuries. From this, what have I learned?

II

This I sensed, standing by my mother's bedside after she had died. The awesome power—so sudden after man's long medical martyrdom—will itself make our failure to distribute that power ridiculous. It was this realization that night of September 9, 1948, that determined me to pause and take stock of what this sudden gift of life has already meant to us in the U. S. A. From the Fifth Century, B.C., days of good old Doctor Hippocrates, right down to living memory, life-saving has been largely confined to fishing drowning people out of the water and rescuing folks from burning buildings. Now—in the wink of an eye in terms of history—science pulls the fangs of plagues from which hundreds of millions of human beings have had to die, defenseless. I had been writing about individual medical discoveries—while an epidemic of medical miracles has been actually lengthening—by one-third—the average duration of our lives. It wasn't insulin alone, it was the terrific new power of chemical medicine that had made my mother live five years longer *with* diabetes than she was expected to live at the time she came down with it.

The general enormous shoving-back of death? It began to become understandable when I stopped to think of the medical weapons, accepted today, but non-existent 30 years ago when my father died, and many of them unimagined 10 years ago.

In 1917 there were no toxoid preventives for diphtheria or lockjaw. No sulfas to cure blood-poisoning, pneumonia, meningitis, or the bubonic plague that once murdered two-thirds of Europe's people in one medieval pandemic. No atabrine or DDT to combat malaria that is reliably supposed to have been the principal factor in destroying ancient Greek civilization. Not a synthetic vitamin to fight murderous malnutrition—or with the new synthetic hormones —to guard unborn babies and extend our prime of life. The greatest of all death-fighters, the anti-biotics like penicillin, streptomycin and aureomycin had not yet begun bubbling in the chemists' kettles. X-rays and radium hadn't yet been tamed from their deadliness into powerful life-savers against accessible cancer. Surgeons hadn't dared operations now curing hopeless tuberculosis and staving off cerebral hemorrhage, heart failure, and kidney disease due to malignant high blood pressure.

In terms of lives saved, the contrast in these 30 years is amazing. Infants under one year of age died at the ghastly rate of 94 in 1,000 babies born alive, in 1917. Then healthmen, led by Herman Bundesen, that rough-and-tumble death fighter in Chicago, found that faulty pasteurization was failing to wipe death out of milk, and that careless, incompetent, unscientific obstetrics was killing thousands of newborn. The result of correcting this mass child-murder? The nation's infant death rate by 1947 had tumbled two-thirds, in these 30 years saving 2,600,000 children who would have died.

(Just the same in Chicago, leading the nation, 28 in 1,000 infants under one year old are still dying. Herman Bundesen says savagely there is no irreducible minimum to this death and not Bundesen, but the fact of the existence of science, will drive it down toward zero.)

Prospects for life among pre-school children—age one to four—are still more astounding. Microbe-hunter G. Ramon of the Pasteur Institute in Paris, by what was really a ridiculously simple chemical trick, turned the strangling toxin of the diphtheria microbe into a gentle, life-guarding toxoid. Thirty years ago, diphtheria accounted for more than half of all the deaths from the four principal childhood diseases. Last year the disease was nationally negligible; in Chicago not a single child died from diphtheria which 30 years ago accounted for the deaths of many hundreds of children in a year.

A similar inoculation is taking the murderous sting out of whooping cough; sulfas and penicillin are cutting down mortality from scarlet fever and pneumonia following measles—completing the armament against the four former principal pre-school-age child-killers. In our three momentous decades, deaths from diphtheria, whooping cough, scarlet fever, and measles have in the aggregate dropped 80 per cent. The chief cause of pre-school-age child death is no longer disease—it's accidents.

How long will it be before there are no deaths from those four principal diseases, none at all? Though the healthmen and doctors will have to do the work, the fact that the work can be done dictates the answer.

When my father died in 1917 there was almost universal medical defeatism about a chemical cure ever being found for TB and pneumonia. Thousands of chemicals had been tested. They all, alas, killed animals and men before they killed the TB microbe and the pneumococcus. The trouble? It was simply that the chemists, microbe hunters, and doctors had tried the wrong chemicals. The diseases themselves, as Boss Kettering says, had no objection to being cured. And it's just as hard to find the wrong chemical against a sickness as it is to find the right one. That began to be apparent when, in England, in 1938, L. E. H. Whitby used sulfa-pyridine to chase the pneumococcus out of dying mice; it saved human beings too, albeit it nauseated some badly, which only set going a terrific cookery of thousands of new sulfas till American Cyanamid's chemist, Dick Roblin, at the head of a chemical commando of Ph.D.'s, concocted what is at present the king of them all, sulfa-diazine.

Now physicians are throwing a one-two punch—penicillin plus sulfa-diazine—at the pneumococcus. Lobar pneumonia is on the ropes and groggy. Thirty years ago it was smiting about 85,000 Americans with a gasping blue-faced death; and that mass tragedy has faded by more than 80 per cent so that only 20,000 Americans died from pneumococcal lobar pneumonia in 1947.

How many of these need to die? When lobar pneumonia is caught early, as it is at Permanente Hospital where Garfield's health plan has swept away the fear of the cost of illness, pneumonia's former general death rate of 25 per 100 has been cut down to 1.1— transformed from a great killer to almost a minor infection.

And TB? For many years there has been rejoicing that this microbic murderer—it took 145,000 Americans in 1917—is on the downtrend; yet it's hardly an occasion for dancing in the streets about the conquest of a disease that is still killing 50,000 Americans, annually. One deadly bottleneck has been not enough hospitals for the long bed-rest and active treatment by pneumothorax and surgery needed to cure the TB victims.

At last this stymie seems broken. Dr. Selman Waksman and his mold-hunters at Rutgers University discovered streptomycin. Many TB-fighters have been guardedly excited about its power over the tubercle microbe. The world's ace TB-fighter, Dr. E. J. O'Brien of Detroit—nobody mistakes Pat O'Brien's boldness for overenthusiasm—reports that this mold magic has doubled the number of former absolutely incurable victims who can now be saved by deribbing operations . . . after preliminary streptomycin.

Hard-hitting Pat further says that the anti-biotic has also made possible the cutting in half of the earlier cases—there are hundreds of thousands of these—who have had to undergo pneumothorax and other lengthy treatment to have a chance for cure. This may release the necessary sanatorium beds for a rapid and final blitz against the white death.

Typhoid fever—by healthmen's and engineer's sanitation and pasteurization—has had its murder cut down by 99 per cent in our great 30 years. Diarrheal diseases that made away with 80,000 of our citizens in 1917, killed only 8,000 in 1947.

The end of these stirring 30 years sees the beginning of the twilight of the microbes that have murdered billions. Malaria 30 years ago was a sinister life-sapper and killer in our south. In 1947 just 213 people in the U. S. A. are reported to have died of it, and the reliability of most of these death certificates is questionable. It is now actually hard to find a case of malaria, because of mosquito-fighting DDT and atabrine and the new far quicker-acting and less disagreeable drug, aralen; officers of the National Malaria Society are seriously debating changing their organization's name.

Deaths from syphilis, most sinister of plagues because of its secrecy and shame, have dropped from 21,000 to 13,000 in the past ten years; and in the past two years the U. S. Public Health Service reports a 20 per cent drop in new cases discovered. The deadly chain of syphilitic infection can now be broken, by penicillin and—more powerfully and rapidly as it is now done in Chicago—by the one-day (pardon me, 30-hour) treatment in which penicillin is combined with arsenicals, bismuth, and artificial fever.

Two most terrifying diseases attacking the nervous system—epidemic meningitis and lockjaw—have shown a death-rate drop of 76 per cent in the past 30 years. Meningitis epidemics are stopped in their tracks by sulfa-diazine; and lockjaw can be prevented when its toxoid is universally combined in one prophylactic shot with the anti-diphtheria inoculation, the withholding of which from a single child is murder. Even those super-tiny ultra-microbes, viruses hitherto incurable—like virus pneumonia—are succumbing to what promises to be the greatest of all the anti-biotics, aureomycin.

All very well, microbe murder is on the way out, you admit. But what of killers like cancer and heart disease, not conquered but even on an apparent increase? The recent years of our three great decades have seen the encouraging number of these deaths now attackable. You recall the grand old man of American medicine, two chapters back, who pointed out that cancer is one of the easiest of all diseases to cure while localized and accessible? If we could get all cancer victims to early and competent treatment, he says, out of 180,000 now annually dying—50,000 could live. That potential will force popular demand that the doctors, surgeons, pathologists, and radiologists get busy and save these lives.

The terrific toll of 420,000 deaths attributed to heart disease— its an apparent 100 per cent increase since 1917—may disturb us but it is not quite so appalling as it seems. Countless thousands are now signed out as perishing from heart disease because other science has saved them to live to a great old age; the death certificates of other countless thousands are marked heart disease—simply because hearts stopped beating and there is no other cause of death easily discernible, and no autopsies to try to give the answer.

Dr. Paul D. White of Harvard University—he is a remarkable blend of hard-headed and optimistic—has broken down the real killer diseases of the heart into the principal causes. Look at the progress. Heart failure from thyroid diseases and diphtheria has all but vanished; syphilitic heart disease, big killer 30 years ago, in 1947 claimed only 4,000 victims and may soon be in limbo; sub-acute bacterial endocarditis—you recall it was 97 per cent fatal—is now curable in almost 90 per cent of cases. Its murder has been estimated at 10,000 victims yearly. Is it likely that the citizenry will tolerate its continuance once it's generally known to be curable?

Rheumatic fever, by repeated attacks triggering rheumatic heart disease, kills an estimated 40,000 of our younger population. There's excellent evidence that the hemolytic streptococcus is the microbe criminal setting up an allergy that explodes as rheumatic fever. Sulfas, and better yet, penicillin, and maybe most practical of all so far as its safety goes, aureomycin, can prevent streptococcus infections. That will guard the rheumatically susceptible hearts of hundreds of thousands of children and younger grown-ups whose rheumatic threat can be recorded by competent physicians.

This leaves death-fighters face-to-face with two principal wreckers of the human heart—malignant hypertension (high blood pressure) and coronary heart disease.

Against heart enlargement and failure from hypertension, there is a hope, definite even if its realization involves stern and drastic measures. Dr. Max Minor Peet, of the University of Michigan, and independently Drs. Alfred Adson and Winchell Craig of the Mayo Clinic for the past 16 years have been perfecting an operation upon the sympathetic nervous system. They interrupt the sympathetic nerve paths to the abdomen, where it seems that a nefarious nervous stimulation stirs up the kidneys to brew a sinister hypertensive poison. The operation lowers the high blood pressure in a good percentage of sufferers; and the five- to ten-year survival rate of heart-threatened hypertensives is on a definite upgrade after these operations.

It is not the final answer, which already gives a hint of being chemical, but when you're a victim you don't ask for future answers, you ask to live. And the demand of more and more victims will force the perfection of this sympathectomy operation by more and more surgeons who'll be saving more and more people while foundations against heart disease or high blood pressure scurry round for research money to help chemists find a simple cure.

But the master-killer, especially of men in mid-life and after, is coronary heart disease—blood clots forming inside and blocking the blood vessels nourishing the heart, killing its blood-pumping muscles. While the prime cause is unknown, against the lethal results there's a gleam of hope. Two chemicals, dicoumarol and heparin, both of which retard the clotting of blood, are being used to check the danger of this blood-clotting inside the arteries of the heart. Dr. Leo Loewe—who conquered sub-acute bacterial endocarditis—has just reported a marked reduction of death in coronary attacks. He uses heparin in a safe and practical form—the heparin/Pitkin thought up by our maverick friend, Ralph Shaner.

Heparin/Pitkin is injected, under the skin, as soon as possible after the coronary attack has occurred. It prevents the spread of the deadly blood clots; used promptly, it often makes the damage to vital heart muscle inconsequential. When one attack has announced deadly peril to the heart, the victim lives under the looming threat of others. Heparin/Pitkin, injected every few days under the skin, frequently prevents further mischief in the coronary arteries.

Will heart-threatened hundreds of thousands be content to wait till millions of dollars of research money now being raised (a laudable enterprise, mind you) finally brings in the discovery of what causes coronary disease? Or will those threatened ask, Please, Doctor cardiologist, please, Doctor general practitioner, will you give us a whirl at this possible protection while the researchers are looking for the ultimate cause?

III

Why are there so few healthy aged? Why should old age be almost synonymous with sickness? Sadder than death and more cruel than pain is the feeling of millions of the old that they are burdens. In a home for old people—the Home and Hospital of the Daughters of Jacob, in the Bronx in upper New York City—there were some 500 old people from 65 to 110 years of age. It made me sit up when Dr. Henry A. Rafsky, who is attending gastro-enterologist and President of the Medical Board of this home, told me that this was the first human geriatrics laboratory in the world. Ten years ago, as in all such institutions, there was the atmosphere of sadness of ageing derelicts all thrown up on life's shore, all old crocks listless, rheumy-eyed, power of concentration feeble, drive gone, waiting to die. They could be dimly thankful for food and shelter, but why go on living?

Henry Rafsky was head of the staff in charge of caring for their numerous ailments. He was not a geriatrician. He is a tall, keen, gray-eyed, very genial (but extremely busy with time only for small doses of that geniality) gastro-enterologist. He is famous for demonstrating how many treatments are not cures for peptic ulcer. He became celebrated for sticking a gastroscope down a patient's gullet and taking the first color-photograph of a severe peptic ulcer and this he prizes as an art connoisseur would treasure a good van Gogh. Medically he is dishearteningly conservative, and he is proud that so far—and then he crosses his fingers—he has not published a medical mistake. You would not have suspected him of entertaining scientifically heretical ideas. Gastro-enterologically he was very regular. Now—it would not be in the cards for a geriatrician to believe you could do anything much but palliate old age—Henry Rafsky turned maverick.

Henry asked a highly heretical question. Are people really as old as their arteries? The authoritative world of geriatrics answered yes—unanimous.

Mulishly and, I must say, mystically, Henry Rafsky said no. He scraped together a bit of research money—you may be sure not from insurance companies or any foundation alleging a geriatric interest—and he got together a research team of fellow mavericks to examine chemically into the functions of the livers of these poor old fogies existing in the Home and Hospital of the Daughters of Jacob. There were obvious signs of liver disease in a few of them. But hold it. Chemically, the livers of almost every one of them were badly underpar.

And this was Rafsky's simple science: the liver is the chemical laboratory of the human body.

It was Henry Rafsky's merit that he asked only the most simple questions, ones that a child could answer—if the child were a precocious organic chemist. Why this deterioration of all these livers? The home was famous, in line with the most excellent Jewish tradition, for its nutritious diet, tasty gastronomically and beautifully balanced scientifically. Adequate and then some, according to the standards of the Board of Nutrition of the National Research Council.

Now Henry Rafsky asked what was by all scientific knowledge a silly question, in view of the supposed fact that a diet is adequate whether you're a baby or a slippered pantaloon. Henry propounded: though adequate for youngsters, was this diet good enough for these ancients? Not a textbook, not a monograph in the immense scientific lore of the hidden hunger admitted that there might be any difference, that diet that would make a baby bounce might actually be poison to the liver of an old man or old lady.

Rafsky and his biochemical team set to work in their cluttered, ridiculously cramped little laboratory. Rafsky's questions, though so simple, had the merit that they would give him a clear yes or clear no for an answer. The biochemical tests? They showed that the great majority of these decrepit old people—though eating that wonderfully nutritious diet—were deficient fantastically in vitamins and protein.

Ten years after Henry began asking those questions, Herman Bundesen and I went to the Home and Hospital of the Daughters of Jacob. And now you should see those old people who used to be waiting to die. Now lively, and it was strange how few of them were dying. The waiting list is increasing, with the result that the directors are compelled to erect an additional building.

"Does it boil down to this: that we're as old as our liver, not as old as our arteries?" I asked Henry.

He turned on his benevolent wrinkle-eyed smile. "I don't say so," he said. He was super-cautious. You see he'd never had to take back, scientifically, anything he'd published. "But that's my theory," he added. "Give us just a little more time, and we'll tell you for sure . . . One way or the other," he ended, conservatively.

If Henry Rafsky's theory is right, if it turns out that we're actually as old as our livers, not as old as our arteries, then there's a better answer than bigger old folks' homes. And if this newly discovered liver deficiency is detected and corrected not in old age—but in mid-life—and this liver deficiency is no theory but cold scientific fact—then us older owners of now possible husky livers will go on working, self-supporting into a far advanced active age, a new strange twilight. (I'd like to stick around to see if that's so; I will, if Henry is right and we have good luck.)

IV

Thirty years ago pernicious anemia was 100 per cent lethal. Now, without Dr. George Minot and Dr. William P. Murphy knowing why liver was good for it, it's estimated that there are at least 100,000 people in the U. S. A.—alive and healthy—who owe that health and life to liver and its extracts. The patients didn't care about the doctors not knowing why liver worked; the people kept coming faithfully for their more or less uncomfortable liver shots, patiently while the chemists cooked for 24 years in their laboratories, first finding the B vitamin, folic acid, which controlled pernicious anemia—but only partly—and at last, just now, discovering the magic vitamin B-12—of which incredibly tiny doses seem to control this formerly invincible death completely.

If there was a little bit more of this rough-and-ready life-saving spirit against great killers, like cancer, more hundreds of thousands could easily now be living.

Even so, looking back over this past 30 years, there is a victory for the doctors—the humblest now play their part in it—that's the fantastic opposite of all wars in history. Look at the majestic downward slope of America's general death rate—1917 to 1947—there's only one year's interruption of that downgrade, the flu murder of 1918—and it tells us the accelerating rise of hundreds of thousands of lives rescued yearly.

In these three decades the lives saved have totaled, in round numbers, ten million.

These are only figures; but each digit means a sweetheart saved for a lover, or a breadwinner for a family, or a child for its parents, or a mother for her children. Each digit is a unit of a greater store of mankind's productive energy, of happiness—not for all—but for very many. Each digit, adding up to these increasing millions who used to have to die, increases the human force that will back up embattled health planners, like Garfield, who has cooked up a bookkeeping helping people to come for medical care right away when they fall sick and the earlier they come the less chance they have to die.

A voice from the rear of the hall protests to the effect that it is not entirely the doctors who have saved these ten million. Granted. It is the healthmen, it is that vague non-human physician known as the "rising standard of living," it is maybe the doles of the New Deal, it is surely the organic chemists making vitamin wizardry against malnutrition. It's all these, as well as the doctors. But the voice heckles again: "Look at the curve of your down-trending death rate. Why didn't it flatten out or go upward during the war? Half the doctors were away from the civilian population taking care of the soldiers and sailors. What good are doctors?"

It's admitted that this is a phenomenon requiring learned analysis of which insurance actuaries and public health biometricians alone are capable. Yet this paradox of the death rate going down despite half the doctors gone, might have a simple explanation: medicine's power is now so terrific that a doctor can save ten lives where a few years ago he couldn't rescue one.

What has loomed in the last few years of this life among the doctors is that their glorious forward march may be thrown into a confused retreat, may turn out to mean nothing at all. The human activity that has given physicians their life-saving arsenal is the very same that is now putting all human society, if not all human life, in jeopardy. This activity is science, the hunt for truth. For many years I esteemed men of science—truth hunters—above physicians. What would doctors be but bedside comforters and medieval quack-salvers if it were not for the pure scientists and especially the organic chemists?

During these past 30 years, the men of basic science in addition to enabling doctors to save these millions of lives, have set a sinister current in the opposite direction. These 30 years have grown more somber with lies—used scientifically—and with bloodshed and starvation—employed artistically—and now at last we all live with a foreboding of possible total human disaster. Till a few years ago I had thought that men of basic science—truth hunters—would be the human beings who were brave, brainy, and honest enough to lead us to a happier tomorrow.

I have known men of science—notably Ivan Pavlov and Charles F. Kettering—who hold a fierce belief that the scientific method points the one way out of the world's despair. Isn't that hunt for truth the most disinterested of all human action and by far the noblest? Wouldn't the purity of this hunt for truth ennoble the all-around characters of the hunters? Mightn't they become examples for us all to follow toward truth and life out of our present morass of lies and death?

As I grew to know men of science more intimately—especially as they contended for political power in their own scientific organizations—it became clear that the regard for truth on the part of many

of them too often failed to go beyond the protocols of their laboratory experiments. It was amazing: a man could be the most honest
experimenter and devious in his dealing with his fellowmen. The
supposed sanctity of the hunt for truth in general failed to make
saints of the hunters. It was astounding: too often it seemed to turn
them into especially subtle character assassins and connivers. With
the exception of a handful of scientific immortals like Pasteur and
Pavlov, they did not seem to possess either the clairvoyance or the
faith to make them prophets, guides in our dangerous human adventure.

There are a few—notably Boss Kettering—who are true to their
science, self-reliant, brave and very cold. You find any fact, says Boss
Ket, and you cannot put it back into oblivion. You cannot put the
brakes on any discovery, not even that of the atom bomb, and you
shouldn't try to; you've got to go on with it even if we're all blown
to hell with it. What you should do is to step up the study of
human nature, you may even find a chemical, a vitamin, a hormone,
a simple pill to take the devil out of human nature . . . This is
Boss Ket's faith and when you hear him give out with it, it is not
bleak, there is religion, there is glowing hope, there is white-hot fire
in it.

But there's only one Boss Kettering; and among most of the
truth hunters I've met, there are men who are geniuses in their
special work, but in their sense of a possible high destiny of their
truth hunt many of them seem to me to be—timid.

Kettering's versatile genius has enabled him to hunt truth and
at the same time establish his personal economic independence. But
in general the brains of our men of science seem to be for hire,
by industry, by the foundations set up by millionaires, by the military, and by political global strategists. They're glorified technicians, most of them, and they're a dime a dozen. At the beginning
of the war I sensed this. Then came the last year of the war and into
the discard went my hopes for a pervading nobility of truth hunters. Though they had invented plenty of instruments for mass murder before, now our men of science pulled off their altruistic masks.
The hunt for truth now showed itself to be not only bright with

promise of a new strong and happy mankind but dark with the power to destroy us utterly. Science? It is a two-edged sword.

I had to disentangle the activities of the men who fight for life (doctors and healthmen) from the men who hunt for truth—giving life with one hand and death with the other. It was a bitter day when my old friend, H. L. Mencken (he is fortunate, he says, to have been born with no more public spirit than a cat), taunted me. He showed me how I had had the hunt for truth and the fight for life all mixed up together.

"I hope that you insert something about the atomic bomb in your book," said Henry. "It is, I believe, the greatest of American inventions, and the greatest glory of Christianity since the hanging of Martin Luther. Please don't forget that the noble patriots who developed the bomb also devised an entirely new disease, to wit, galloping cancer."

The men of science did seem to be aghast at the explosions they set off at Alamagordo, Hiroshima, Nagasaki, and Bikini. Even Professor Einstein—who helped convince our late President to embark on a gamble of two billions to develop the most exquisite murder in history—urged the collection of more money for an organization to prevent the atom bomb from doing all of us in.

A member of the board of trustees of a university that had led all others in the practical smashing of the atom told me of an episode taking place on the day of the glorious news from Hiroshima. On that afternoon, two of the greatest of the developers of atomic fission, taking a constitutional with their respective wives, met on the campus. They stopped. They exchanged salutations. In despond they looked at each other. They sat down on the curb in the quiet street. They both wept.

v

The doctors. Are they the only hope in science—for brotherhood—if in it there is any hope at all? The science of the doctors is crude by the standards of the molecular physicists and the micro-chemists. Yet, as students of cause and effect in their treatment of the sick, they, the doctors, are still men of science—and this is their significance: by the nature of their calling they use only the good edge of the scientific two-edged sword. In this function most of them are modest; they have no spiritual pretension, and do not know their own power. What, for example, would happen if some dedicated doctor would arise on the floor of a national medical convention, glorify the immense life-saving progress of medical science during the past 30 years, and propose that the doctors try to fuse their good Samaritan science with religion, to give true dignity to all human life?

What would happen, I asked Dr. Herman Kabat, the medical maverick who is making many rise and walk. I answered my own question: "Such a man would be hooted off any medical convention floor." Herman Kabat does not share my pessimism. He has the steel of the truth hunter beneath his gentleness as a physician. At Wake Robin in December, 1948, Herman Kabat came to the defense of the physicians. He looked out over Lake Michigan, out into the impenetrable gray of the horizon. He launched into a soliloquy whose sense was as follows:

We must not be too tough on the doctors. They're so busy to keep from being chained up by the government that they're on the defensive. The best they have to offer is that we have the finest medical care in the world, when they should be telling us here's the best we could possibly give if the government would lay off and let us show what we could do about medical care. For this project, the doctors are now accumulating helpers, volunteers. (Herman smiled shrewdly and then went on.) Who are these helpers? More and more millions of people who know at last that the chips are down. Too bad the A-bomb had to kill all those non-combatants in Japan, but there may have been good even in that filthy murder. The advance of science has at last reached the point where the issue is absolutely clear. The issue is live-or-die. In the world's caste system men must at last perforce be brothers; there's a meeting of extremes; the Wall Street bankers are menaced by the A-bomb, no place even for them to hide; the Hottentots are dimly grasping the importance of a quart of milk a day; the Hindus will soon know their lives can be saved by aureomycin; low and high know it's better to have milk and aureomycin than to have A-bombs and bacterial warfare and systematic starvation. The people are teaching this ethical, this social A B C to the doctors. They're the doctors' encouragers out of their primordial social timidity, their excessive individualism. These are the helpers of the doctors. Truck drivers, housewives, GI's—all see the issue of live-or-die, more and more clearly. They will back up the doctors in anything the doctors want to do. If the doctors happen now to be too busy frantically defending their *status quo* so that they are a bit laggard in distributing their power over live-or-die, then truck drivers, housewives, and GI's will surely say: Let's get going. (Herman Kabat's eyes were glowing not with fanaticism but with a mysterious kindliness.) What excites our plain citizens more? he asked. The new B-50's that can fly round the world with plenty of cargo space for bombs for Russia? Or the Berlin airlift has kept our late enemies living? (Herman smiled with a strange serenity and went on.) Where the plain citizens are so strong is that they are so simple. Yes, idiotically simple. As they see the issue of live-or-die clearer, they'll act on just that little slogan. Look how they've already bit into the lag between finding life-saving science and saving life with it. Do you think that women would *now* wait 80 years—as they actually did from the days of the discovery of the prevention of childbed fever by Ignaz Semmelweis in the 1850's till the days in the middle 1930's when it was at last put into action in our country to cut down the maternal death rate? If they didn't get that protection, there'd be riots in the lobbies of the hospitals.

Herman wound it up. No, he was not being any kind of pollyanna, he was not being idiotically optimistic. Sure we do not know what is going to happen. Sure science is a two-edged sword. Sure we may all be blown to smithereens. But the dizzy, murderous, life-saving onrush and upsurge of science? That's all to the good. Because it has made the issue of live-or-die no longer dodgeable by the citizens. It's again by the skin of our teeth that we may pull out as in all somber crises in human life from before human record. When *Genus homo* knows the chips are really down, it is his pri-

mordial human characteristic not to just sit on his hands and take
it. . . .

Herman made me feel very fine. He had something there. For
years, in tens of thousands of letters pouring into Wake Robin, in
newspapers, in town meetings of citizens, I myself had been stirred
by the evidence of this mass popular answer, this roaring answer
to the question, to live or to die—we'll live! It is the deep murmur
of the affirmative, of an overwhelming demand to make operative
the legend of the good Samaritan, the ultimate and only duty of
the doctors.

Newspaper dispatch, March 28, 1948. Headline: BLOOD POISONING
VICTIM GETS AID AFTER SNOW TREK. It was the saving of the life of
Shirley Dallas, 13 years old, of Forestville, Michigan. For two days
doctors couldn't reach her because of snow-blocked roads. She was
going to die, and then?

A state highway department snow-plow cleared away a six-mile
stretch of highway at a mile-an-hour pace last night so that Dr.
D. M. Baird, of Deckerville, could get through to treat Shirley,
dying, in a Forestville hotel. And then?

Townsfolk of Forestville, armed with snow shovels, in the dead
of night lamed their backs and endangered their coronaries, and for
six hours hacked away at the snowdrifts. The people of the town
met the state snowplow outside their village. Collectively, they, all
of them good Samaritans, made the work of their medical good
Samaritan possible.

I laughed, and showed Herman Kabat a frayed newspaper clip-
ping. SIX CHILDREN START RUSH OF BLOOD DONORS, said the headline in the New York *Herald Tribune*. "It was as much as a pint
of your blood was worth to be an adult and to be walking the
streets of the Williamsburgh section of Brooklyn, yesterday," began
that newspaper story.

It was the answer of those six Brooklyn kids to the plight of
Susanna, the two-year-old, brown-eyed daughter of Mr. and Mrs.
Vito Giordano. Shirley was suffering from the sinister Mediter-
ranean anemia. She would have to have periodic blood transfusions till she reached maturity. Then at last she'd no longer need

them, because her body, relieved of its burden of growing, would at last be able to manufacture her red blood cells fast enough to keep her alive, said the newspaper story.

Shirley's father and mother had already given so much of their blood to the blood bank, to match each transfusion of its special blood for Shirley, that they had become so weak they couldn't give any more and now for Shirley it seemed to be the end.

But then the six Brooklyn street gamins heard of it. They went to the Red Cross and offered their own blood. No go. They were too young. And then, what did those youngsters do?

They went out into the streets and button-holed passers-by.

"There's a baby sick," they said. Their eyes were wide with pleading. They insisted: "There's this baby sick, she needs blood," they said. "Will *you* help her?"

That afternoon they marched 15 donors into the Red Cross.

They were irresistible. The astounded Red Cross functionaries exclaimed they'd never seen such blood go-getters. Then other children of their School Settlement House joined them, canvassing for blood, more and more blood, till there was more than enough for Shirley, till they began getting unheard-of quantities of blood for the Red Cross donor campaign, in general. Then Supreme Court Justice George J. Beldock, president of Brooklyn's Youth United, working in Brooklyn's eight settlement houses with a membership of 16,000 youngsters, heard of this. The Judge called a meeting immediately to implement this children's crusade in all eight settlements. Shirley Giordano would live, and how many more? Now the public-spirited dignitaries of the Red Cross would realize what Cy Young, doctor to Michigan's five million, was so sure of: that there should be no commerce in human blood in the matter of saving a human life. The Red Cross officials now could realize what those six Brooklyn kids knew in their bones: that there's enough blood to save all of the thousands still dying because of the miserable slowness of our organizing to distribute it or because now—when it's not yet free—the vast majority haven't the money to buy life-saving blood at its market cost of $25 or more per pint.

Those Brooklyn kids knew there is enough blood to drown the

world if you care enough about getting it for a baby who is sick, or for a man or a woman, if you care enough to put the emotion into asking for it.

Now I remembered all that and more, and Kabat had something there about the ordinary citizens being the encouragers of the doctors. These fantastic outbursts of community and even nationwide concern for one threatened youngster or woman or man are aroused by what? By the crisis of live-or-die. Remember the country shoving Christmas ahead for little Nubbins Hoffman in Colorado because the doctors thought he was going to die of cancer before Christmas? Nobody asked for their presents back when Nubbins fooled them and stayed alive. I remember the citizens of Chicagoland just now going wild over little 14-year-old Roberta Lee Mason who was so horribly burned saving the lives of her four brothers and sisters. The region chipped in to give her as good or better medical care than their own children would get, better than a little rich girl's care, offering their blood, pouring in $17,000 for the unions to build a house where her home had burned down, having it ready before Roberta would be out of the hospital.

When we ordinary citizens once realize how much of the power of live-or-die the doctors now have, we will at last grasp it that when they let us die needlessly, they are really killing us; we will understand that they are then guilty of negligent homicide; then we will get sore; and then we will take drastic action in the direction of justice in this matter of live-or-die—whether it will be the right kind of action is another question. Already more and more people are telling the doctors: "Let's get going, we want to live."

V I

I remember my mother, two days before she died; she was breathless from having hurried to the lookout to watch the morning rainbow—the most perfect we had ever seen—arched across the western sky with its feet fading into Lake Michigan very close to us. Mother had always been a great skeptic, and she looked up at me as she held on to me: "It's supposed to mean hope, isn't it?" she asked, smiling ironically. But she was anything but skeptical about medical science that had kept her alive so long. "I'll swallow any vitamin you give me," she said.

"I'll take any shot from Dr. Edna, even if it kills me, so long as it gives me a chance to keep going," she said, laughing.

Two days later she called for her last shot, and Dr. Edna, with mother's blood pressure already very low, got the injection with great skill into a vein I don't see how she found. Mother's last observable emotion was her faith in Dr. Edna and her last act was cooperating with her.

It was in the spring before my mother died that Dr. Edna revealed why my mother would later have such faith in her. Edna brought new hope for wayfarers on man's rough road.

This was on a sunny day exceptionally warm for April, at Wake Robin; ice floes at last out of the Lake so we could hear the surf again after the long silence of winter; clear sky above the budding black oaks and maples alive with the haunting warble of bluebirds migrating north toward nesting; from far away on the Lake the ventriloquial honking of a flock of Canada geese resting on their way north for mating. Rhea, Sid Garfield, Dr. Edna and I sat all day outside round the big table with its legs the stumps of a clump of cherry trees Rhea and I had cut down many years ago when we were young, clearing the woods to begin building the little shack now grown into Wake Robin. And now we were how much older?

What I remember even more than the lift in the music of the bluebirds and the Canadas was Edna—unknown small-town doctor —groping to give a new thought to Sid Garfield, famous as the discoverer of how to bring modern medical care to people so they could pay for it. Dr. Edna, who ran her own individual cure store, was all for Sid's group medicine, but she had something new to add to it. Both of them were clean-cut, young, tough, no malarkey, with the mark of competence stamped on them. Serious lines carved by uphill struggle were plain on both their faces—on Edna's because you'd better not be a doctor if you're a woman, on Sid's because you'd better not be a doctor if you try changing the economics of distributing medical care.

Sid was disgusted with the patching and mending of broken-down human machines that was most of medicine and almost all of surgery. . . . "It's most of it garbage collecting," said Sid.

Then Edna began telling us. She was excellently trained in the specialty of pediatrics; she had wanted to make a life of building a new kind of child, super-children; she had been forced—by the deplorable lack of group organization in medical practice—to spend the bulk of her time as a plain family doctor; while the doctors of her city of 18,000 esteemed Edna highly, it seemed there was not enough work to support a full-time pediatrician. Yet she had made the best of that disappointment. She was a blend of super-modern specialist and old-fashioned doctor (you don't find many of them any more) who doesn't mind making house calls. The citizens of the town and the country around didn't mind it that Dr. Edna would come out any time of the day and the night no matter the snow or the freezing rain. She had a terrific practice and was working far over capacity.

This April day at Wake Robin it was exciting to hear family doctor Edna leap out ahead of Sid Garfield who directed a great prepaid group medical care project for more than a hundred thousand people up and down the West Coast.

"What we ought to be doing is teaching people how to keep *away* from the doctors," said Edna. "Mothers could do a lot of things themselves that they pay me to do. If they'd do them, then I could go on from there."

Edna leaned forward, telling all of us, and her eyes were really sparking. There was a new spirit in this handsome, slender young woman with black hair tinged with gray, with blue-gray eyes steely yet kindly and with an intensity that had in them a bit of Joan of Arc. Her special new spirit she showed by the total absence of an ancient medical characteristic that was as old as the first doctor's priestcraft: this was the doctor's curious belief in his sole possession of mysteries forever beyond the understanding of ordinary citizens—"the laity" as the older doctors still call us. To Edna this high-and-mightiness was nonsense. She was all for patients understanding her science.

"Of course I'm for your prepayment plan by the people to groups of specialists," said Edna. "It brings them to you early—it makes curative medicine, what do you call it, a vanishing economy. But how much do you do to keep people away from you altogether?" she asked.

As a doctor Edna struck me as being way out ahead, because of her fierce conviction that she could teach most people most of her professional stuff.

"Why, my child patients know what I'm doing," said Edna. "The other day I came into a home and a three-year-old looked up at me and said, 'I don't have to have any more penicillin now, do I, Doctor?' and that little kid pronounced penicillin perfectly!"

Edna kept piling into Sid, who took it with his usual enigmatic slit-eyed smile. "Is most of what we do so difficult, so remarkable?" asked Edna.

She seemed to me to be a new kind of medical animal, she was a hybrid, a cross between the front-line family doctor and the health-man. She was all for Herman Bundesen who had got his world-famous book, *Our Babies*, to more than 12,000,000 mothers, who used it to take a great deal of medical care of their own infants. Here was Edna going out beyond Bundesen, teaching mothers to be assistant doctors to do a lot of what's supposed to be a pediatrician's work on their youngsters on up through adolescence. She was a new type of medical professor though her medical college was only her crowded office and most of her students hadn't gone further than high school. She urged all mothers crowding her waiting room with their bawling babies to get Dr. Benjamin Spock's *Baby and Child Care,* in the Pocket Book edition. If a mother couldn't afford that, Edna bought the book for her; and at the county seat's well baby clinic (Edna ran that in addition to her heavy practice) there was a fund to supply Dr. Spock's book to hundreds of mothers.

"They tell me it's their *Bible,*" said Edna, "and it keeps hundreds of calls away from my office."

By the book and by personal talks Edna was turning, she said, hundred of mothers into her medical assistants: changing the feed-

ing of their youngsters as they grew older; knowing how much
they should weigh at what year; correcting their thumb-sucking and
loss of appetite; analyzing their not sleeping; spotting signs of rickets
that might later mean bad bone structure and broken-down feet;
using vitamins to speed lagging growth and to boost anti-microbic
resistance; punctually bringing their children for all preventive
inoculations; knowing when penicillin and the new, marvelous
aureomycin might be indicated to keep colds and measles from turning into deadly pneumonia; becoming psychologists to conquer in-
hibitions and fears and teaching sex candidly to guard them from
becoming problem children or juvenile delinquents.

Into Edna's office came more and more mothers with their children to learn to be doctors from this woman doctor who did not
look medically down her nose at them. "I haven't nearly the number of home calls to make that I had when this began, seven years
ago," said Edna. "My office? Booked solid. But I try to make it more
and more for teaching, less and less for doctoring.

"If I could only get them all to keeping their children from getting
sick, the mothers doing my work at home, lightening that awful
office load—then I could really start practicing the new medicine—
then I could go on from there."

She was gallant and she was very tired. Look what she would be
free to do when all the mothers, finally, were doctors for their own
youngsters! Then she could concentrate on the tough ones, on rheumatic heart disease, preventing the respiratory disease that triggered
it. Practicing psychotherapy on the early mental quirks that might
be danger signals of later schizophrenia. Drawing blood for the
chemistry to detect pre-diabetics—diabetes the one supposedly con-
trollable disease the death rate of which was so alarmingly rising.
Spotting early cancer—really early. Finding out by chemistry, X-ray,
and ophthalmology whether a given high blood pressure was perilous. Drawing blood for liver function tests which might predict a
future breakdown fatal to the brain or the kidneys or the heart.

"For God's sake," she said, "why don't we learn how to teach
the well to take care of themselves . . . to keep away from the
doctors?"

That was a memorable day at Wake Robin. Almost 40 years before in medical school I had heard old Dean Victor C. Vaughan of the University of Michigan pronounce that medicine was the one profession working to destroy the reason for its own existence. This was the first time I had seen a practicing doctor trying to put Dean Vaughan's prophecy into all-out action.

"Here's a new type of specialist, Sid," I said, nodding at Edna. "Remember the five dollars per visit it costs you each time your health plan subscribers come to Permanente—they paying only one dollar each time?"

"You mean—" began Sid.

"I mean doctors like Edna might cut down your overhead."

VII

What really made Edna and Sid lone wolves, what put their backs to the wall, was that, from time immemorial, doctors had considered the art and science of medicine as their sole prerogative. *The doctors own medicine, lock, stock, and barrel.* Sid's basic crime was giving the citizens a say as to how to pay for their medicine. And now Edna—beginning to teach citizens how to keep away from the doctors? They were both of them traitors to their trade!

Among the doctors themselves there is at last the whisper of a hint of help for mavericks like Sid and Edna. A group of the ultra-élite of American medicine—there are more than 160 of them as this is written—have signed a protest to the American Medical Association to which they all belong not in good but in the highest standing, not politically, but *medically.*

One of the leading members of this protesting committee has been quoted as saying: "We don't want government medicine, but neither do we want a program entirely planned and dictated by the medical profession."

"We shouldn't profess to know everything," said a leading member of the protesting committee.

This wasn't only humility, it wasn't only common decency, it was revolutionary. Because the citizens of the U. S. A. have been dirt under the feet of "the leadership" of the American Medical Association. The club the leadership has used to beat up all attempts to assert the medical rights of the citizens has been this: You can't know anything about medical care unless you are an M.D.

The protesting committee of distinguished physicians said, in part, over their signatures:

"We believe that the fundamental failure of the American Medical Association in its attitudes and policies bearing on the general problem of medical care has been its unwillingness fully to acknowledge the need of improvement. . . ."

This was a final destruction of the myth that our medical care is all right because it is superior to that of Burma and Bulgaria. These were not lay citizens protesting, but distinguished doctors.

The committee protested the failure of the leadership of the American Medical Association "to come forward with a comprehensive constructive program which would be of clear advantage to the public as well as to the profession itself."

This was epoch-making. Here were men of the highest medical repute, men every bit as anxious as the leadership of the A.M.A. itself to forestall government medicine, admitting that medicine should be practiced for the public as well as for the doctors.

Terminating its protesting statement, the committee said: "The undersigned believe that now is the time to voice our disapproval of the leadership and policies of the Association on the extension of medical care."

Disapproval of the leadership? This was truly historic. No doctors who were not crackpot socializers, no doctors who were middle-of-the-road, no doctors of high achievement had ever before dared to challenge their Association's leadership, not right out in the open, not in voices above a frightened whisper.

Among those disapproving this leadership so that all citizens reading the newspapers could know it? Dr. George Minot, Nobel Prize winner for conquering pernicious anemia; Dr. Evarts Graham, father of lung surgery; Dr. Ernest Goodpasture, Sedgwick medalist for his great work in the field of viruses; Dr. Paul A. O'Leary of the Mayo Clinic, world-famed authority on syphilis. And the other signers were the peers of these mentioned, all deserving not only the respect but the complete confidence and admiration of the more than 150,000 physicians of the U. S. A.

With characteristic promptness—never at a loss for the wrong word—the A.M.A. leadership issued a retort discourteous to the effect that these were doctors talking out of their "plaster towers" and not representatives of the practice of medicine. And yet, when he read those names, I wonder if the leadership of the American Medical Association didn't shiver in his shoes even if ever so little?

This forthright denunciation may mean a final turning of a corner on our rough road toward decent medical care. Or it may mean nothing. For in every trade union, which is precisely what the A.M.A. has so far been, no more no less, any protesting group no matter how well intentioned, no matter how high in good will, can only work at reform in its spare moments. The leadership? He is in there working to hold his power 24 hours every day. Knowing this, who can be sanguine about a change in leadership?

Trying to pierce the inscrutable future for a real hope that our road toward life shall be less rough, we must look back to the past, back over the rough road on which our ancestors have wept and bled and toiled and sweat from the days of the cave-men toward our present struggle for kindliness, for brotherhood, for a pervading spirit of the good Samaritan. When we were all cold, there arose that hardy fire-bringer, Prometheus. When we were all going to drown, a fore-sighted gentleman, old Noah, built his seagoing Ark. When the Christian church was corrupt, dreamy Saint Francis of Assisi came to restore a bit of the brotherhood taught by the Man of Galilee. When the Christian church was putting down honest Protestants by the cruel technique of Torquemada, then Voltaire roared: "Stamp out the Infamy," and his voice gave men new courage. When our own Union was threatened with bloody disintegration, Lincoln died to guard us from this danger of the House Divided so that we're still of some hope to a divided world.

Will a medical prophet soon appear to lead us out of the present infamy of the sick man being personally taxed for his medical care at the very moment he is least able to pay for it? Will a Prometheus bring us fire against the cold of medical neglect? He will appear, if he does, as a maverick. As of now we do not spy him. Just the same, remembering back over this life among the doctors, remembering how the mavericks of this chronicle have more and more of the devotion, the awe, of more and more millions of citizens, it seems to me that the times are building up for his coming.

Bibliographic Note

A formal bibliography is omitted because it would almost make a volume in itself. The following were technically, and many of them philosophically, helpful in the assembling of material and in the writing about our life among the doctors:

CHAPTER I: Dr. Thomas Parran, Dr. Edward Francis.

CHAPTER II: Dr. C. C. Young; Minna Crooks Young; Dr. L. G. Christian; Dr. G. D. Cummings; Dr. J. T. Tripp; Dr. Pearl Kendrick.

CHAPTERS III TO VI, INCL.: Dr. Karl Friedrich Meyer; Dr. Tom Douglas Spies; Dr. J. W. MacQueen; Dr. Norman Jolliffe; Dr. R. R. Williams; Dr. W. H. Sebrell; Dr. C. G. King; Dr. Horace Eddy Robinson; Miss Jean Grant; Miss Frances Bomer; Mr. M. Lee Marshall; Mr. James S. Adams; Mr. Hugh Comer.

CHAPTER VII: Dr. Herman N. Bundesen; Dr. William I. Fishbein; Dr. Walter M. Simpson; Dr. H. Worley Kendell; Dr. Theodore G. Bauer; Dr. George X. Schwemlein; Dr. Paul A. O'Leary; Mr. Charles F. Kettering; Mr. Edwin Sittler.

CHAPTER VIII: Dr. Alvin F. Coburn; Adge Coburn.

CHAPTER IX: Dr. Ralph D. Shaner; Dr. Leo Loewe; Mr. John L. Smith; Dr. H. T. Hyman.

CHAPTER X: Dr. O. C. Wenger; Miss Regina Kaplan, R.N.; Miss Georgia Hauke; Miss Charlotte Reamey.

CHAPTER XI: Dr. Herman Kabat; Sara Kabat; Dr. Tracy J. Putnam; Miss Maggie Knott; Mr. Henry J. Kaiser, Jr.; Mr. Gordon Tolman; Louise Tobey Dean; Mr. Curtis Rockwell Gray; Dr. Ralph D. Shaner.

CHAPTER XII: Those helping us on this chapter ask to remain anonymous because of danger of medical molestation.

CHAPTER XIII: Dr. Sidney R. Garfield; Virginia Garfield; Dr. Cecil Cutting; Millie Cutting; Dr. Paul FitzGibbon; Dr. Morris F. Collen; Dr. Ray Lyman Wilbur; Dr. Karl Friedrich Meyer; Dr. William P. Shepard; Dr. Harold R. Brunn; Dr. William Donald; Corporal Wilmer Patrick Shea; Mr. Henry J. Kaiser, Sr.; Mr. Edgar F. Kaiser.

CHAPTER XIV: Dr. Ralph D. Shaner; Dr. Edna Schrick; Dr. Henry A. Rafsky.

Index